About Visionlearning

Science is about more than facts. It's about the process of discovery of the world around you. That's why the learning materials Visionlearning provides include more than just scientific concepts. They explore the stories of the people behind the science and how we have come to know what we know. Our learning modules present scientific concepts in the context of their discovery and our current state of state of knowledge on the topic.

Visionlearning provides free online, high-quality content for teaching and learning science. Through modular readings, assessments, interactive animations, a comprehensive science glossary, and other features, our site promotes science education, focuses readers on the process of scientific discovery, and conveys the act of being a scientist. Our module design has been extensively tested and reviewed by students and teachers, and incorporate a number of proven features aimed toward improving literacy and concept understanding. We want to make sure that everyone has access to the information they need to become scientifically literate.

The materials presented in this book are available on our free website where they are supplemented by resources that cannot be printed in book form. In each chapter of this book, you will find a text-and-image-based reading. These lessons are written by professional scientists and educators who ensure that they are accurate and concise to avoid overloading students with extraneous information. At the top of each lesson is a pre-reader, which contains questions to stimulate prior knowledge on the topic, a general overview of what the module will cover, and some definitions of terms users should understand before reading. In the online versions, a table of contents provides an outline of the entire module.

Audio recordings of the module can be streamed while on the website. These audio files help aural learners, struggling readers, and language learners by modeling intonation, inflection, and pronunciation of difficult terms and names. Audio is provided in both English and Spanish.

Glossary terms in the online lessons are hyperlinked to a pop-up glossary to allow easy access to unfamiliar definitions. Hovering over the term provides a quick, on-screen definition. Clicking the term opens a lightbox with additional information (including an audio pronunciation), and the glossary page for the term provides even more.

Comprehension Checkpoints are questions placed in strategic spots throughout each module to promote good reading techniques. These checkpoints ask the reader a specific question related to the content immediately preceding, helping them to stop and think about what they have just read. Immediate feedback helps them know if they need to re-read, or if they have understood a concept correctly.

Because interaction helps to focus students' attention, most of our online lessons contain interactive learning tools embedded within the body of the lesson. These animations help illustrate points and concepts addressed in the reading. (In this book, references are given when an online animation is available.)

Finally, each Visionlearning module contains a module-specific quiz written with Bloom's Taxonomy in mind. Feedback to quiz answers are provided at the end of this book. We hope that you enjoy using these materials. Happy learning!

For Amy, John, Carina, Aidan, and all of our students
who have inspired this work

Origins: Understanding the Science of Discovery

Anthony Carpi, PhD
Professor of Environmental Chemistry and Toxicology
John Jay College of Criminal Justice, the City University of New York
New York, NY

Anne E. Egger, PhD
Assistant Professor, Geological Sciences and Science Education
Central Washington University
Ellensburg, WA

Visionlearning, Inc.
www.visionlearning.com

Acknowledgments

This work has benefitted from the reviews and feedback of many peer reviewers, and their time and dedication are greatly appreciated. We also thank our readers for submitting comments online that have helped us refine and improve the accuracy and quality of this material. Funding for the Visionlearning project has been provided by the National Science Foundation Course, Curriculum, and Laboratory Improvement Program, and the U.S. Department of Education Fund for the Improvement of Post-Secondary Education. However, this content does not necessarily represent the policy of, or endorsement by, the Federal Government.

Image Copyrights: p.2 Public domain; p.4 Visionlearning, Inc.; p.5 TOMS science team & the Scientific Visualization Studio, NASA GSFC; p.8 Visionlearning, Inc.; p.12 Visionlearning, Inc.; p.14 Visionlearning, Inc.; p.14 NASA; p.16 Epogee, Ltd.; p.17 Visionlearning, Inc.; p.18 NASA; p.19 Huntington Library; p.21 NASA/WMAP; p.24 Visionlearning, Inc.; p.27 Visionlearning, Inc.; p.29 Public domain; p.33 Visionlearning, Inc.; p.34 Visionlearning, Inc.; p.35 Visionlearning, Inc.; p.37 Visionlearning, Inc.; p.38 Visionlearning, Inc.; p.42 Visionlearning, Inc.; p.43 Visionlearning, Inc.; p.48 Visionlearning, Inc.; p.49 Visionlearning, Inc.; p.55 Visionlearning, Inc.; p.56 Visionlearning, Inc.; p.60 Visionlearning, Inc.; p. 68 Pat_Hastings/Shutterstock; p.69 Visionlearning, Inc.; p.70 Visionlearning, Inc.; p.71 Visionlearning, Inc.; p.72 Visionlearning, Inc.; p.77 Visionlearning, Inc.; p.82 Visionlearning, Inc.; p.83 Visionlearning, Inc.; p.84 Visionlearning, Inc.; p.85 Visionlearning, Inc.; p.89 NASA; p.91 JPL; p.92 Visionlearning, Inc.; p.94 Visionlearning, Inc.; p.98 Public domain; p.99 Public domain; p.101 Visionlearning, Inc.; p.102 Visionlearning, Inc.; p.103 Visionlearning, Inc.; p.108 Anne Egger; p.109 Anne Egger; p.110 Anne Egger; p.111 Anne Egger; p.112 Visionlearning, Inc.; p.113 Figure modified from This Dynamic Earth, a publication from the U.S. Geological Survey; p.118 Visionlearning, Inc.; p.119 Visionlearning, Inc.; p.120 Visionlearning, Inc.; p.121 Visionlearning, Inc.; p.122 Visionlearning, Inc.; p.126 Shutterstock; p.127 Visionlearning, Inc.; p.127 Healthy Mouse image Tony Wear, 2009; Dead Mouse image South 12th Photography, 2009; Used under license from Shutterstock, Inc.; p.128 Visionlearning, Inc.; p.134 Visionlearning, Inc.; p.135 Visionlearning, Inc.; p.136 Visionlearning, Inc.; p.137 Museum of London; p.138 Visionlearning, Inc.; p.139 Visionlearning, Inc.; p.144 Visionlearning, Inc.; p.151 Public domain; p.153 Public domain; p.154 Public domain; p. 162 Image courtesy of Special Collections, University of Houston Libraries; p.163 Emory University; p.170 Public domain; p.171 Public domain; p.172 Corel Corporation; p.177 Visionlearning, Inc.; p.183 Corel Corporation; p.187 Visionlearning, Inc.; p.193 Public domain; p. 193 Corel Corporation; p.200 Public domain; p.202 NASA; p.203 Visionlearning, Inc.; p.210 Visionlearning, Inc.; p.216 Adapted from IMO (2007); p.220 Visionlearning, Inc.; p.223 Public domain; p.224 University of Wisconsin-Madison Space Science and Engineering Center; p.225 Visionlearning, Inc. image adapted from image in Jones et al. 1986; p.227 IPCC; p.232 Visionlearning, Inc.; p.234 Public domain; p.236 Anne Egger; p.237 Anne Egger

Production Director: Heather Falconer
Web Programmer: Russ Demarest
Translator: Oscar Cifuentes
This text was printed directly from author provided files

Requests for permission or inquiries should be emailed to:
vision@visionlearning.com

http://www.visionlearning.com

Kendall Hunt
publishing company

www.kendallhunt.com
Send all inquiries to:
4050 Westmark Drive
Dubuque, IA 52004-1840

Copyright © 2014 by Visionlearning, Inc.

ISBN 978-1-4652-5645-4

Contents

The Practice of Science:
An Introduction to Research Methods

by Anthony Carpi, PhD, Anne E. Egger, PhD

Did you know that that even though people talk about "the scientific method," there is more than one way to do research? Examples throughout history, even as early as 5000 BCE, reveal that the practice of science is not a simple step-by-step path that leads to certain answers. Rather, the real scientific method is much less predictable and much more interesting.

Module Summary

Scientists use multiple methods to investigate the natural world and these interconnect and overlap, often with unexpected results. This module gives an overview of scientific research methods, data processing, and the practice of science. It discusses myths that many people believe about the scientific method and provides an introduction to our Research Methods series.

Terms you should know:

interpretation = an explanation of patterns observed in the data

method = a procedure, a process, a systematic way of doing something

observation = the act of noticing something; a record of that which has been noticed

When some people think of science, they think of formulas and facts to memorize. Many of us probably studied for a test in a science class by memorizing the names of the four nucleotides in DNA (adenine, cytosine, guanine, and thymine) or by practicing with one of Newton's laws of motion, like $f = ma$ (force equals mass times acceleration). While this knowledge is an important part of science, it is not all of science. In addition to a body of knowledge that includes formulas and facts, science is a practice by which we pursue answers to questions that can be approached scientifically. This practice is referred to collectively as scientific research, and while the techniques that scientists use to conduct research may differ between disciplines, the underlying principles and objectives are similar. Whether you are talking about biology, chemistry, geology, physics, or any other scientific field, the body of knowledge that is built through these disciplines is based on the collection of data that are then analyzed and interpreted in light of other research findings. How do we know about adenine, cytosine, guanine, and thymine? These were not revealed by chance, but through the work of many scientists collecting data, evaluating the results, and putting together a comprehensive theory that explained their observations.

The recorded roots of formal scientific research lie in the collective work of a number of individuals in ancient Greek, Persian, Arab, Indian, Chinese, and European cultures, rather than from a single person or event. The Greek mathematician Pythagoras is regarded as the first person to promote a scientific hypothesis when, based on his descriptive study of the movement of stars in the sky in the 5th century BCE, he proposed that the Earth was round. The Indian mathematician and astronomer Aryabhata used descriptive records regarding the movement of objects in the night sky to propose in the 6th century CE that the Sun was the center of the solar system. In the 9th century, Chinese alchemists invented gunpowder while performing experiments attempting to make gold from other substances. And the Middle Eastern scientist Alhazen is credited with devising the concept of the scientific experiment while researching properties related to vision and light around 1000 CE.

Figure 1: *The front cover and an inner page from De Revolutionibus showing Copernicus's hypothesis regarding the revolution of planets around the sun (from the 2nd edition, Basel, 1566).*

These and other events demonstrate that a scientific approach to addressing questions about the natural world has long been present in many cultures. The roots of *modern* scientific research methods, however, are considered by many historians to lie in the Scientific Revolution that occurred in Europe in the 16th and 17th centuries. Most historians cite the beginning of the Scientific Revolution as the publication of *De Revolutionibus Orbium Coelestium* (*On the Revolutions of the Heavenly Spheres*) in 1543 by the Polish astronomer Nicolaus Copernicus. Copernicus's careful observation and description of the movement of planets in relation to the Earth led him to hypothesize that the Sun was the center of the solar system and the planets revolved around the Sun in progressively larger orbits in the following order: Mercury, Venus, Earth, Mars, Jupiter, and Saturn (Figure 1). Though Copernicus was not the first person to propose a heliocentric view of the solar system, his systematic gathering of data provided a rigorous argument that challenged the commonly held belief that Earth was the center of the universe.

Figure 2: *Sir Isaac Newton*

The Scientific Revolution was subsequently fueled by the work of Galileo Galilei, Johannes Kepler, Isaac Newton (Figure 2), and others, who not only challenged the traditional geocentric view of the universe, but explicitly rejected the older philosophical approaches to natural science popularized by Aristotle. A key event marking the rejection of the philosophical method was the publication of *Novum Organum: New Directions Concerning the Interpretation of Nature* by Francis Bacon in 1620. Bacon was not a scientist, but rather an English philosopher and essayist, and *Novum* is a work on logic. In it, Bacon presented an inductive method of reasoning that he argued was superior to the philosophical approach of Aristotle. The Baconian method involved a repeating cycle of observation, hypothesis, experimentation, and the need for independent verification. Bacon's work championed a method that was objective, logical, and empirical and provided a basis for the development of scientific research methodology.

Bacon's method of scientific reasoning was further refined by the publication of *Philosophiæ Naturalis Principia Mathematica* (*Mathematical Principles of Natural Philosophy*) by the English physicist and mathematician Isaac Newton in 1686. *Principia* established four rules that have become the basis of modern approaches to science. In brief, Newton's rules proposed that the simplest explanation of natural phenomena is often the best, countering the practice that was common in his day of assigning complicated explanations derived from belief systems, the occult, and observations of natural events. And *Principia* maintained that special explanations of new data should not be used when a reasonable explanation already exists, specifically criticizing the tendency of many of Newton's contemporaries to embellish the significance of their findings with exotic new explanations.

Bacon and Newton laid the foundation that has been built upon by modern scientists and researchers in developing a rigorous methodology for investigating natural phenomena. In particular, the English statisticians Karl Pearson and Ronald Fisher significantly refined scientific research in the 20th century by developing statistical techniques for data analysis and research design (see our Statistics in Science module). And the practice of science continues to evolve today, as new tools and technologies become available and our knowledge about the natural world grows. The practice of science is commonly misrepresented as a simple, four- or five-step path to answering a scientific question, called "The Scientific Method." In reality, scientists rarely follow such a straightforward path through their research. Instead, scientific research includes many possible paths, not all of which lead to unequivocal answers. The *real* scientific method, or practice of science, is much more dynamic and interesting.

Comprehension Checkpoint

Scientific research, if done correctly, follows a straightforward five-step path and leads to definite answers.

A) True
B) False

More than one Scientific Method

The typical presentation of the Scientific Method (Figure 3) suggests that scientific research follows a linear path, proceeding from a question through observation, hypothesis formation, experimentation and finally producing results and a conclusion. However, scientific research does not always proceed linearly. For example, prior to the mid 1800s, a popular scientific hypothesis held that maggots and microorganisms could be spontaneously generated from the inherent *life-force* that existed in some foods. Louis Pasteur doubted this hypothesis and this led him to conduct a series of experiments that would eventually disprove the theory of spontaneous generation (see our Experimentation in Scientific Research module). Pasteur's work would be difficult to characterize using Figure 3 – while it did involve experimentation, he did not develop a hypothesis prior to his experiments. Instead he was motivated to disprove an existing hypothesis. Or consider the work of Grove Karl Gilbert who conducted research on the Henry Mountains in Utah in the late 1800s (see our Description in Scientific Research module). Gilbert was not drawn to the area by a pressing scientific question, but rather he was sent there by the US government to explore the region. Further, Gilbert did not perform a single experiment in the Henry Mountains; his work was based solely on observation and description, yet no one would dispute that Gilbert was practicing science. The traditional and simplistic Scientific Method presented in Figure 3 does not begin to reflect the richness or diversity of scientific research, let alone the diversity of scientists themselves.

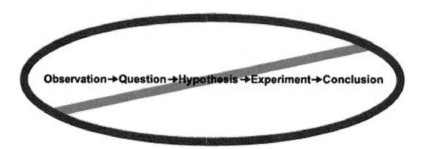

Figure 3: The classic view of The Scientific Method *is misleading in its representation of scientific practice.*

Scientific research methods

Scientific research is a robust and dynamic practice that employs multiple methods toward investigating phenomena, including experimentation, description, comparison, and modeling. Though these methods are described separately both here and in more detail in subsequent modules, many of these methods overlap or are used in combination. For example, when NASA scientists purposefully slammed a 370 kg spacecraft named Deep Impact into a passing comet in 2005, the study had some aspects of descriptive research and some aspects of experimental research (see our Experimentation in Scientific Research module). Many scientific investigations largely employ one method, but different methods may be combined in a single study, or a single study may have characteristics of more than one method. The choice of which research method to use is personal and depends on the experiences of the scientists conducting the research and the nature of the question they are seeking to address. Despite the overlap and interconnectedness of these research methods, it is useful to discuss them separately to understand the principal characteristics of each and the ways they can be used to investigate a question.

Experimentation: Experimental methods are used to investigate the relationship(s) between two or more variables when at least one of those variables can be intentionally controlled or manipulated. The resulting effect of that manipulation (often called a treatment) can then be measured on another variable or variables. The work of the French scientist Louis Pasteur is a classic example. Pasteur put soup broth in a series of flasks, some open to the atmosphere and others sealed. He then measured the effect that the flask type had on the appearance of microorganisms in the soup broth in an effort to study the source of those microorganisms. (See our Experimentation in Scientific Research module)

Description: Description is used to gather data regarding natural phenomena and natural relationships and includes observations and measurements of behaviors. A classic example of a descriptive study is Copernicus's observations and sketches of the movement of planets in the sky in an effort to determine if Earth or the Sun is the orbital center of those objects. (See our Description in Scientific Research module)

Comparison: Comparison is used to determine and quantify relationships between two or more variables by observing different groups that either by choice or circumstance are exposed to different treatments. Examples of comparative research are the studies that were initiated in the 1950s to investigate the relationship between cigarette smoking and lung cancer in which scientists compared individuals who had chosen to smoke of their own accord with non-smokers and correlated the decision to smoke (the treatment) with various health problems including lung cancer. (See our Comparison in Scientific Research module)

Modeling: Both physical and computer-based models are built to mimic natural systems and then used to conduct experiments or make observations. Weather forecasts are an example of scientific modeling that we see every day, where data collected on temperature, wind speed, and direction are used in combination with known physics of atmospheric circulation to predict the path of storms and other weather patterns. (See our Modeling in Scientific Research module)

These methods are interconnected and are often used in combination to fully understand complex phenomenon. Modeling and experimentation are ways of simplifying systems towards understanding causality and future events. However, both rely on assumptions and knowledge of existing systems that can be provided by descriptive studies or other experiments. Description and comparison are used to understand existing systems and are used to examine the application of experimental and modeling results in real-world systems. Results from descriptive and comparative studies are often used to confirm causal relationships identified by models and experiments. While some questions lend themselves to one or another strategy due to the scope or nature of the problem under investigation, most areas of scientific research employ all of these methods as a means of complementing one another towards clarifying a specific hypothesis, theory, or idea in science.

Comprehension Checkpoint

Scientific research methods, such as *experimentation, description, comparison,* and *modeling*:

A) are interconnected and are often used in combination.

B) are more effective if used alone

Research methods in practice:
The investigation of stratospheric ozone depletion

Scientific theories are clarified and strengthened through the collection of data from more than one method that generate multiple lines of evidence. Take, for example, the various research methods used to investigate what came to be known as the "ozone hole."

Early descriptive and comparative studies point to problem: In 1957, the British Antarctic Survey (BAS) began a descriptive study of stratospheric ozone levels in an effort to better understand the role that ozone plays in absorbing solar energy (MacDowall & Sutcliffe, 1960). For the next 20 years, the BAS recorded ozone levels and observed seasonal shifts in ozone levels, which they attributed to natural fluctuations. In the mid 1970s, however, the BAS began to note a dramatic drop in ozone levels that they correlated with the change of seasons in the Antarctic. Within a decade, they noted that a seasonal "ozone hole" (Figure 4) had begun to appear over the South Pole (Farman et al., 1985).

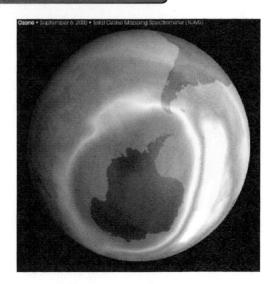

Figure 4: A picture of the Antarctic Ozone Hole in 2000, one of the largest holes on record. Ozone levels are given in Dobson Units, a measurement specific to stratospheric ozone research and named in honor of G.M.B. Dobson, one of the first scientists to investigate atmospheric ozone.

The development of new technology opens novel research paths: Concurrent with the early BAS studies, the British scientist James Lovelock was working on developing new technology for the detection of trace concentrations of gases and vapors in the atmosphere (Lovelock, 1960). One instrument that Lovelock invented was a sensitive electron capture detector that could quantify atmospheric levels of chlorofluorocarbons (CFCs). At the time, CFCs were widely used as refrigerants and as propellants in aerosol cans and they were thought to be stable in the atmosphere and thus harmless chemicals. In 1970, Lovelock began an observational study of atmospheric CFCs and found that the chemicals were indeed very stable and could be carried long distances from major urban air pollution sources by prevailing winds. Under the impression that CFCs were chemically inert, Lovelock proposed that the chemicals could be used as benign atmospheric tracers of large air mass movements (Lovelock, 1971).

Modeling and experimental research are used to draw causal connections: In 1972, F. Sherwood Rowland, a chemist at the University of California at Irvine, attended a lecture on Lovelock's work. Rowland became interested in CFCs and began studying the subject with a colleague at Irvine, Mario Molina. Molina and Rowland were familiar with modeling research by Paul Crutzen, a researcher at the National Center for Atmospheric Research in Colorado, that had previously shown that nitrogen oxides are involved in chemical reactions in the stratosphere and can influence upper atmosphere ozone levels (Crutzen, 1970). They were also familiar with modeling research by Harold Johnston, an atmospheric chemist at the University of California at Berkeley, which suggested that nitrogen oxide emissions from supersonic jets could reduce stratospheric ozone levels (Johnston, 1971). With these studies in mind, they consulted experimental research published by Michael Clyne and Ronald Walker, two British chemists, regarding the reaction rates of several chlorine-containing compounds (Clyne & Walker, 1973). In 1974, Molina and Rowland published a landmark study in the journal *Nature* in which they modeled chemical kinetics to show that CFCs were not completely inert, and that they could be transported to high altitudes where they would break apart in strong sunlight and release chlorine radicals (Molina & Rowland, 1974). Molina and Rowland's model predicted that the chlorine radicals, which are reactive, would cause the destruction of significant amounts of ozone in the stratosphere.

Descriptive and comparative research provide real-world confirmation: In 1976, a group of scientists led by Allan Lazrus at the National Center for Atmospheric Research in Boulder, Colorado, used balloons to carry instruments aloft that could sample air at high altitudes. In these samples, they were able to detect the presence of CFCs above the troposphere – confirming that CFCs did indeed reach the stratosphere and that once there, they could decompose in light (Lazrus et al., 1976). Further research conducted using balloons and high-atmosphere aircraft in the 1980s confirmed that chlorine and chlorine oxide radicals contribute to the loss of ozone over the Antarctic (McElroy et. al., 1986). By the late 1980s, scientists began to examine the possible link between ozone loss and skin cancer because high levels of ultraviolet light, as would exist under an ozone hole, can cause skin cancer. In areas such as Southern Chile, where the Antarctic ozone hole overlaps with a populated land mass, a significant correlation was indeed found between the growing ozone hole and increasing rates of skin cancer (Abarca & Casiccia, 2002).

As a result of this collection of diverse yet complementary scientific evidence, the world community began to limit the use of CFCs and ratified the Montreal Protocol in 1988, which imposed strict international limits on CFC use. In 1995, Molina, Rowland, and Crutzen shared the Nobel Prize in chemistry for their research that contributed to our understanding of ozone chemistry.

The ozone story (further detailed in our online Resources associated with this module; see The Ozone Depletion Phenomenon) highlights an important point: scientific research is multi-dimensional, non-linear, and often leads down unexpected pathways. James Lovelock had no intention of contributing to the ozone depletion story; his work was directed at quantifying atmospheric CFC levels. Although gaining an understanding of the ozone hole may appear as a linear progression of events when viewed in hindsight, this was not the case at the time. While each researcher or research team built on previous work, it is more accurate to portray the relationships between their studies as a web of networked events, not as a linear series. Lovelock's work led Molina and Rowland to their ozone depletion models, but Lovelock's work is also widely cited by researchers developing improved electron capture detectors. Molina and Rowland not only used Lovelock's work, but they drew on the research of Crutzen, Johnston, Clyne, Walker and many others. Any single research advance was subsequently pursued in a number of different directions that complemented and reinforced one another – a common phenomenon in science. The entire ozone story required modeling, experiments, comparative research, and descriptive studies to develop a coherent theory about the role of ozone in the atmosphere, how we as humans are affecting it, and how we are also affected by it.

Comprehension Checkpoint

The ozone research story shows that, in practice, scientific research is

A) a linear step-by-step procedure.

B) an interconnected web of related studies.

The real practice of science

Scientific research methods are part of the practice through which questions can be addressed scientifically. These methods all produce data that are subject to analysis and interpretation and lead to ideas in science such as hypotheses, theories, and laws. Scientific ideas are developed and disseminated through the literature where individuals and groups may debate the interpretations and significance of the results. Eventually, as multiple lines of evidence add weight to an idea it becomes an integral part of the body of knowledge that exists in science and feeds back into the research process. Figure 5 provides a graphical overview of the materials we have developed to explain the real practice of science, and the key elements are explained below.

The Scientific Community: Scientists (see our Scientists and the Scientific Community module) draw on their background, experiences, and even prejudices in deciding on the types of questions they pursue and the research methods that they employ, and they are supported in their efforts by the scientific institutions and the community in which they work (see our Scientific Institutions and Societies module). Human nature makes it impossible for any scientist to be completely objective,

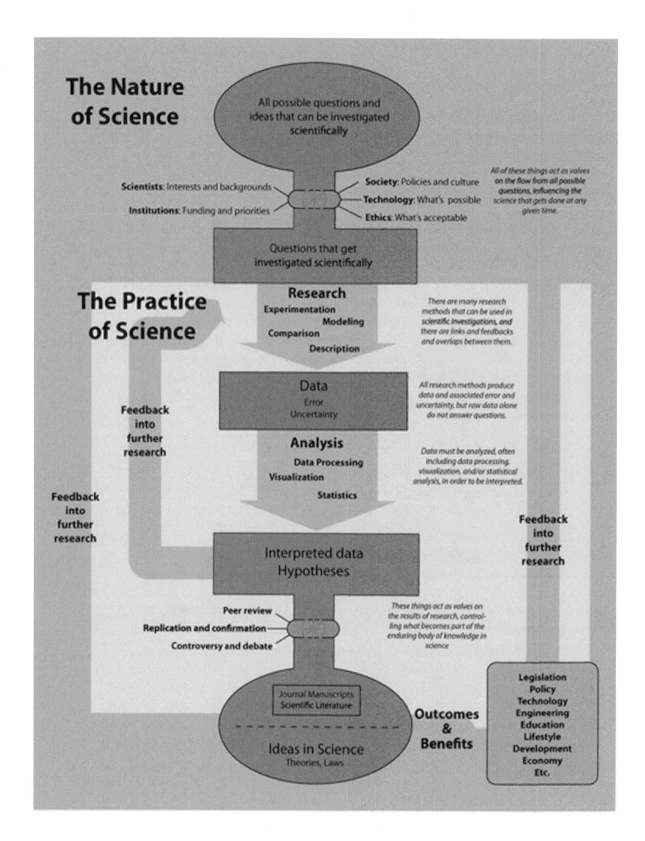

The Nature of Science

All possible questions and ideas that can be investigated scientifically

Scientists: Interests and backgrounds

Institutions: Funding and priorities

Society: Policies and culture

Technology: What's possible

Ethics: What's acceptable

All of these things act as valves on the flow from all possible questions, influencing the science that gets done at any given time.

Questions that get investigated scientifically

The Practice of Science

Research
Experimentation
Modeling
Comparison
Description

There are many research methods that can be used in scientific investigations, and there are links and feedbacks and overlaps between them.

Data
Error
Uncertainty

All research methods produce data and associated error and uncertainty, but raw data alone do not answer questions.

Analysis
Data Processing
Visualization
Statistics

Data must be analyzed, often including data processing, visualization, and/or statistical analysis, in order to be interpreted.

Feedback into further research

Feedback into further research

Interpreted data
Hypotheses

Feedback into further research

Peer review

Replication and confirmation

Controversy and debate

These things act as valves on the results of research, controlling what becomes part of the enduring body of knowledge in science

Journal Manuscripts
Scientific Literature

Ideas in Science
Theories, Laws

Outcomes & Benefits

Legislation
Policy
Technology
Engineering
Education
Lifestyle
Development
Economy
Etc.

Figure 5: *A graphical overview of our modules that detail how science is practiced – multiple research methods are influenced by many factors, and the process has feedback loops leading to new ideas and research studies.*

but an important aspect of scientific research is that scientists are open to any potential result. Science emphasizes the use of multiple lines of evidence as a check on the objectivity of both individual scientists and the community at large. Research is repeated, multiple methods are used to investigate the same phenomenon, and scientists report these methods and their interpretations when publishing their work. Assuring the objectivity of data and interpretation is built into the culture of science. These common practices unite a community of science made up of individuals and institutions that are dedicated to advancing science. Rowland, Molina, Lovelock, and Crutzen each were guided by their personal interests and supported by their respective institutions. For example, in addition to his work with CFCs, James Lovelock is credited with proposing the Gaia hypothesis that all living and non-living things on the planet interact with one another much like a large, single organism. This perspective influenced his interest in looking at the movement of large air masses across the globe, work that was supported by funding from the National Aeronautics and Space Administration (NASA).

Data: Science is a way of understanding the world around us that is founded on the principal of gathering and analyzing data (see our Data Analysis and Interpretation module). In contrast, before the popularization of science, philosophical explanations of natural phenomena based on reasoning rather than data were common, and these led to a host of unsupported ideas, many of which have proven incorrect. For example, in addition to his ideas on vision, the Greek philosopher Empedocles also reasoned that because most animals are warm to the touch, they must contain fire inside of them (see our States of Matter module). In contrast, the initial conclusion of the presence of a hole in the stratospheric ozone layer was based on years of data collected by scientists at the British Antarctic Survey. The amount of uncertainty and error (see our Uncertainty, Error, and Confidence module) associated with these data was critical to record as well – a small error in Dobson units would have made the hole seemingly disappear. Using statistical methods (see our Statistics in Science module) and data visualization techniques (see our Using Graphs and Visual Data in Science module) to analyze data, the scientists at the BAS drew on their own experience and knowledge to interpret those data, demonstrating that the "hole" was more than a seasonal, natural shift in ozone levels.

Ideas in science: Scientific research contributes to the body of scientific knowledge, held in record in the scientific literature (see our Utilizing the Scientific Literature module) so that future scientists can learn from past work. The literature does not simply hold a record of all of the data that scientists have collected: it also includes scientists' interpretations of those data. To express their ideas, scientists propose hypotheses to explain observations. For example, after observing, collecting, and interpreting data, Lovelock hypothesized that CFCs could be used by meteorologists as benign tracers of the movement of large air masses. While Lovelock was correct in his prediction that CFCs could be used to trace air movement, later research showed that they are not benign. This hypothesis was just one piece of evidence that Molina and Rowland used to form their theory of ozone depletion. Scientific theories (see our Theories, Hypotheses, and Laws module) are ideas that have held up under scrutiny and are supported by multiple lines of evidence. The ozone depletion theory is based on results from all of the studies described above, not just Lovelock's work. Unlike hypotheses, which can be tenuous in nature, theories rely on multiple lines of evidence and so are durable. Still, theories may change and be refined as new evidence and analyses come to light. For example, in 2007, a group of NASA scientists reported experimental results showing that chlorine peroxide, a compound formed when CFCs are transported to the stratosphere and which participates in the destruction of ozone, has a slower reaction rate in the presence of ultraviolet light than previously thought (Pope et al., 2007). The work by Pope and his colleagues does not dispute the theory of ozone destruction; rather, it does suggest that some modifications may be necessary in terms of the reaction rates used in atmospheric chemistry models.

Despite the fact that different scientists use different methods, they can easily share results and communicate with one another because of the common language that has developed to present and interpret data and construct ideas. These shared characteristics allow studies as disparate as atmospheric chemistry, plant biology, and paleontology to be grouped together under the heading of "science." Although a practicing scientist in any one of those disciplines will require very specialized factual knowledge to conduct their research, the broad similarities in methodology allow that knowledge to be shared across many disciplines

Key Concepts for this chapter

▶ The practice of science involves many possible pathways. The classic description of the scientific method as a linear or circular process does not adequately capture the dynamic yet rigorous nature of the practice.

▶ Scientists use multiple research methods to gather data and develop hypotheses. These methods include experimentation, description, comparison, and modeling.

▶ Scientific research methods are complementary; when multiple lines of evidence independently support one another, hypotheses are strengthened and confidence in scientific conclusions improves.

References

Abarca, F., & Casiccia, C. C. (2002). Skin cancer and ultraviolet-B radiation under the Antarctic ozone hole: Southern Chile, 1987-2000. *Photodermatology, Photoimmunology & Photomedicine*, 18(6), 294-302.

Agar, D. (2001). Arabic studies in physics and astronomy during 800-1400 AD. Retrieved September 22, 2008, from the University of Jyväskylä.

Clyne, M. A. A., & Walker, R. F. (1973). Absolute rate constants for elementary reactions in the chlorination of CH_4, CD_4, CH_3Cl, CH_2Cl_2, $CHCl_3$, $CDCl_3$ and $CBrCl_3$. *Journal of the Chemical Society, Faraday Transactions 1*, 69, 1547–1567.

Cohn, D. (2004). *The life and times of Louis Pasteur*. University of Louisville.

Crutzen, P. J. (1970). The influence of nitrogen oxides on the atmospheric ozone content. *Quarterly Journal of the Royal Meteorological Society*, 96(408), 320-325.

Environment Canada. (2006). *Protocol to the Vienna Convention on Substances that Deplete the Ozone Layer* (Montreal Protocol).

Farman, J. C., Gardiner, B. G., & Shanklin, J. D. (1985). Large losses of total ozone in Antarctica reveal seasonal ClOx/NOx interaction. *Nature*, 315, 207-210.

Johnston, H. (1971). Reduction of stratospheric ozone by nitrogen oxide catalysts from supersonic transport exhaust. *Science*, 173(3996), 517.

Kelly, J. (2004). *Gunpowder*. New York: Basic Books.

Lazrus, A. L., Gandrud, B. W., Woodard, R. N., & Sedlacek, W. A. (1976). Direct measurements of stratospheric chlorine and bromine. *Journal of Geophysical Research*, 81(C6), 1067-1070.

Lovelock, J. E. (1960). A photoionization detector for gases and vapors. *Nature*, 188, 401.

Lovelock, J. E. (1971). Atmospheric fluorine compounds as indicators of air movements. *Nature*, 230(5293), 379.

MacDowall, J., & Sutcliffe, R. C. (1960). Some observations at Halley Bay in seismology, glaciology and meteorology [and discussion]. Proceedings of the Royal Society of London. Series A, *Mathematical and Physical Sciences*, 256(1285), 149-197.

McElroy, M. B., Salawitch, R. J., Wofsy, S. C., & Logan, J. A. (1986). Reductions of Antarctic ozone due to synergistic interactions of chlorine and bromine. *Nature*, 321, 759-762.

Molina, M. J., & Rowland, F. S. (1974). Stratospheric sink for chlorofluoromethanes: Chlorine atom-catalysed destruction of ozone. *Nature*, 249(5460), 810.

Newton, I. (1686). Book 3: The system of the world. *Philosophiae Naturalis Principia Mathematica*, translated by Andrew Motte, 1729.

Pasteur, L. (1880). De l'atténuation du virus du choléra des poules. *Comptes rendus de l'Academie des Sciences*, 91, 673.

Pope, F. D., Hansen, J. C., Bayes, K. D., Friedl, R. R., & Sander, S. P. (2007). Ultraviolet absorption spectrum of chlorine peroxide, ClOOCl. *Journal of Physical Chemistry A*, 111(20), 4322-4332.

Rowland, F. S. (2004). The changing atmosphere. April 5, Lecture to Bibliotheca Alexandrina, Egypt. Retrieved September 22, 2008.

Williams, H. S. (1999). *A history of science*. Seattle, WA: The World Wide School.

Wyckoff, S. How did scientific inquiry begin? *Scientific inquiry*, ACEPT, Arizona State University.

Take the Quiz ► ► ►

The Practice of Science Quiz

1. There are no examples of scientific research prior to the *Scientific Revolution* in Europe in the 16th century.

   A) True

   B) False

2. Which of the following is NOT a component of all scientific research methods?

   A) being open to potential results

   B) gathering data

   C) having other scientists review methods and findings

   D) manipulating variables

3. In *Novum Organum*, Francis Bacon wrote about

   A) a method of reasoning that involves a repeating cycle of observation, hypothesis, and experimentation.

   B) a method of reasoning that involves philosophy instead of observation and study.

   C) a challenge to the heliocentric view of the universe.

   D) a methodology for analyzing data that involves statistical analysis of data.

4. The problem with the traditional presentation of the scientific method as seen below is that

   A) scientific research rarely proceeds in a neat, linear fashion.

   B) experimentation is not the only research method available to scientists.

   C) not all research studies begin with a question.

   D) all of the choices are correct

5. The research that led to the adoption of the international agreement known as the Montreal Protocol that limited the use of chlorofluorocarbons (CFCs)

   A) involved only modeling.

   B) involved only experiments.

   C) involved several different methods.

   D) involved a type of method that cannot be easily classified.

Answers and feedback can be found on Page 244

The Nature of Scientific Knowledge

by Anthony Carpi, PhD and Anne Egger, PhD

Did you know that it was not Magellan, Columbus, or even Copernicus who first proposed that the world was round? Rather, 2,000 years before these Europeans, Greek philosophers referred to the Earth as a sphere. An accumulation of evidence over the centuries confirmed that the Earth was round long before explorers sailed around the world.

Module Summary

This module explores the nature of scientific knowledge by asking what science is. It emphasizes the importance of a scientific way of thinking and shows how observation and testing add to the body of scientific knowledge. Focusing on astronomy and physics, the module highlights the work of scientists through history who have contributed to our understanding of the age of the universe as a means of conveying the nature of scientific knowledge.

Terms you should know:

process = method, procedure; series of actions or steps

evidence = support for an idea, opinion, or hypothesis

It seems preposterous to us today that people once thought that the Earth was flat. Who could have possibly thought of our planet as a giant disk with the stars and heavens above, and boulders, tree roots, and other things below? But this was the dominant view of Earth in much of the world before the 2nd century BCE, though the details differed from culture to culture. And it was not explorers who sailed around the world that finally laid the idea to rest, but an accumulation of evidence long before this.

Greek philosophers referred to a spherical Earth as early as the 6th century BCE. They observed that the moon appeared to be a sphere and therefore inferred that Earth might also be spherical. Two hundred years later, in the 4th century BCE, the Greek philosopher Aristotle observed that the shadow of the Earth on the moon during a lunar eclipse is always curved, thus providing some of the first evidence that Earth is spherical. In the 3rd century BCE, the mathematician Eratosthenes observed that at noon on the summer solstice in the ancient Egyptian city of Syene, the sun was directly overhead as objects did not cast a shadow. Eratosthenes was from Alexandria, Egypt, some 500 miles to the north, and he knew that a tall tower cast a shadow in that city at the same time on the summer solstice. Using these observations and measurements of shadow length and distance, he inferred that the surface of

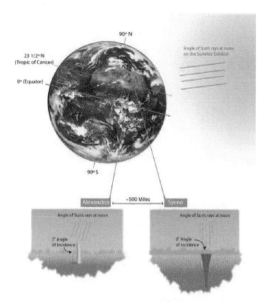

Figure 1: Representation of Eratosthenes' studies demonstrating the curvature of Earth and the geometry used to calculate the circumference of the planet.

Figure 2: Earthrise *taken on December 24, 1968, from the Apollo 8 mission.*

the Earth is curved and he calculated a remarkably accurate estimate of the circumference of the planet (Figure 1). Some years later, the Greek geographer Strabo added to this evidence when he observed that sailors saw distant objects move downward on the horizon and disappear as they sailed away from them. He proposed that this was because Earth was curved and those sailors were not simply moving further away from the objects but also curving around the planet as they sailed.

Aristotle, Eratosthenes, and Strabo didn't call themselves scientists, yet they were using the process of science by making observations and providing explanations for those observations. Thus, we knew that Earth was a sphere long before Ferdinand Magellan's men sailed all the way around it in 1522 or before Apollo 8 astronauts sent back pictures of Earth from space in 1968 (Figure 2), documenting its spherical shape. In fact, those astronauts had to be absolutely confident that the Earth was a rotating sphere, orbiting the sun, or they would never have been able to get into orbit. It is the nature of science and scientific knowledge that gave them that confidence, and understanding the difference between scientific knowledge and other types of knowledge is critical to understanding science itself.

What is science?

Science consists of two things: a body of knowledge and the process by which that knowledge is produced. This second component of science provides us with a way of thinking and knowing about the world. Commonly, we only see the "body of knowledge" component of science. We are presented with scientific concepts in statement form – Earth is round, electrons are negatively charged, our genetic code is contained in our DNA, the universe is 13.7 billion years old – with little background about the process that led to that knowledge and why we can trust it. But there are a number of things that distinguish the scientific process and give us confidence in the knowledge produced through it.

So then, what is the scientific process? The scientific process is a way of building knowledge and making predictions about the world in such a way that they are testable. The question of whether Earth is flat or round could be put to the test, it could be studied through multiple lines of research, and the evidence evaluated to determine whether it supported a round or flat planet. Different scientific disciplines typically use different methods and approaches to investigate the natural world, but testing lies at the core of scientific inquiry for all scientists.

As scientists analyze and interpret their data (see our Data Analysis and Interpretation module), they generate hypotheses, theories, or laws (see our Theories, Hypotheses, and Laws module), which help explain their results and place them in context of the larger body of scientific knowledge. These different kinds of explanations are tested by scientists through additional experiments, observations, modeling, and theoretical studies. Thus, the body of scientific knowledge builds on previous ideas and is constantly growing. It is deliberately shared with colleagues through the process of peer review (see our Peer Review module), where scientists comment on each other's work, and then through publication in the scientific literature (see our Utilizing the Scientific Literature module), where it can be evaluated and integrated into the body of scientific knowledge by the larger community. And this is not the end: One of the hallmarks of scientific knowledge is that it is subject to change, as new data are collected and reinterpretations of existing data are made. Major theories, which are supported by multiple lines of evidence, are rarely completely changed, but new data and tested explanations add nuance and detail.

A scientific way of thinking is something that anyone can use, at any time, whether or not they are in the process of developing new knowledge and explanations. Thinking scientifically involves asking questions that can be answered analytically by collecting data or creating a model and then testing one's ideas. A scientific way of thinking inherently includes creativity in approaching explanations while staying within the confines of the data. Thinking scientifically does not mean rejecting your culture and background, but recognizing the role that they play in your way of thinking. While testable explanations are a critical component of thinking scientifically, there are other valid ways of thinking about the world around us that do not always yield testable explanations. These different ways of thinking are complementary – not in competition – as they address different aspects of the human experience.

It's easy to be confident in the scientific process and our knowledge when we can provide irrefutable evidence, as we were able to do by orbiting around the Earth in a spaceship and taking pictures of an obviously round planet. But most scientific investigations do not lead to results that are so easily supported, and yet we still rely on and trust the knowledge produced through the process of science. Why do we trust it? Because it works. Science has a long history of creating knowledge that is useful and that gives us more insight into our surroundings. Take one of the statements above: The universe is 13.7 billion years old. Why should we have confidence in this statement?

Comprehension Checkpoint

The scientific process is a way of building knowledge and making predictions that

A) can be tested.

B) are accepted as scientific law.

The age of the universe

How old is the universe? How can we possibly know the age of something that was created not simply before human history, but before our planet came into being? This is a difficult question to address scientifically, so much so that through the early 20th century many scientists assumed that the universe was infinite and eternal, existing for all of time.

Machines and entropy

The first indication that the universe may not have existed for all of time came from an unlikely source: the study of engines. In the 1820s, Sadi Carnot was a young officer on leave from the French military. While taking classes at various institutions in Paris, he became interested in industrial problems, and was surprised to see that no scientific studies had been undertaken on the steam engine, a relatively new invention at the time and a poorly understood one. Carnot believed that engines could be better understood – a characteristic common to scientists is that they work to better understand things – and so he studied the transfer of energy in engines. He recognized that no engine could be 100% efficient because some energy is always lost from the system as heat (Figure 3), and he published his ideas in a book titled *Reflections on the Motive Power of Fire and on Machines Fitted to Develop that Power*, which presented a mathematical description of the amount of work that could be generated by an engine, called the Carnot cycle (Carnot, 1824).

Carnot's work didn't receive much attention during his lifetime, and he died of cholera in 1832 when he was only 36 years old. But others began to realize the importance of his work and built upon it. One of those scientists was Rudolf Clausius, a German physicist who showed that Carnot's principle was not limited to engines, but in fact applied to all systems in which there was a transfer of energy. Clausius' application of an explanation for one phenomenon to many others is also characteristic of science, which assumes that processes are universal.

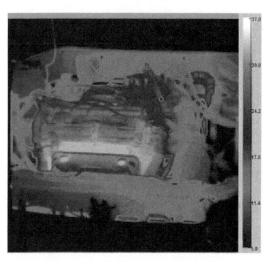

Figure 3: *An infrared image of a running engine showing the temperature of various parts of the engine. Higher temperatures (lighter portions of the image) indicate greater heat loss. The loss of heat represents a loss of efficiency in the engine, and a contribution to the increasing entropy of the universe.*

In 1850, Clausius published a paper in which he developed the Second Law of Thermodynamics, which states that energy always flows from a high energy state (for example, a system that is hot) to a low energy state (one that is cold) (Clausius, 1850). In later work, Clausius coined the term *entropy* to describe the energy lost from a system when it is transferred, and as an acknowledgement of the pioneering work of Sadi Carnot in providing the foundation for his discoveries, Clausius used the symbol S to refer to the entropy of a system.

But how do engines and entropy relate to the age of the universe? In 1865, Clausius published another paper that restated the Second Law of Thermodynamics as "the entropy of the universe tends to a maximum." If the universe was infinite and existed for all time, the second law of thermodynamics says that all of the energy within the universe would have been lost to entropy by now. In other words, the stars themselves would have burned out long ago, dissipating their heat into surrounding space. The fact that there are still active stars must mean that the universe has existed for a finite amount of time, and was created at some specific point in time. Perhaps the age of that point in time could be determined?

Redshift and the Doppler Effect

At about the same time, an Austrian physicist by the name of Christian Doppler was studying astronomy and mathematics. Doppler knew that light behaved like a wave, and so began to think about how the movement of stars might affect the light emitted from those stars. In a paper published in 1842, Doppler proposed that the observed frequency of a wave would depend on the relative speed of the wave's source in relation to the observer, a phenomenon he called a "frequency shift" (Doppler, 1842). He made an analogy to a ship at sail on the ocean, describing how the ship would encounter waves on the surface of the water at a faster rate (and thus higher frequency) if it were sailing into the waves than if it were traveling in the same direction as the waves.

You might be familiar with the frequency shift, which we now call the Doppler Effect in his honor, if you have ever listened to the sound of traffic while standing on the side of the road. The familiar high-to-low pitch change is an example of the effect – the actual frequency of the waves emitted is not changing, but the speed of the passing vehicle affects how quickly those waves reach you. Doppler proposed that we would see the same effect on any stars that were moving: Their color would shift toward the red end of the spectrum if they were moving away from Earth (called a *redshift*) and toward the blue end of the spectrum if they were moving closer (called a *blueshift*) (see Figure 4). He expected to be able to see this shift in binary stars, or pairs of stars that orbit around each other. Eventually, Doppler's 1842 paper, entitled "On the coloured light of the double stars and certain other stars of the heavens," would change the very way we look at the universe. However, at the time, telescopes were not sensitive enough to confirm the shift he proposed.

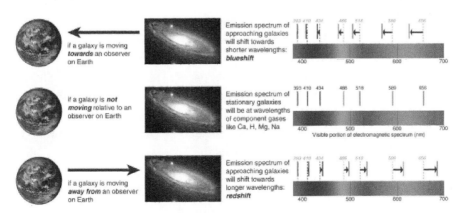

Figure 4: *A representation of how the perceived spectrum of light emitted from a galaxy is affected by its motion.*

Doppler's ideas became part of the scientific literature and by that means became known to other scientists. By the early 1900s, technology finally caught up with Doppler and more powerful telescopes could be used to test his ideas. In September of 1901, an American named Vesto Slipher had just completed his undergraduate degree in mechanics and astronomy at Indiana University. He got a job as a temporary assistant at the Lowell Observatory in Flagstaff, Arizona, while continuing his graduate work at Indiana. Shortly after his arrival, the observatory obtained a three-prism spectrograph, and Slipher's job was to mount it to the 24-inch telescope at the observatory and learn to use it to study the rotation of the planets in the solar system. After a few months of problems and trouble-shooting, Slipher was able to take spectrograms of Mars, Jupiter, and Saturn. But Slipher's personal research interests were much farther away than the planets of the solar system. Like Doppler, he was interested in studying the spectra of binary stars, and he began to do so in his spare time at the observatory.

Over the next decade, Slipher completed a Masters degree and a PhD at Indiana University, while continuing his work at Lowell Observatory measuring the spectra and Doppler shift of stars. In particular, Slipher focused his attention on stars within spiral nebulae (Figure 5), expecting to find that the shift seen in the spectra of the stars would indicate that the galaxies those stars belonged to were rotating. Indeed, he is credited with determining that galaxies rotate, and was able to determine the velocities at which they rotate. But in 1914, having studied 15 different nebulae, he announced a curious discovery at a meeting of the American Astronomical Society in August:

> In the great majority of cases the nebulae are receding; the largest velocities are all positive....The striking preponderance of the positive sign indicates a general fleeing from us or the Milky Way.

Figure 5: *The Andromeda galaxy, one of the spiral nebulae studied by Vesto Slipher, as seen in infrared light by NASA's Wide-field Infrared Survey Explorer.*

Slipher had found that most galaxies showed a redshift in their spectrum, indicating that they were all moving away from us in space, or receding (Slipher, 1915). By measuring the magnitude of the redshift, he was able to determine the recessional velocity or the speed at which objects were "fleeing". Slipher had made an interpretation from his observations that put a new perspective on the universe, and in response, he received a standing ovation for his presentation.

Slipher continued his work with redshift and galaxies and published another paper in 1917, having now examined 25 nebulae and seen a redshift in 21 of them. Georges Lemaître, a Belgian physicist and astronomer, built on Slipher's work while completing his PhD at the Massachusetts Institute of Technology. He extended Slipher's measurements to the entire universe, and calculated mathematically that the universe must be expanding in order to explain Slipher's observation. He published his ideas in a 1927 paper called "A homogeneous Universe of constant mass and growing radius accounting for the radial velocity of extragalactic nebulae" (Lemaître, 1927), but his paper met with widespread criticism from the scientific community. The English astronomer Fred Hoyle ridiculed the work, and coined the term "Big Bang" theory as a disparaging nickname for Lemaître's idea. And none other than Albert Einstein criticized Lemaître, writing to him, "Your math is correct, but your physics is abominable" (Deprit, 1984).

Einstein's criticism had a personal and cultural component, two things we often over-look in terms of their influence on science. Several years earlier, Einstein had published his general theory of relativity (Einstein, 1916). In formulating the theory, Einstein had encoun-tered one significant problem: General relativity predicted that the universe had to be ei-ther contracting or expanding – it did not allow for a static universe. But a contracting or expanding universe could not be eternal, while a static, non-moving universe could, and the prevailing cultural belief at the time was that the universe was eternal. Einstein was strongly influenced by his cultural surroundings. As a result, he invented a "fudge factor," which he called the cosmological constant, that would allow the theory of general relativity to be con-sistent with a static universe. But science is not a democracy or plutocracy; it is neither the most common or most popular conclusion that becomes accepted, but rather the conclusion that stands up to the test of evidence over time. Einstein's cosmological constant was being challenged by new evidence.

Comprehension Checkpoint

Scientists are not influenced by their personal experiences, their beliefs, or the culture of which they are a part.

A) True

B) False

The expanding universe

In 1929, an American astronomer working at the Mt. Wilson Observatory in southern California made an important contribution to the discussion of the nature of the universe. Edwin Hubble had been at Mt. Wilson for 10 years, measuring the distances to galaxies, among other things. In the 1920s, he was working with Milton Humason, a high school drop-out and assistant at the observatory. Hubble and Humason plotted the distances they had calculated for 46 different galaxies against Slipher's recession velocity and found a linear relationship (see Figure 6) (Hubble, 1929).

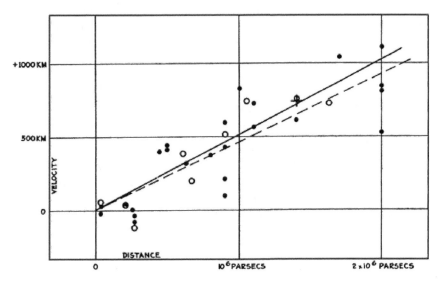

Figure 6: The original Hubble dia-gram. The relative velocity of galaxies (in km/sec) is plotted against distance to that galaxy (in parsecs; a parsec is 3.26 light years). The slope of the line drawn through the points gives the rate of expansion of the universe (the Hubble Constant). (Originally Figure 1, from "A Relation Between Distance and Radial Velocity Among Extra-Galactic Nebulae," Proceedings of the National Academy of Sciences, Volume 15, Issue 3, 1929: p. 172. © Huntington Library, San Marino, CA.)

In other words, their graph showed that more distant galaxies were receding faster than closer ones, confirming the idea that the universe was indeed expanding. This relationship, now referred to as Hubble's Law, allowed them to calculate the rate of expansion as a function of distance from the slope of the line in the graph. This rate term is now referred to as the Hubble constant. Hubble's initial value for the expansion rate was 500 km/sec/Megaparsec, or about 160 km/sec per million-light-years. (You can learn more about Linear Equations at www.visionlearning.com.)

Knowing the rate at which the universe is expanding, one can calculate the age of the universe by in essence "tracing back" the most distant objects in the universe to their point of origin. Using his initial value for the expansion rate and the measured distance of the galaxies, Hubble and Humason calculated the age of the universe to be approximately 2 billion years. Unfortunately, the calculation was inconsistent with lines of evidence from other investigations. By the time Hubble made his discovery, geologists had used radioactive dating techniques to calculate the age of Earth at about 3 billion years (Rutherford, 1929) – or older than the universe itself! Hubble had followed the process of science, so what was the problem?

Even laws and constants are subject to revision in science. It soon became clear that there was a problem in the way that Hubble had calculated his constant. In the 1940s, a German astronomer named Walter Baade took advantage of the blackouts that were ordered in response to potential attacks during World War II and used the Mt. Wilson Observatory in Arizona to look at several objects that Hubble had interpreted as single stars. With darker surrounding skies, Baade realized that these objects were, in fact, groups of stars, and each was fainter, and thus more distant, than Hubble had calculated. Baade doubled the distance to these objects, and in turn halved the Hubble constant and doubled the age of the universe. In 1953, the American astronomer Allan Sandage, who had studied under Baade, looked in more detail at the brightness of stars and how that varied with distance. Sandage further revised the constant, and his estimate of 75 km/sec/Megaparsec is close to our modern day estimate of the Hubble constant of 72 km/sec/Megaparsec, which places the age of the universe at 12 to 14 billion years old.

The new estimates developed by Baade and Sandage did not negate what Hubble had done (it is still called the Hubble constant, after all), but they revised it based on new knowledge. The lasting knowledge of science is rarely the work of an individual, as building on the work of others is a critical component of the process of science. Hubble's findings would have been limited to some interesting data on the distance to various stars had it not also built on, and incorporated, the work of Slipher. Similarly, Baade and Sandage's contribution were no less significant because they "simply" refined Hubble's earlier work.

Since the 1950s, other means of calculating the age of the universe have been developed. For example, there are now methods for dating the age of the stars, and the oldest stars date to approximately 13.2 billion years ago (Frebel et al., 2007). The Wilkinson Microwave Anisotropy Probe (see the Research links on this module for more detail) is collecting data on cosmic microwave background radiation (Figure 7). Using these data in conjunction with Einstein's theory of general relativity, scientists have calculated the age of the universe at 13.7 ± 0.2 billion years old (Spergel et al., 2003). The convergence of multiple lines of evidence on a single explanation is what creates the solid foundation of scientific knowledge.

Figure 7: Visual representation of the cosmic microwave background radiation, and the temperature differences indicated by that radiation, as collected by the Wilkinson Microwave Anisotropy Probe.

−200μK ▮▬▬▬▬▬▬▬▬▬▬▬▬▬▬▬▬▮ 200μK

Comprehension Checkpoint

Major ideas in science are rarely the work of

A) individuals.

B) multiple researchers.

Why should we trust science?

Why should we believe what scientists say about the age of the universe? We have no written records of its creation, and no one has been able to "step outside" of the system, as astronauts did when they took pictures of Earth from space, to measure its age. Yet the nature of the scientific process allows us to accurately state the age of the observable universe. These predictions were developed by multiple researchers and tested through multiple research methods. They have been presented to the scientific community through publications and public presentations. And they have been confirmed and verified by many different studies. New studies, or new research methods, may be developed that might possibly cause us to refine our estimate of the age of the universe upward or downward. This is how the process of science works; it is subject to change as more information and new technologies become available. But it is not tenuous – our age estimate may be refined, but the idea of an expanding universe is unlikely to be overturned. As evidence builds to support an idea, our confidence in that idea builds.

Upon seeing Hubble's work, even Albert Einstein changed his opinion of a static universe and called his insertion of the cosmological constant the "biggest blunder" of his professional career. Hubble's discovery actually confirmed Einstein's theory of general relativity, which predicts that the universe must be expanding or contracting. Einstein refused to accept this idea because of his cultural biases. His work had not predicted a static universe, but he assumed this must be the case given what he had grown up believing. When confronted with the data, he recognized that his earlier beliefs were flawed, and came to accept the findings of the science behind the idea. This is a hallmark of science: While an individual's beliefs may be biased by personal experience, the scientific enterprise works to collect data to allow for a more objective conclusion to be identified. Incorrect ideas may be upheld for some amount of time, but eventually the preponderance of evidence helps to lead us to correct these ideas. Once used as a term of disparagement, the "Big Bang" theory is now the leading explanation for the origin of the universe as we know it.

There are other questions we can ask about the origin of the universe, not all of which can be answered by science. Scientists can answer when and how the universe began, but cannot calculate the reason why it began, for example. That type of question must be explored through philosophy, religion, and other ways of thinking. The questions that scientists ask must be testable. Scientists have provided answers to testable questions that have helped us calculate the age of the universe, like how distant certain stars are and how fast they are receding from us. Whether or not we can get a definitive answer, we can be confident in the process by which the explanations were developed, allowing us to rely on the knowledge that is produced through the process of science. Someday we may find evidence to help us understand why the universe was created, but for the time being science will limit itself to the last 13.7 or so billion years of phenomena to investigate.

Key Concepts for this chapter

▶ Science consists of a body of knowledge and the process by which that knowledge is developed.

▶ The core of the process of science is generating testable explanations, and the methods and approaches to generating knowledge are shared publicly so that they can be evaluated by the community of scientists.

▶ Scientists build on the work of others to create scientific knowledge.

▶ Scientific knowledge is subject to revision and refinement as new data, or new ways to interpret existing data, are found.

References

Carnot, S. (1824). *Réflexions sur la puissance motrice du feu, et sur les machines propres à développer oette puissance.* Paris: Gauthier-Villars.

Clausius, R. (1850). Ueber die bewegende Kraft der Wärme und die Gesetze, welche sich daraus für die Wärmelehre selbst ableiten lassen. *Annalen der Physik, 155*(3), 368-397.

Deprit, A. (1984). *Monsignor Georges Lemaitre.* Paper presented at the Big-Bang Cosmology Symposium in honour of G. Lemaitre.

Doppler, C. (1842). Uber das farbige Licht der Doppelsterne und einiger anderer Gestirne des Himmels [On the colored light of the double stars and certain other stars of the heavens]. *Abh. Kniglich Bhmischen Ges. Wiss, 2,* 467-482.

Einstein, A. (1916). Die grundlage der allgemeinen relativitätstheorie. *Annalen der Physik, 354*(7), 769-822.

Frebel, A., Christlieb, N., Norris, J. E., Thom, C., Beers, T. C., & Rhee, J. (2007). Discovery of HE 1523-0901, a strongly r-process-enhanced metal-poor star with detected uranium. *The Astrophysical Journal Letters, 660*(2), L117-L120.

Hubble, E. (1929). A relation between distance and radial velocity among extra-galactic nebulae. *Proceedings of the National Academy of Sciences of the United States of America, 15*(3), 168.

Lemaître, G. (1927). Un univers homogène de masse constante et de rayon croissant rendant compte de la vitesse radiale des nébuleuses extra-galactiques. *Annales de la Société scientifique de Bruxelles, 47,* 49-59.

Rutherford, E. (1929). Origin of actinium and age of the Earth. *Nature, 123*(3096), 313-314.

Slipher, V. M. (1915). Spectrographic observations of nebulae. *Popular Astronomy, 23,* 21-24.

Spergel, D. N., Verde, L., Peiris, H. V., Komatsu, E., Nolta, M. R., Bennett, C. L., . . . Kogut, A. (2003). First-year Wilkinson Microwave Anisotropy Probe (WMAP) observations: Determination of cosmological parameters. *The Astrophysical Journal Supplement Series, 148*(1), 175.

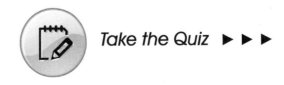

Take the Quiz ▶ ▶ ▶

The Nature of Scientific Knowledge Quiz

1. An important component of the scientific process is that the findings of science are

    A) testable.

    B) absolute.

    C) true.

    D) uncertain.

2. We could be certain that the Earth was round only after pictures of the planet were taken from space in 1968.

    A) True

    B) False

3. How did the Second Law of Thermodynamics contribute to our understanding of the age of the universe?

    A) It suggested that the universe is infinitely old.

    B) It suggested that the universe must be finite in age.

    C) It suggested that the universe is contracting.

    D) It suggested that the universe must be finite in size.

4. Study the line spectra in Section 1 of the image. This spectrum represents the normal emission lines for elements traditionally found in stars (H, He, Ca, Na, etc.). The two sets of line spectra in Section 2 represent the observed spectra for stars SN1 and SN2. What can be said about the movement of these stars based on these spectra?

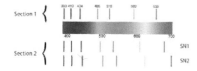

    A) Both stars are moving away from the observer; however, SN2 is moving *faster*.

    B) Both stars are moving away from the observer; however, SN2 is moving *slower*.

    C) Both stars are moving toward the observer; however, SN2 is moving *slower*.

    D) Both stars are moving toward the observer; however, SN2 is moving *faster*.

5. Edwin Hubble created the figure below from a combination of his and Vesto Slipher's research data. What does the data in the figure show?

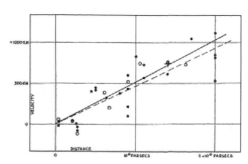

    A) The velocity of a star is directly proportional to its distance.

    B) The stars are receding from one another..

    C) The universe is expanding..

    D) Star brightness is a function of velocity.

6. Einstein incorrectly believed that the universe was static because his theory of relativity predicted a static universe.

    A) True

    B) False

7. Which of the following statements BEST describes the process by which we have come to understand the age of the universe?

    A) The age of the universe cannot be known through scientific means.

    B) Scientists have identified a single way to measure the age of the universe.

    C) Over time, newer studies have built upon, revised, and improved our understanding of the age of the universe.

    D) Scientists have worked independently to test and answer unique questions using only their own data.

Answers and feedback can be found on Page 245

Energy: An Introduction

by Zachary Hartman, PhD and Anthony Carpi, PhD

> Did you know that when you warm your hands by rubbing them together fast, you are changing energy from one form to another? There are many different forms of energy, any of which can be changed into other forms. This conversion of energy is what makes all of our daily activities possible.

Module Summary

The concept of energy has fascinated scientists and philosophers for thousands of years. This module describes early ideas about energy and traces the development of our modern understanding of energy through the work of Joule and Faraday. Potential and kinetic energy are distinguished, and the six main forms of energy are described. The module highlights energy conversion and discusses how energy is measured.

Terms you should know:

field of force = the area around one object in which it can exert influence on another object

kinetic = relating to the motion of objects

thermal = relating to heat

work = using force to move an object; a process in which one form of energy is converted into another.

Energy touches upon everything we do. From the lights we turn on in the morning, to the car we drive to work or school, to our ability to read this page. Energy is both a constant in the human existence while also representing the process of change. All of our daily activities are possible because of the conversion of one form of energy to another. As such, scientists and even philosophers through the ages have tried to understand and come to terms with the concept. Yet until recently, a clear understanding of energy has escaped us. So how did we come to understand it?

Ancient Greek philosophers thought that all matter and processes could be described in terms of combinations of four elements: earth, air, water and fire (see our Module Early Ideas about Matter for more information). They associated the first three elements, earth, air, and water, with the physical conditions of objects – how hard, soft, or wet things were. Fire, on the other hand, was associated with the heat of objects, their motion, or even the life-force of living beings. In other words, they associated the "element" fire with the amount of energy in things. The Greek philosopher Heraclitus went a step further. He proposed that fire was the ultimate manifestation of all matter, "All things are an interchange for fire, and fire for all things, just like goods for gold and gold for goods." While the association of all forms of energy with fire was grossly oversimplified the idea that energy underlies all aspects of nature hints at our modern understanding of energy and would be revisited by Albert Einstein some 2,500 thousand years after Heraclitus.

The four-element theory was championed by Aristotle and other influential philosophers of Ancient Greece, but in practice this theory provided a very poor framework by which we could come to understand the universe, especially with respect to energy. Yet due to Aristotle's influence, the philosophy held strong against all challengers for almost 2,000 years. A true understanding of energy eluded Western science throughout most of the middle ages.

In 1687, the legendary scientist Isaac Newton published his "Mathematical Principles of Natural Philosophy" (casually known as the Principia), in which he described the laws governing bodies in motion. The Principia gave a thorough, mathematical description of the laws of motion, providing the first accurate description of the energy associated with moving objects – mechanical energy. Since Newton's time, scientists have described in great detail other major forms of energy, including thermal, chemical, electrical, electromagnetic, and nuclear.

What is energy?

At its foundation, energy is a very simple concept. The term was first invented by Thomas Young in 1807 after the Greek word energeia, which roughly translates to "activity." Energy is the ability for an object to perform work on another object. At its core, this is a simple definition; however, it can manifest itself in many ways.

Mechanical Energy

Mechanical energy is the energy possessed by an object because of its movement or position. We often describe mechanical energy in two different forms, potential and kinetic. Potential energy is so-called "stored" energy because it is the energy an object possesses as a result of its position in relation to a field of force, such as gravity. For example, when we lift a ball off the ground into the air, the object gains potential energy as it is moving to a position in which gravity will cause it to drop to the ground if we release it. If we then drop the ball, the potential energy that is present is converted into kinetic energy, which is the energy associated with the motion of an object. The concepts of potential and kinetic energy do not apply only to mechanical energy. A battery that is not connected to a circuit is considered to have potential energy that can be converted to electrical energy if the circuit is closed. Potential energy is found in other energy forms, as well.

The conversion of potential into kinetic energy is demonstrated in the following example using a weight and pulley (see Figure 1). As the individual lifts the weight against the force of gravity, the potential energy rises. Dropping the weight will convert this potential energy into kinetic energy momentarily as the object is falling. The higher we lift the object, the more potential energy we impart as it is further from the surface of the earth, and so the more kinetic energy it releases as it falls. You can try this experiment yourself; the link below allows you to lift and drop a 100-kg weight. You can observe how potential and kinetic energy are related to each other by "freezing" the weight at different heights during its fall.

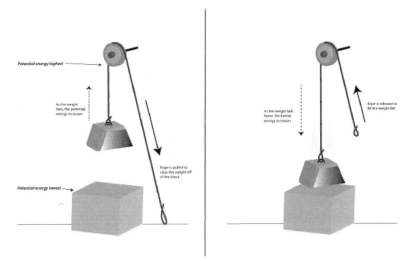

Figure 1: *Illustration of potential and kinetic energy in a solid object.*

Thermal Energy

Thermal energy is also associated with motion, but in this case it is the motion of objects at the atomic level. Thermal energy is derived from the kinetic energy of atoms or molecules within a system. In other words, the atoms and molecules of all substances are in constant motion at any temperature above absolute zero, and this is true even for solids. The thermal energy of a material, as measured by its temperature, is related to the motion of the atoms and molecules within that material – hot materials contain molecules moving very rapidly, while colder materials have molecules moving more slowly.

So what's the difference between thermal and mechanical energy? Put simply, it's the scale of the problem. For example, if you touch a hot pan, the atoms of metal are moving very quickly, and they can transfer the thermal energy on that atomic level, causing pain and even burns. Mechanical energy is the energy released when you drop the pan because it is hot.

Chemical Energy

Chemical energy is also related to atoms and molecules, but it is a function of their structure and interaction as opposed to their motion. As described in our Chemical Bonding module, atoms and molecules can bond with one another as a result of their electron structure. Similar to when we lift or drop an object within a gravitational field of force, the bonding of two atoms represents an interaction within an electromagnetic field of force. And this interaction results in a change of energy. In some cases chemical changes require the input of energy, while in other cases chemical changes give off energy in the form of heat, mechanical energy (such as during an explosion), or electrical energy (such as in a battery).

Nuclear Energy

Atoms also contain energy stored as a function of their internal structures. Within the nucleus of the atom, the strong nuclear force keeps protons and neutrons bound together. The breaking or forming of these nuclear interactions can take up or release nuclear energy. These processes can occur naturally, as when a radioactive element like uranium decays. In fact, the heat from naturally-occurring radioactive elements in the Earth's crust contributes substantially to the production of heat at the Earth's core. They can also be stimulated to occur artificially, and the nuclear energy released by these stimulated radioactive processes is what powers nuclear power plants.

Electromagnetic Energy

Another form of energy is associated with particles even smaller than atoms. Electromagnetic energy is caused by the motion of photons, which are packets of energy that behave both like particles and like waves. Photons make up all the forms of electromagnetic radiation that we are familiar with, like visible, infrared, and ultraviolet light, radio waves, and microwaves, as well as those we might be less familiar with, like gamma radiation. Electromagnetic energy often causes changes in the energy level of electrons within atoms, or the motion of atoms and molecules. For example, water molecules can absorb microwave radiation, which causes them to vibrate, increasing their thermal energy, and heating your food in the process. And ultraviolet waves can cause damage to the molecules in your skin itself, causing a sunburn even in the absence of thermal energy.

Electrical Energy

Electrical energy also is based in the movement of particles associated with atoms, but in this case it is the flow of electrons within a system. Electrical energy can be generated in a number of ways. For example, certain chemical reactions, such as those that take place in batteries, cause electrons to flow. In addition, physically moving a conductor like a metal in a magnetic field can generate electrical current. And light can also stimulate the flow of electrons in certain materials, such as photovoltaic cells. Once electrical current is generated, it can flow through materials that have "loosely" attached electrons, specifically metals, making then good conductors of electricity.

Other Forms of Energy

While we are most likely to encounter these six forms of energy in daily life, they are not the only ways that energy can be seen. In general, however, other forms of energy are really special descriptions of the six forms we've discussed. Sound energy, for example, can create concussive forces through vibration of air particles. This is really a specific form of mechanical energy. The key point is that you will encounter energy in a large variety of ways.

Comprehension Checkpoint

_____ energy has to do with the motion of molecules, while

_____ energy has to do with the flow of electrons.

A) Thermal, electrical

B) Mechanical, nuclear

Energy manifests in so many different forms that at first glance it may seem impossible to relate them. In fact, for a long time scientists thought each form of energy represented a unique property about the universe. For example, it was thought that work (mechanical energy) and heat (thermal energy) were two completely separate entities!

This concept of separate forms of energy was finally successfully challenged by James Prescott Joule (1818–1889), a Scottish chemist who contributed several important experimental findings to our understanding of energy. His most famous experiment, published in 1845, used a paddle wheel to show that different forms of energy are interchangeable. This concept was not entirely discovered by Joule; several researchers attempted to demonstrate that heat and energy were interconvertible before Joule, but their experiments were poorly designed, leading to ambiguous results that were challenged. Joule, through diligent planning and careful measurement, was the first scientist to back this concept with solid data. To do this, Joule built a special pulley system and a sealed water vessel that was insulated from the environment. He used a system of weights to perform a precise amount of work on the paddle wheel,

Figure 2: James Joule

which, in turn, caused the water in the vessel to move. The friction associated with stirring the water inside a vessel raised the temperature of the water, which could be measured using a thermometer. His experimental data showed that a weight of 772 pounds falling one foot would raise the temperature of one pound of water by one degree Fahrenheit. In doing this, Joule was the first to clearly demonstrate beyond the shadow of a doubt that mechanical energy could be changed into thermal energy.

In many ways, this concept of transforming motion into energy is very obvious to us in modern times. If you rub your hands together, they get hotter due to friction. It's important to note, however, that scientists of James Joule's day did not find this concept intuitive. They thought that heat was caused by a substance stored within hot objects called "caloric," and as this substance moved, you could get work (for more about the caloric theory of heat, refer to our Thermodynamics I module). By understanding that thermal energy and mechanical energy were two different forms of the same thing, Joule demonstrated a critical concept and added greatly to our understanding of energy.

Interestingly, the idea that forms of energy could not be converted was not limited to the interplay between mechanical and thermal energy. Prior to the 1800s, the relationship between electricity, magnetism, and light eluded scientists. They were each said to require a different "ether" and had unique properties. This changed, however, when Michael Faraday invented the electric generator in 1821. Faraday had been experimenting with devices to maintain a constant electric current. He found that he could achieve this by rotating a copper disk within a magnetic field. Remarkably, he found that he could cause the opposite effect as well: Running a current through the disk triggered the disc to rotate. Faraday was able to demonstrate that, with the right design, this rotation could be used to power a shaft. Faraday had invented a precursor to the electric motor and in doing so was one of the first scientists to show that electrical and mechanical energy could be interconverted.

Certainly, there are many different ways of conversions of energy. Describing each could fill volumes of books: Heat released by nuclear energy drives the formation of steam and is used to turn giant turbines to generate electricity, our body's use of chemical energy to power our muscles, and the list goes on. It is possible to transform any form of energy into any other.

Measuring energy

As discussed already, all of the different manifestations of energy are related. They all describe a system's ability to perform some kind of work. As such, they can all be measured using the same unit. Because James Joule was among the first scientists to document the phenomenon of energy conversion, and because his observations were so carefully detailed in his writings, we now call the unit used to measure energy the joule. This unit formally describes the energy it takes to produce one newton of force over a distance of one meter or the electrical energy it takes to pass one ampere of current through a one-ohm resistor for one second.

While it is important to recognize that we only use one unit to convey the amount of energy used or given off in a process, it is also important to recognize that we rarely, if ever, can directly measure the energy output itself. Measuring the amount of energy converted in a process is usually done by analyzing changes in other parameters, like temperature, and then calculating backwards to joules.

For example, if you needed to know how much chemical energy is stored in a block of wood – and if you don't have access to tables with that information – there is no tool that we can use to say "that wood contains this much chemical energy." In order to determine the amount of energy contained in the substance, we must release that energy by burning the block of wood and then measuring the temperature change in the surroundings (this is usually measured using calorimetry, a technique you can read more about in the Thermody-namics I module).

Without experiment , it would not be possible to know the quantity of energy in an object. As such, measuring energy is perhaps one of the more elusive concepts encountered when we discuss energy. Energy is the potential to do work; however, until it gets used up, we cannot observe how much energy we had!

From astronomy to zoology, all forms of natural science rely on an understanding of energy to some degree. In the physical sciences, our understanding of energy flow helps to predict chemical reactions, determine the trajectory of objects, and many other processes. In the life sciences, energy is used to study how enzymes work and why different biomolecules interact in certain ways. Energy is a fundamental concept for all students of science, and it is a cornerstone for existence at large.

Key Concepts for this chapter

► Energy is defined as the capacity to perform work.

► Energy comes in many forms, such as mechanical, chemical, heat, etc. and all are interchangeable to some extent.

► James Joule was instrumental in establishing the concept of inter-changeability of different forms of energy and quantitatively measured those changes in certain systems.

References

Newton, Isaac, *Philosophiae Naturalis Principia Mathematica* ("Mathematical Principles of Natural Philosophy"), London, 1687; Cambridge, 1713; London, 1726.

Joule, James, On the Existence of an Equivalent Relation between Heat and the ordinary Forms of Mechanical Power. [In the letter to the Editors of the '*Philosophical Magazine.*'] series 3, vol. xxvii, p. 205

Take the Quiz ► ► ►

Energy Quiz

1. Which of the following did the Greeks believe composed all matter?

   A) earth, air, fire, heart

   B) solids, liquids, gases

   C) earth, air, water, fire

   B) atoms

2. Which of the Greek philosophers was the most important champion of the theory of matter from Question 1?

   A) Aristotle

   B) Heraclitus

   C) Plato

   D) Hippocrates

3. How do we define energy?

   A) The life-force moving through objects.

   B) The ability to perform work.

   C) The ability to turn on a light. .

   D) The ability to cook food.

4. Which of these is not one of the main forms of energy?

   A) mechanical

   B) electrical

   C) nuclear

   D) psychic

5. Which of the following statements is correct?

   A) Potential energy can be converted to kinetic energy.

   B) Potential energy of an object rises as you lift it higher from the ground.

   C) Potential energy does not apply only to mechanical energy; it can be found in electrical, chemical, and other forms, as well.

   D) All of the choices are true.

6. Which of the following statements about energy is incorrect?

   A) Energy cannot be destroyed or created; it can only change forms.

   B) Mechanical energy cannot be converted into electrical energy.

   C) The chemical energy stored in objects can be used to drive machines.

   D) Work is performed by expending energy.

7. What was the main contribution of James Joule to our understanding of energy?

   A) He gave us the energy unit Joule, which he named after himself.

   B) He built the first electric generator, showing the world that energy can change forms.

   C) He was the first to carefully prove that mechanical energy can be converted to thermal energy, demonstrating they were not caused by different essences.

   D) He was the first to show that microorganisms in beer brewing were responsible for the alcohol content.

Answers and feedback can be found on Page 246

Early Ideas about Matter:
From Democritus to Dalton

by Anthony Carpi, PhD

Did you know that some ancient Greeks believed that all matter was made up of four substances: fire, air, water, and earth? They believed that rabbits were soft because they had more water than earth. Although this idea seems silly now, it contains a fundamental principle of atomic theory: that matter is made up of a small number of fundamental elements.

Module Summary

Tracking the development of our understanding of the atomic structure of matter, this module begins with the contributions of ancient Greeks, who proposed that matter is made up of small particles. The module then describes how Lavoisier's Law of Conservation of Mass and Proust's Law of Definite Proportions contributed to Dalton's modern atomic theory.

Terms you should know:

element = a pure chemical substance that is made of only one kind of atom
matter = physical substances

Early humans easily distinguished between materials that were used for making clothes, those that could be shaped into tools, or those that were good to eat. Then they gave these things the names, such as "fur," "stone," or "rabbit." However, these people did not have our current understanding of the substances that made up those objects. Empedocles, a Greek philosopher and scientist who lived on the south coast of Sicily between 492 BCE and 432 BCE, proposed one of the first theories that attempted to describe the things around us. Empedocles argued that all matter was composed of four elements: fire, air, water, and earth. The ratio of these four elements affected the properties of the matter (Figure 1). Stone was thought to contain a high amount of earth, while a rabbit was thought to have a higher ratio of both water and fire, thus making it soft and giving it life.

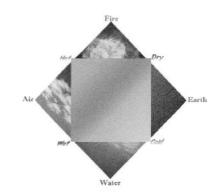

Figure 1

Empedocles's theory was quite popular, but it had a number of problems. For example, regardless of how many times you break a stone in half, the pieces never resemble any of the core elements of fire, air, water, or earth. Despite these problems, Empedocles's theory was an important development in scientific thinking because it was among the first to suggest that some substances that looked like pure materials, like stone, were actually made up of a combination of different "elements."

The atom is proposed

A few decades after Empedocles, Democritus, another Greek who lived from 460 BCE to 370 BCE, developed a new theory of matter that attempted to overcome the problems of his predecessor. Democritus's ideas were based on reasoning rather than science, and drew on the teachings of two Greek philosophers who came before him: Leucippus and Anaxagoras. Democritus knew that if you took a stone and cut it in half, each half had the same properties as the original stone. He reasoned that if you continued to cut the stone into smaller and smaller pieces, at some point you would reach a piece so tiny that it could no longer be divided. Democritus called these infinitesimally small pieces of matter *atomos*, meaning 'indivisible'. He suggested that atomos were eternal and could not be destroyed. Democritus theorized that atomos were specific to the material that they made up, meaning that the atomos of stone were unique to stone and different from the atomos of other materials, such as fur (Figure 2). This was a remarkable theory that attempted to explain the whole physical world in terms of a small number of ideas.

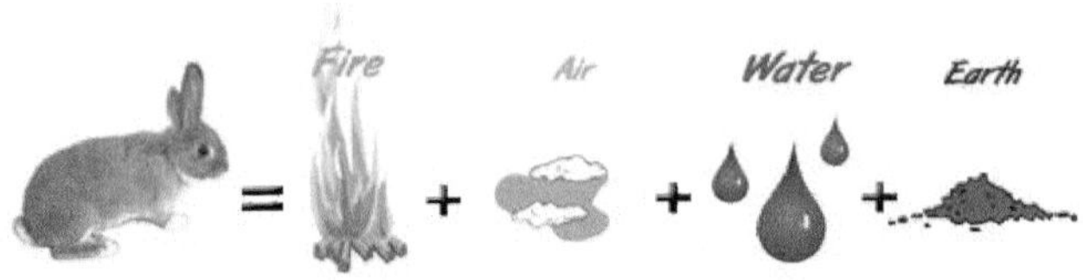

Figure 2

Ultimately, though, Aristotle and Plato, two of the best-known philosophers of Ancient Greece, rejected the theories of Democritus. Aristotle accepted the theory of Empedocles, adding his own (incorrect) idea that the four core elements could be transformed into one another. Because of Aristotle's great influence, Democritus's theory would have to wait almost 2,000 years before being rediscovered.

In the 17th and 18th centuries CE, several key events helped revive the theory that matter was made of small, indivisible particles. In 1643, Evangelista Torricelli, an Italian mathematician and pupil of Galileo, showed that air had weight and was capable of pushing down on a column of liquid mercury (thus inventing the barometer). This was a startling finding. If air – this substance that we could not see, feel, or smell – had weight, it must be made of something physical. But how could something have a physical presence, yet not respond to human touch or sight? Daniel Bernoulli, a Swiss mathematician, proposed an answer. He developed a theory that air and other gases consist of tiny particles that are too small to be seen, and are loosely packed in an empty volume of space. The particles could not be felt because unlike a solid stone wall that does not move, the tiny particles move aside when a human hand or body moves through them. Bernoulli reasoned that if these particles were not in constant motion they would settle to the ground like dust particles; therefore he pictured air and other gases as loose collections of tiny billiard-ball-like particles that are continuously moving around and bouncing off one another.

Law of Conservation of Mass

Many scientists were busy studying the natural world at this time. Shortly after Bernoulli proposed his theory, the Englishman Joseph Priestley began to experiment with red mercury calx in 1773. Mercury calx, a red solid stone, had been known and coveted for thousands of years because when it is heated, it appears to turn into mercury, a silver liquid metal. Priestley had observed that it does not just turn into mercury; it actually breaks down into two substances when it is heated, liquid mercury and a strange gas. Priestley carefully collected this gas in glass jars and studied it. After many long days and nights in the laboratory, Priestley said of the strange gas, "What surprised me more than I can well express was that a candle burned in this air with a remarkably vigorous flame." Not only did flames burn strongly in this gas, but a mouse placed in a sealed container of this gas lived for a longer period of time than a mouse placed in a sealed container of ordinary air. Priestley's discovery revealed that substances could combine together or break apart to form new substances with different properties. For example, a colorless, odorless gas could combine with mercury, a silver metal, to form mercury calx, a red mineral (Figure 3).

Figure 3: Mercury calx

Priestley called the gas he discovered *dephlogisticated air*, but this name would not stick. In 1778, Antoine Lavoisier, a French scientist, conducted many experiments with dephlogisticated air and theorized that the gas made some substances acidic. He renamed Priestley's gas *oxygen*, from the Greek words that loosely translate as 'acid maker'. While Lavoisier's theory about oxygen and acids proved incorrect, his name stuck. Lavoisier knew from other scientists before him that acids react with some metals to release another strange and highly flammable gas called *phlogiston*. Lavoisier mixed the two gases, phlogiston and the newly renamed oxygen, in a closed glass container and inserted a match. He saw that phlogiston immediately burned in the presence of oxygen and afterwards he observed droplets of water on the glass container. After careful testing, Lavoisier realized that the water was formed by the reaction of phlogiston and oxygen, and so he renamed phlogiston *hydrogen*, from the Greek words for 'water maker'.

Lavoisier also burned other substances such as phosphorus and sulfur in air, and showed that they combined with air to make new materials. These new materials weighed more than the original substances, and Lavoisier showed that the weight gained by the new materials was lost from the air in which the substances were burned. From these observations, Lavoisier established the Law of Conservation of Mass, which says that mass is not lost or gained during a chemical reaction.

Comprehension Checkpoint

Elements are used up when they fuel chemical reactions, so resulting substances have less mass.

A) True

B) False

Modern atomic theory

Priestley, Lavoisier, and others had laid the foundations of the field of chemistry. Their experiments showed that some substances could combine with others to form new materials; other substances could be broken apart to form simpler ones; and a few key "elements" could not be broken down any further. But what could explain this complex set of observations? John Dalton, an exceptional British teacher and scientist, put together the pieces and developed the first modern atomic theory in 1803. To learn more about Priestley's and Lavoisier's experiments and how they formed the basis of Dalton's theories, try the interactive experiment *Dalton's Playhouse* available through the online version of this module.

Dalton made it a regular habit to track and record the weather in his home town of Manchester, England. Through his observations of morning fog and other weather patterns, Dalton realized that water could exist as a gas that mixed with air and occupied the same space as air. Solids could not occupy the same space as each other; for example, ice could not mix with air. So what could allow water to sometimes behave as a solid and sometimes as a gas? Dalton realized that all matter must be composed of tiny particles. In the gas state, those particles floated freely around and could mix with other gases, as Bernoulli had proposed. But Dalton extended this idea to apply to all matter – gases, solids and liquids. Dalton first proposed part of his atomic theory in 1803 and later refined these concepts in his classic 1808 paper *A New System of Chemical Philosophy* (which you can access through a link under the Resources tab on the online version of this module).

Dalton's theory had four main concepts:

1. **All matter is composed of indivisible particles called atoms.** Bernoulli, Dalton, and others pictured atoms as tiny billiard-ball-like particles in various states of motion. While this concept is useful to help us understand atoms, it is not correct as we will see in later modules on atomic theory.

2. **All atoms of a given element are identical; atoms of different elements have different properties.** Dalton's theory suggested that every single atom of an element such as oxygen is identical to every other oxygen atom; furthermore, atoms of different elements, such as oxygen and mercury, are different from each other. Dalton characterized elements according to their atomic weight; however, when isotopes of elements were discovered in the late 1800s, this concept changed.

3. **Chemical reactions involve the combination of atoms, not the destruction of atoms.** Atoms are indestructible and unchangeable, so compounds, such as water and mercury calx, are formed when one atom chemically combines with other atoms. This was an extremely advanced concept for its time; while Dalton's theory implied that atoms bonded together, it would be more than 100 years before scientists began to explain the concept of chemical bonding.

4. **When elements react to form compounds, they react in defined, whole-number ratios.** The experiments that Dalton and others performed showed that reactions are not random events; they proceed according to precise and well-defined formulas. This important concept in chemistry is discussed in more detail shortly.

Comprehension Checkpoint

An element is made up of

A) one kind of atom.

B) different types of atoms that combine chemically.

Some of the details of Dalton's atomic theory require more explanation.

Elements: As early as 1660, Robert Boyle recognized that the Greek definition of *element* (earth, fire, air, and water) was not correct. Boyle proposed a new definition of an element as a fundamental substance, and we now define elements as *fundamental substances that cannot be broken down further by chemical means.* Elements are the building blocks of the universe. They are pure substances that form the basis of all of the materials around us. Some elements can be seen in pure form, such as mercury in a thermometer; some we see mainly in chemical combination with others, such as oxygen and hydrogen in water. We now know of approximately 116 different elements. Each of the elements is given a name and a one- or two-letter abbreviation. Often this abbreviation is simply the first letter of the element; for example, hydrogen is abbreviated as H, and oxygen as O. Sometimes an element is given a two-letter abbreviation; for example, helium is He. When writing the abbreviation for an element, the first letter is always capitalized and the second letter (if there is one) is always lowercase.

Atoms: A single unit of an element is called an atom. The atom is the most basic unit of matter, which makes up everything in the world around us. Each atom retains all of the chemical and physical properties of its parent element. At the end of the 19th century, scientists would show that atoms were actually made up of smaller, "subatomic" pieces, which smashed the billiard-ball concept of the atom (see our Atomic Theory I: The Early Days module).

Compounds: Most of the materials we come into contact with are compounds, substances formed by the chemical combination of two or more atoms of the elements. A single "particle" of a compound is called a molecule. Dalton incorrectly imagined that atoms "hooked" together to form *molecules.* However, Dalton correctly realized that compounds have precise formulas. Water, for example, is always made up of two parts hydrogen and one part oxygen. The chemical formula of a compound is written by listing the symbols of the elements together, without any spaces between them. If a molecule contains more than one atom of an element, a number is subscripted after the symbol to show the number of atoms of that element in the molecule. Thus the formula for water is H_2O, never HO or H_2O_2.

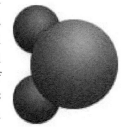

Figure 4: Water molecule

Comprehension Checkpoint

The formula for water can be written as either H_2O or HO_2.

A) True

B) False

Law of Definite Proportions

The idea that compounds have defined chemical formulas was first proposed in the late 1700s by the French chemist Joseph Proust. Proust performed a number of experiments and observed that no matter how he caused different elements to react with oxygen, they always reacted in defined proportions. For example, two parts of hydrogen always reacts with one part oxygen when forming water; one part mercury always reacts with one part oxygen when forming mercury calx. Dalton used Proust's Law of Definite Proportions in developing his atomic theory.

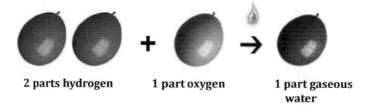

2 parts hydrogen   **1 part oxygen**   **1 part gaseous water**

The law also applies to multiples of the fundamental proportion, for example:

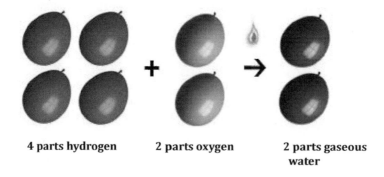

4 parts hydrogen   **2 parts oxygen**   **2 parts gaseous water**

In both of these examples, the ratio of hydrogen to oxygen to water is 2 to 1 to 1. When reactants are present in excess of the fundamental proportions, some reactants will remain unchanged after the chemical reaction has occurred.

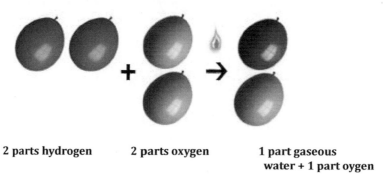

2 parts hydrogen   **2 parts oxygen**   **1 part gaseous water + 1 part oygen**

The story of the development of modern atomic theory is one in which scientists built upon the work of others to produce a more accurate explanation of the world around them. This process is common in science, and even incorrect theories can contribute to important scientific discoveries. Dalton, Priestley, and others laid the foundation of atomic theory, and many of their hypotheses are still useful. However, in the decades after their work, other scientists would show that atoms are not solid billiard balls, but complex systems of particles. Thus they would smash apart a bit of Dalton's atomic theory in an effort to build a more complete view of the world around us.

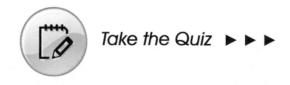

Take the Quiz ► ► ►

Early Ideas about Matter Quiz

1. Joseph Priestley discovered
    A) oxygen.
    B) America.
    C) mercury.
    D) hydrogen.

2. Who proposed the first atomic view of matter?
    A) Priestley
    B) Democritus
    C) Empedocles
    D) Lavoisier

3. The anscient Greeks believed that matter was composed of four basic materials. Which one of the following was not one of the four?
    A) water
    B) gold
    C) earth
    D) fire

4. Which one of the following is not part of Dalton's atomic theory?
    A) Matter is composed of atoms.
    B) Atoms change into other atoms in chemical reactions.
    C) Atoms of different elements have different properties.
    D) Atoms of the same element have the same chemical properties.

5. A substance that cannot be broken down by chemical means into simpler substances is called a(n)
    A) element.
    B) compound.
    C) mixture.
    D) solid.

6. Which one of the following statements concerning the relationship between the number of elements and the number of compounds is correct?
    A) The number of elements is much larger that the number of compounds.
    B) The number of elements must equal the number of compounds.
    C) The number of compounds is much larger than the number of elements.
    D) The number of elements and compounds is approximately the same.

7. The number of known elements at this time is approximately
    A) 100.
    B) infinite.
    C) 50.
    D) 116.

8. Which one of the following symbols represents an element?
    A) HF
    B) NO
    C) CO
    D) He

9. Which one of the following symbols represents a compound?
    A) He
    B) N
    C) Co
    D) CO2

Quiz continued on next page ▶ ▶ ▶

10. Substances A and B combine chemically to form C. Substance C must be:

    A) a solution

    B) a mixture

    C) a compound

    D) an element

11. Although all parts of Dalton's atomic theory are important, which one of the postulates is crucial to explain the observations summarized by the Law of Definite Proportions?

    A) Matter is composed of atoms

    B) Atoms are very small

    C) Atoms of the same elements have the same properties

    D) Atoms chemically combine with other atoms in fixed, whole-number ratios

12. No matter how much extra oxygen is available, 12 grams of carbon always combines with 32 grams of oxygen. This best illustrates the law of:

    A) conservation of mass

    B) multiple proportions

    C) definite proportions

    D) conservation of energy

13. 12 grams of carbon react with 32 grams of oxygen to form exactly 44 grams of carbon dioxide. This is a good example of

    A) Democritus' theory

    B) Priestley's experiments

    C) the law of multiple proportions

    D) the law of conservation of mass

14. Who first proposed the law of definite proportions?

    A) Dalton

    B) Empedocles

    C) Proust

    D) Priestley

Answers and feedback can be found on Page 248

Atomic Theory I: The Early Days

by Anthony Carpi, PhD

Did you know that scientists used to think that atoms resembled billiard balls or raisin bread, although neither of these views proved accurate? Atoms are so tiny that 20 million hydrogen atoms could fit on this dash -. In spite of their incredibly small size, scientists have come to an accurate understanding of atomic structure.

In this module

Modern atomic theory has evolved dramatically from the 19th century view of the atom as a small, solid sphere resembling a billiard ball. This module explores that story: from the discovery of electrons and protons in the late 19th century to the planetary model of the atom in the early 20th century. The module explains the function of subatomic particles as well as their relative size and weight. The concepts of atomic number and atomic mass are introduced.

Terms you should know:

charge = a quantity of electricity

particle = a tiny piece of matter

Until the final years of the nineteenth century, the accepted model of the atom resembled that of a billiard ball – a small, solid sphere. In 1897, J. J. Thomson dramatically changed the modern view of the atom with his discovery of the electron. Thomson's work suggested that the atom was not an "indivisible" particle as John Dalton had suggested but a jigsaw puzzle made of smaller pieces.

Thomson's notion of the electron came from his work with a nineteenth century scientific curiosity: the cathode ray tube. For years scientists had known that if an electric current was passed through a vacuum tube, a stream of glowing material could be seen; however, no one could explain why. Thomson found that the mysterious glowing stream would bend toward a positively charged electric plate. Thomson theorized, and was later proven correct, that the stream was in fact made up of small particles, pieces of atoms that carried a negative charge. These particles were later named *electrons*.

After Eugen Goldstein's 1886 discovery that atoms had positive charges, Thomson imagined that atoms looked like pieces of raisin bread, a structure in which clumps of small, negatively charged electrons (the "raisins") were scattered inside a smear of positive charges. In 1908, Ernest Rutherford, a former student of Thomson's, proved Thomson's raisin bread structure incorrect.

Rutherford proposes a planetary model of an atom

Rutherford performed a series of experiments with radioactive alpha particles. While it was unclear at the time what the alpha particle was, it was known to be very tiny. Rutherford fired tiny alpha particles at solid objects such as gold foil. He found that while most of the alpha particles passed right through the gold foil, a small number of alpha particles passed through at an angle (as if they had bumped up against something) and some bounced straight back like a tennis ball hitting a wall. Rutherford's experiments suggested that gold foil, and matter in general, had holes in it! These holes allowed most of the alpha particles to pass directly through, while a small number ricocheted off or bounced straight back because they hit a solid object.

In 1911, Rutherford proposed a revolutionary view of the atom. He suggested that the atom consisted of a small, dense core of positively charged particles in the center (or nucleus) of the atom, surrounded by a swirling ring of electrons. The nucleus was so dense that the alpha particles would bounce off of it, but the electrons were so tiny, and spread out at such great distances, that the alpha particles would pass right through this area of the atom. Rutherford's atom resembled a tiny solar system with the positively charged nucleus always at the center and the electrons revolving around the nucleus.

The positively charged particles in the nucleus of the atom were called protons. Protons carry an equal, but opposite, charge to electrons, but protons are much larger and heavier than electrons.

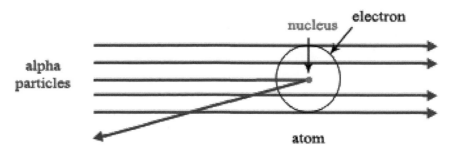

Figure 1: Interpreting Rutherford's Gold Foil Experiment

Comprehension Checkpoint

Rutherford proposed that the atom resembled
  A) a billiard ball.
  B) a solar system.

Chadwick discovers the neutron

In 1932, James Chadwick discovered a third type of sub-atomic particle, which he named the neutron. Neutrons help stabilize the protons in the atom's nucleus. Because the nucleus is so tightly packed together, the positively charged protons would tend to repel each other normally. Neutrons help to reduce the repulsion between protons and stabilize the atom's nucleus. Neutrons always reside in the nucleus of atoms and they are about the same size as protons. However, neutrons do not have any electrical charge; they are electrically neutral.

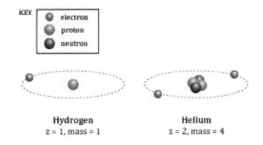

Figure 2

Atoms are electrically neutral because the number of protons (+ charges) is equal to the number of electrons (- charges) and thus the two cancel out. As the atom gets larger, the number of protons increases, and so does the number of electrons (in the neutral state of the atom). The illustration below (Figure 2) compares the two simplest atoms, hydrogen and helium. (You can view a simulation in the online version of this module.)

Comprehension Checkpoint

Neutrons have

A) a positive charge to balance out electrons

B) no electrical charge

Size, number, and weight of atoms

Atoms are extremely small. One hydrogen atom (the smallest atom known) is approximately 5×10^{-8} mm in diameter. To put that in perspective, it would take almost 20 million hydrogen atoms to make a line as long as this dash -. Most of the space taken up by an atom is actually empty because the electron spins at a very far distance from the nucleus. For example, if we were to draw a hydrogen atom to scale and used a 1-cm proton (about the size of this picture - ●), the atom's electron would spin at a distance of ~0.5 km from the nucleus. In other words, the atom would be larger than a football field!

Atoms of different elements are distinguished from each other by their number of protons (the number of protons is constant for all atoms of a single element; the number of neutrons and electrons can vary under some circumstances). To identify this important characteristic of atoms, the term *atomic number* (z) is used to describe the number of protons in an atom. For example, z = 1 for hydrogen and z = 2 for helium.

Another important characteristic of an atom is its weight, or *atomic mass*. The weight of an atom is roughly determined by the total number of protons and neutrons in the atom. While protons and neutrons are about the same size, the electron is more than 1,800 times smaller than the two. Thus the electrons' weight is inconsequential in determining the weight of an atom – it's like comparing the weight of a flea to the weight of an elephant. Refer to the animation in the online version of this module to see how the number of protons plus neutrons in the hydrogen and helium atoms corresponds to the atomic mass.

Atomic Theory I Quiz

1. Who was the first person to suggest that the atom was made up of smaller parts?

   A) James Chadwick

   B) John Dalton

   C) J.J. Thomson

   D) Ernest Rutherford

2. Cathode rays are beams of

   A) protons.

   B) electrons.

   C) alpha particles.

   D) neutrons.

3. Based on his experiments, what did Rutherford propose?

   A) atoms had a dense nucleus

   B) all of the choices

   C) atoms are mostly empty space

   D) the nucleus is positively charged

4. The proton has

   A) the opposite charge and a larger mass than the electron.

   B) the opposite charge and a smaller mass than the electron.

   C) the same charge and the same mass as the electron.

   D) the same charge and a smaller mass than the electron.

5. The neutron has

   A) about the same size and charge as a proton.

   B) about the same size and charge as an electron.

   C) no charge and about the same size as a proton.

   D) no charge and about the same size as a an electron.

6. How many protons are in the helium atom?

   A) one

   B) two

   C) four

   D) five

7. The number of protons in an atom is called the

   A) nucleus.

   B) atomic weight.

   C) atomic mass.

   D) atomic number.

8. Which of the following is a valid definition of atomic weight? Atomic weight is

   A) the number of protons in an atom.

   B) the number of protons and electrons.

   C) the number of electrons in an atom.

   D) the number of protons and neutrons.

9. What is the atomic mass of helium?

   A) one

   B) two

   C) six

   D) four

10. Which is the correct organization of the subatomic particles in an atom?

   A) Neutrons and electrons reside inside of a small nucleus. Protons revolve around the nucleus.

   B) Electrons reside inside of a small nucleus. Protons and neutrons revolve around the nucleus.

   C) Protons and electrons reside inside of a small nucleus. Neutrons revolve around the nucleus.

   D) Protons and neutrons reside inside of a small nucleus. Electrons revolve around the nucleus.

Quiz continued on next page ▶ ▶ ▶

11. The electron has a

   A) positive charge and relatively small mass.

   B) positive charge and relatively large mass.

   C) negative charge and relatively small mass.

   D) negative charge and relatively large mass.

Answers and feedback can be found on Page 250

Atomic Theory II:
Ions, Isotopes, and Electron Shells

by Anthony Carpi, PhD

Did you know that different elements give off distinct colors when heated? This is because electrons "jump" away from the nucleus when they are excited. When the electrons "fall" back, they release energy in the form of light. Anyone who has seen the glow of neon lights has seen this process in action.

Module Summary

Focusing on advances in atomic theory over the past century, this module explores how Niels Bohr's discovery of line spectra led to his theory that each atom has multiple electron "shells" – the energy levels occupied by electrons. Ions and isotopes are defined, and the quantum behavior of electrons is demonstrated through animations.

Terms you should know:

emit = give off; send forth

level = a position that is defined in relation to a different position

spectrum (plural: spectra) = a continuing range such as of color or frequency; a series of colors arranged by wavelength as in a rainbow

In our module Atomic Theory I: The Early Days we learned about the basic structure of the atom. Normally, atoms contain equal numbers of protons and electrons. Because the positive and negative charges cancel each other out, atoms are normally electrically neutral. But, while the number of protons is always constant in any atom of a given element, the number of electrons can vary.

Ions

When the number of electrons changes in an atom, the electrical charge changes. If an atom gains electrons, it picks up an imbalance of negatively charged particles and therefore becomes negative. If an atom loses electrons, the balance between positive and negative charges is shifted in the opposite direction and the atom becomes positive. In either case, the magnitude (+1, +2, -1, -2, etc.) of the electrical charge will correspond to the number of electrons gained or lost. Atoms that carry electrical charges are called ions (regardless of whether they are positive or negative). For example, Figure 1 shows a positive hydrogen

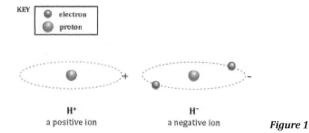

Figure 1

H⁺
a positive ion

H⁻
a negative ion

ion (which has lost an electron) and a negative hydrogen ion (which has gained an extra electron). The electrical charge on the ion is always written as a superscript after the atom's symbol. View an animation of this in the online version of this module.

Isotopes

The number of neutrons in an atom can also vary. Two atoms of the same element that contain different numbers of neutrons are called isotopes. For example, normally hydrogen contains no neutrons. An isotope of hydrogen does exist that contains one neutron (commonly called *deuterium*). The atomic number (z) is the same in both isotopes; however the atomic mass increases by one in deuterium as the atom is made heavier by the extra neutron (Figure 2). View an animation of this in the online version of this module.

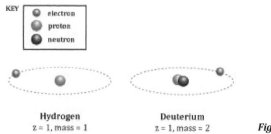

Figure 2

Hydrogen
z = 1, mass = 1

Deuterium
z = 1, mass = 2

Comprehension Checkpoint

Isotopes are atoms of the same element that have a different number of

A) protons.

B) neutrons.

Electron Shells

Ernest Rutherford's view of the atom consisted of a dense nucleus surrounded by freely spinning electrons (see our Atomic Theory I module). In 1913, the Danish physicist Niels Bohr proposed yet another modification to the theory of atomic structure based on a curious phenomenon called *line spectra*.

When matter is heated, it gives off light. For example, turning on an ordinary light bulb causes an electric current to flow through a metal filament. This heats the filament and produces light. The electrical energy absorbed by the filament excites the atoms' electrons, causing them to "wiggle." This absorbed energy is eventually released from the atoms in the form of light.

When normal white light, such as that from the sun, is passed through a prism, the light separates into a continuous spectrum of colors:

Figure 3: Continuous (white light) spectra

Bohr knew that when pure elements were excited by heat or electricity, they gave off distinct colors rather than white light. This phenomenon is most commonly seen in modern-day neon lights, tubes filled with gaseous elements (typically neon). When an electric current is passed through the gas, a distinct color (most often red) is given off by the element. When light from an excited element is passed through a prism, only specific lines (or wavelengths) of light can be seen. These lines of light are called line spectra. For example, when hydrogen is heated and the light is passed through a prism, the following line spectra can be seen:

Figure 4: Hydrogen line spectra

Each element has its own distinct line spectra. For example:

Figure 5: Helium line spectra

Figure 6: Neon line spectra

To Bohr, the line spectra phenomenon showed that atoms could not emit energy continuously, but only in very precise quantities (he described the energy emitted as *quantized*). Because the emitted light was due to the movement of electrons, Bohr suggested that electrons could not move continuously in the atom (as Rutherford had suggested) but only in precise steps. Bohr hypothesized that electrons occupy specific energy levels. When an atom is excited, such as during heating, electrons can jump to higher levels. When the electrons fall back to lower energy levels, precise quanta of energy are released as specific wavelengths (lines) of light.

Under Bohr's theory, an electron's energy levels (also called electron shells) can be imagined as concentric circles around the nucleus. Normally, electrons exist in the ground state, meaning they occupy the lowest energy level possible (the electron shell closest to the nucleus). When an electron is excited by adding energy to an atom (for example, when it is heated), the electron will absorb energy, "jump" to a higher energy level, and spin in the higher energy level. After a short time, this electron will spontaneously "fall" back to a lower energy level, giving off a quantum of light energy. Key to Bohr's theory was the fact that the electron could only "jump" and "fall" to precise energy levels, as measured in electron volts, or eV, thus emitting a limited spectrum of light. The animation "Bohr's Atom," in the online version of this module, simulates this process in a hydrogen atom and displays the energy absorbed or released in eV units.

Not only did Bohr predict that electrons would occupy specific energy levels, he also predicted that those levels had limits to the number of electrons each could hold. Under Bohr's theory, the maximum capacity of the first (or innermost) electron shell is two electrons. For any element with more than two electrons, the extra electrons will reside in additional electron shells. For example, in the ground state configuration of lithium (which has three electrons) two electrons occupy the first shell and one electron occupies the second shell. This is illustrated in the animation "The Lithium Atom" in the online version of this module.

For further details, the online version of this module includes an animated table showing the electron configurations of the first eleven elements.

Comprehension Checkpoint

At their lowest energy level, electrons are

A) in the ground state.
B) as far as possible from the nucleus.

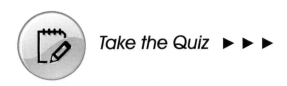

Take the Quiz ▶ ▶ ▶

Atomic Theory II Quiz

1. Ions are:

A) electrons

B) neutrons

C) protons

D) charged atoms

2. Isotopes are atoms of the same element with:

A) different numbers of neutrons

B) different numbers of electrons

C) different atomic numbers

D) different numbers of protons

3. The atomic number is the same in different isotopes of the same element:

A) True

B) False

4. Which part of Dalton's original atomic theory must be modified with the discovery of isotopes?

A) Compounds are formed when elements enter into chemical reactions

B) All atoms of a given element are identical

C) Matter is composed of atoms

D) Atoms combine with other atoms in whole number ratios to form compounds

5. Who was the person to propose the theory of atomic structure based on line spectra?

A) John Dalton

B) Niels Bohr

C) Ernest Rutherford

D) James Chadwick

6. The distinct pattern of colors emitted by excited atoms is called:

A) line spectra

B) rainbow

C) continuous spectra

D) cathode rays

7. Under Bohr's theory of line spectra, the energy in atoms is:

A) quantized

B) infinite

C) zero

D) continuous

8. When an electron is excited, the electron's "distance" from the nucleus:

A) cannot be predicted

B) decreases

C) increases

D) stays the same

9. In the normal or "ground" state, all of the electrons in an atom are:

A) in the nucleus

B) not moving

C) in the lowest possible electron shells

D) in the highest possible energy shells

10. The maximum number of electrons that may reside in the first energy level is:

A) two

B) eight

C) thirteen

D) three

12. The existence of line spectra can be explained by:

A) the unique properties of neon lights

B) atoms crashing into prisms

C) electrons "jumping" and "falling" to and from specific orbitals

D) the unique colors of atoms

Answers and feedback can be found on Page 253

Nuclear Chemistry: An Introduction

by Anthony Carpi, PhD

Did you know that the sun and stars are actually enormous thermonuclear fusion reactors? And that atoms can be split artificially, releasing energy that can be harnessed to generate electrical power? Thanks to pioneers in nuclear chemistry like Marie Curie, we have come to understand different types of radiation and nuclear reactions.

Module Summary

Beginning with the work of Marie Curie and others, this module traces the development of nuclear chemistry. It describes different types of radiation: alpha, beta, and gamma. The module then applies the principle of half-life to radioactive decay and explains the difference between nuclear fission and nuclear fusion.

Terms you should know:

decay = to break down; to decrease over time in size, amount, or force

radiation = particles or energy emitted

transmutation = the transformation of one element into another through nuclear decay or reaction

Traditional chemical reactions occur as a result of the interaction between valence electrons around an atom's nucleus (see our Chemical Reactions module for more information). In 1896, Henri Becquerel expanded the field of chemistry to include nuclear changes when he discovered that uranium emitted radiation. Soon after Becquerel's discovery, Marie Sklodowska Curie began studying radioactivity and completed much of the pioneering work on nuclear changes. Curie found that radiation was proportional to the amount of radioactive element present, and she proposed that radiation was a property of atoms (as opposed to a chemical property of a compound). Marie Curie was the first woman to win a Nobel Prize and the first person to win two (the first, shared with her husband Pierre and Becquerel for discovering radioactivity; the second for discovering the radioactive elements radium and polonium).

Radiation and nuclear reactions

In 1902, Frederick Soddy proposed the theory that "radioactivity is the result of a natural change of an isotope of one element into an isotope of a different element." Nuclear reactions involve changes in particles in an atom's nucleus and thus cause a change in the atom itself. All elements heavier than bismuth (Bi) (and some lighter) exhibit natural radioactivity and thus can "decay" into lighter elements. Unlike normal chemical reactions that form molecules, nuclear reactions result in the transmutation of one element into a different isotope or a different element altogether (remember that the number of protons in an atom defines the element, so a change in protons results in a change in the atom). There are three common types of radiation and nuclear changes:

1. **Alpha Radiation (α)** is the emission of an alpha particle from an atom's nucleus. An α particle contains two protons and two neutrons (and is similar to a He nucleus: $_2^4 He$). When an atom emits an α particle, the atom's atomic mass will decrease by four units (because two protons and two neutrons are lost) and the atomic number (z) will decrease by two units. The element is said to "transmutate" into another element that is two z units smaller. An example of an α transmutation takes place when uranium decays into the element thorium (Th) by emitting an alpha particle, as depicted in the following equation:

$$_{92}^{238} U \longrightarrow {}_2^4 He + {}_{90}^{234} Th$$

(Note: in nuclear chemistry, element symbols are traditionally preceded by their atomic weight (upper left) and atomic number (lower left).

2. **Beta Radiation (β)** is the transmutation of a neutron into a proton and an electron (followed by the emission of the electron from the atom's nucleus: $_{-1}^{0} e$). When an atom emits a β particle, the atom's mass will not change (since there is no change in the total number of nuclear particles); however, the atomic number will increase by one (because the neutron transmutated into an additional proton). An example of this is the decay of the isotope of carbon named carbon-14 into the element nitrogen:

$$_6^{14} C \longrightarrow {}_{-1}^{0} e + {}_7^{14} N$$

3. **Gamma Radiation (γ)** involves the emission of electromagnetic energy (similar to light energy) from an atom's nucleus. No particles are emitted during gamma radiation, and thus gamma radiation does not itself cause the transmutation of atoms; however, γ radiation is often emitted during, and simultaneous to, α or β radioactive decay. X-rays, emitted during the beta decay of cobalt-60, are a common example of gamma radiation.

Comprehension Checkpoint

Radiation can result in an atom having a different atomic number.

A) True
B) False

Radioactive decay proceeds according to a principle called the half-life. The half-life ($T_{1/2}$) is the amount of time necessary for one-half of the radioactive material to decay. For example, the radioactive element bismuth (^{210}Bi) can undergo alpha decay to form the element thallium (^{206}Tl) with a reaction half-life equal to five days. If we begin an experiment starting with 100 g of bismuth in a sealed lead container, after five days we will have 50 g of bismuth and 50 g of thallium in the jar. After another five days (ten from the starting point), one-half of the remaining bismuth will decay and we will be left with 25 g of bismuth and 75 g of thallium in the jar. As illustrated in Figure 1, the reaction proceeds in halves, with half of whatever is left of the radioactive element decaying every half-life period.

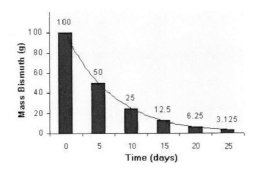

Figure 1: Radioactive Decay of Bismuth-210 ($T_{1/2}$ = 5 days)

The fraction of parent material that remains after radioactive decay can be calculated using the equation:

$$\text{Fraction remaining} = \frac{1}{2^n} \quad \text{(where n - \# of lives elapsed)}$$

The amount of a radioactive material that remains after a given number of half-lives is therefore:

$$\text{Amount remaining} = \text{Original amount} * \text{Fraction remaining}$$

The decay reaction and $T_{1/2}$ of a substance are specific to the isotope of the element undergoing radioactive decay. For example, Bi210 can undergo a decay to ^{206}Tl with a $T_{1/2}$ of five days. ^{215}Bi, by comparison, undergoes β decay to ^{215}Po with a $T_{1/2}$ of 7.6 minutes, and ^{208}Bi undergoes yet another mode of radioactive decay (called electron capture) with a $T_{1/2}$ of 368,000 years!

Comprehension Checkpoint

All radioactive material decays at the same rate.

A) True

B) False

While many elements undergo radioactive decay naturally, nuclear reactions can also be stimulated artificially. Although these reactions also occur naturally, we are most familiar with them as stimulated reactions. There are two such types of nuclear reactions:

1. Nuclear fission: reactions in which an atom's nucleus splits into smaller parts, releasing a large amount of energy in the process. Most commonly this is done by "firing" a neutron at the nucleus of an atom. The energy of the neutron "bullet" causes the target element to split into two (or more) elements that are lighter than the parent atom (Figure 2). You can view an interactive animation of this reaction in the online version of this module.

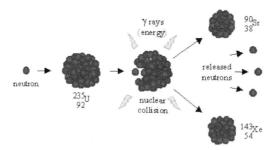

Figure 2: The fission reaction of Uranium-235 (^{235}U)

During the fission of ^{235}U, three neutrons are released in addition to the two daughter atoms. If these released neutrons collide with nearby ^{235}U nuclei, they can stimulate the fission of these atoms and start a self-sustaining nuclear chain reaction. This chain reaction is the basis of nuclear power. As uranium atoms continue to split, a significant amount of energy is released from the reaction. The heat released during this reaction is harvested and used to generate electrical energy. View an interactive animation of these two types of nuclear reactions in the online version of this module.

2. Nuclear fusion: reactions in which two or more elements "fuse" together to form one larger element, releasing energy in the process. A good example is the fusion of two "heavy" isotopes of hydrogen (deuterium: H2 and tritium: H3) into the element helium (Figure 3). You can view an animation of nuclear fusion in the online version of this module.

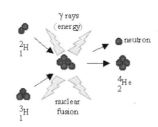

Figure 3: Nuclear fusion of two hydrogen isotopes

Fusion reactions release tremendous amounts of energy and are commonly referred to as thermonuclear reactions. Although many people think of the sun as a large fireball, the sun (and all stars) are actually enormous fusion reactors. Stars are primarily gigantic balls of hydrogen gas under tremendous pressure due to gravitational forces. Hydrogen molecules are fused into helium and heavier elements inside of stars, releasing energy that we receive as light and heat.

Take the Quiz ▶ ▶ ▶

Nuclear Chemistry Quiz

1. Who was the first person to win two Nobel Prizes?

    A) Henri Becquerel

    B) Rosalind Franklin

    C) Marie Curie

    D) Ernest Rutherford

2. Beta radiation is the

    A) transmutation of a neutron into a proton and electron. The proton is emitted.

    B) transmutation of a neutron into a proton and electron. The electron is emitted.

    C) transmutation of a proton into a neutron and electron. The proton is emitted.

    D) transmutation of a proton into a neutron and electron. The electron is emitted.

3. The atomic number decreases by two during what type of radiation?

    A) alpha

    B) beta

    C) gamma

    D) none of the choices

4. X-rays are an example of what type of radiation?

    A) alpha

    B) beta

    C) gamma

    D) transmutation

5. The atomic number increases by one during what type of radioactive decay?

    A) alpha

    B) beta

    C) gamma

    D) none of the choices

6. After three half-lives, what fraction of the original radioactive isotope remains?

    A) 1/4

    B) 1/2

    C) 1/16

    D) 1/8

7. The source of energy produced by the sun is the

    A) burning of fossil fuel.

    B) fusion of hydrogen.

    C) fission of uranium.

    D) none of the choices

8. Nuclear fission is a reaction during which the

    A) nucleus of an atom loses a proton with the release of energy.

    B) nucleus of an atom is fused with another nucleus.

    C) nucleus of an atom is stimulated to split into fragments by some source.

    D) nucleus of an atom spontaneously splits into fragments.

9. In nuclear fusion

    A) large unstable nuclei are fused and then split.

    B) small, relatively stable nuclei are fused together to create a larger atom.

    C) small, relatively stable nuclei are split, releasing energy.

    D) large unstable nuclei are split, releasing energy.

Answers and feedback can be found on Page 255

Gravity: Newtonian Relationships

by Nathaniel Stites, MS

Did you know that the same force that makes an apple fall to the ground holds vast galaxies together? Gravity affects our activities every day, and yet it is not well understood by scientists. However, whether it is a small marble dropping from someone's hand or the motion of planets around the sun, the behavior of objects under the influence of gravity can be described mathematically.

Module Summary

Isaac Newton's description of gravity was not the first explanation of this phenomenon, nor was it the last. This module explores how Newton built on the work of early astronomers and how his theory was confirmed and built upon by others. Mathematical equations are presented for (1) the Law of Universal Gravitation, (2) the Gravitational Constant, (3) Earth's mass, and (4) the gravitational attraction between two people.

Terms you should know:

law = a principle that describes a phenomenon, often mathematically

mass = the amount of matter that an object contains

object = a physical thing; something with mass

What causes objects to fall toward Earth? Why do the planets orbit the sun? What holds galaxies together? If you traveled to another planet, why would your weight change?

All of these questions relate to one aspect of physics: gravity. For all of its influence on our daily lives, for all of its control over the cosmos, and for all of our ability to describe and model its effects, we do not understand the actual mechanisms of gravitational force. Of the four fundamental forces identified by physicists – strong nuclear, electroweak, electrostatic, and gravitational – the gravitational force is the least understood. Physicists today strive toward a "Grand Unified Theory," wherein all four of these forces are united into one physical model that describes the behavior of everything in the universe. At this point in time, the gravitational force is the troublesome one, the force that resists unification.

In spite of the mystery behind the mechanisms of gravity, physicists have been able to describe the behavior of objects under the influence of gravity quite thoroughly. Isaac Newton, a 17th into 18th century English scientist and mathematician (among other things), was the first person to propose a mathematical model to describe the gravitational attraction between objects. Albert Einstein built upon this model in the 20th century and devised a more complete description of gravity in his theory of general relativity. In this module, we will explore Newton's description of gravity and some of the experimental confirmations of his theory that came many years after he proposed his original idea.

The Apple

Whether or not Isaac Newton actually sat under an apple tree while pondering the nature of gravity, the fact that objects fall toward the surface of Earth was well understood long before Newton's time. Everyone has experience with gravity and its effects near the surface of Earth, and our intuitive view of the world includes an understanding that what goes up must come down.

Galileo Galilei (1564–1642) demonstrated that all objects fall to the surface of Earth with the same acceleration, and that this acceleration was independent of the mass of the falling object (see the Concept Simulation *Leaning Tower of Pisa* in the online version of this module). Isaac Newton was no doubt familiar with this concept, and he would eventually formulate a broad and far-reaching theory of gravitation. Newton's theory would encompass not only the behavior of an apple near the surface of Earth, but also the motions of much larger bodies quite far away from Earth.

The Planets

Figure 1: The Solar System

Early conceptions of the universe were "geocentric" – they placed Earth at the center of the universe and had the planets and stars move around Earth. This Ptolemaic Model of the universe dominated scientific thought for many centuries, until the work of such careful astronomers as Tycho Brahe, Nicolaus Copernicus, Galileo Galilei, and Johannes Kepler supplanted this view of the cosmos. The "Copernican Revolution" placed the sun at the center of the solar system and the planets, including Earth, in orbit around the sun (Figure 1). This major shift in perception laid the foundation for Isaac Newton to begin thinking about gravitation as it related to the motions of the planets.

An early unification theory

Just as physicists today are searching for ways to unify the fundamental forces, Isaac Newton also sought to unify two seemingly disparate phenomena: the motion of objects falling toward Earth and the motion of the planets orbiting the sun. Isaac Newton's breakthrough was not that apples fall to Earth because of gravity; it was that the planets are constantly falling toward the sun for exactly the same reason: gravity!

Newton built upon the work of early astronomers, in particular Johannes Kepler, who in 1596 and 1619 published his laws of planetary motion. One of Kepler's central observations was that the planets move in elliptical orbits around the sun. Newton expanded Kepler's description of planetary motion into a theory of gravitation.

Comprehension Checkpoint

What was Newton's most important contribution to our understanding of gravity?

A) Apples fall to Earth because of gravity.

B) Planets are drawn to the sun because of gravity.

Newton's Law of Universal Gravitation

The essential feature of Newton's Law of Universal Gravitation is that the force of gravity between two objects is inversely proportional to the square of the distance between them. Such a connection is known as an "inverse square" relationship. Newton derived this relationship from Kepler's assertion that the planets follow elliptical orbits. To understand this, consider the light radiating from the surface of the sun. The light has some intensity at the surface of the sun. As the light travels away from the sun, its intensity diminishes. The intensity of the light at any distance away from the sun equals the strength of the source divided by the surface area of a sphere surrounding the sun at that radius.

As the distance away from the sun (r) doubles, the area of the sphere surrounding the sun quadruples. Thus, the intensity of the sun's light depends inversely on the square of the distance away from the sun. Newton envisioned the gravitational force as radiating equally in all directions from a central body, just as sunlight in the previous example. Newton recognized that his gravitational model must take the form of an inverse square relationship. Such a model predicts that the orbits of objects around a central body will be conic sections, and years of astronomical observations have borne this out. Although this idea is most commonly attributed to Isaac Newton, the English mathematician Robert Hooke claimed that he originated the idea of the inverse square relationship. Nonetheless, Newton eventually published his theory of gravitation and became famous as a result.

The relationship that Newton came up with looks like this:

$$F = \frac{G\, m_1\, m_2}{r^2}$$

where F is the force of gravity (in units now referred to as newtons), m_1 and m_2 are the masses of the two objects in kilograms (for example, the sun and Earth), r is the distance separating the centers of mass of the objects and G is the "gravitational constant." The equation shows that the force of gravity is directly proportional to the product of the two masses, but inversely proportional to the square of the distance between the centers of those two masses. To understand the formula, keep in mind that the force of gravity *decreases* as distance *increases* (an inverse relationship). The distance (r) is squared due to the relationship between the increasing distance and the growth of the area over which the force is exerted (just as rays of light spread out as they get farther from the sun). Finally, since both masses exert some force due to gravity, it is the product of their masses – not just a single mass – that makes a difference.

This relationship has come to be known as Newton's Law of Universal Gravitation. It is "universal" because all objects in the universe are attracted to all other objects in the universe according to this relationship. Two people sitting across a room from each other are actually attracted gravitationally. As we know from everyday experience, human-sized objects don't crash into each other as a result of this force, but it does exist even if it is very small. Although Newton correctly identified this relationship between force, mass, and distance, he was able only to estimate the value of the gravitational constant between these quantities. The world would have to wait more than a century for an experimental measurement of the constant of proportionality: G.

Comprehension Checkpoint

The farther away two objects are from each other, the stronger the gravitational pull between them

A) True

B) False

Measuring the mass of Earth: The Cavendish experiment

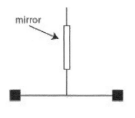

mirror

Figure 2: *The Torsion Balance, devised by Michell and Cevendish to determine the constant of proportionality in Newton's Law of Universal Gravitation*

In 1797 and 1798 Henry Cavendish set out to confirm Newton's theory and to determine the constant of proportionality in Newton's Law of Universal Gravitation. His ingenious experiment, based on the work of John Michell, was successful on both fronts. To accomplish this, Cavendish created a "torsion balance," which consisted of two masses at either end of a bar that was suspended from the ceiling by a thin wire (see Figure 2).

Attached to the wire was a mirror, off of which a beam of light was reflected. Cavendish brought a third mass close to one of the masses on the torsion balance. As the third mass attracted one of the ends of the torsion balance, the entire apparatus, including the mirror, rotated slightly and the beam of light was deflected. Through careful measurement of the angular deflection of the beam of light, Cavendish was able to determine the extent to which the known mass was attracted to the introduced mass. Not only did Cavendish confirm Newton's theory, but also he determined the value of the gravitational constant to an accuracy of about 1 percent (Figure 3).

$$G = 6.67 \times 10^{-11} \text{ N m}^2/\text{kg}^2 \quad \textbf{Figure 3: } \textit{Gravitational constant}$$

Cavendish cleverly referred to his research as "Measuring the Mass of Earth." Since he had determined the value of G, he could do some simple calculations to determine the mass of Earth. By Newton's Second Law, the force between an object and Earth equals the product of the acceleration (g) and the mass of the object (m): F = ma.

Galileo had determined the acceleration of all objects near the surface of Earth in the early 1600s as $g = 9.8 \text{ m/s}^2$.

Therefore, setting this equation equal to Newton's Law of Universal Gravitation described above, Cavendish found:

$$F = mg = \frac{G \, m \, m_E}{r_E^2}$$

where m is the mass of the object, m_E is the mass of Earth, and r_E is the radius of Earth. Solving for the mass of Earth yields the following result:

$$m_E = \frac{gr_E^2}{G} = \frac{(9.8 \text{ m/s}^2)(6.38 \times 10^6 \text{ m})^2}{6.67 \times 10^{-11} \text{ Nm}^2/\text{kg}^2}$$

$$m_E = 5.98 \times 10^{24} \text{ kg}$$

Cavendish had determined the mass of Earth with great accuracy. We can also use this relationship to calculate the force of attraction between two people across a room. To do this, we simply need to use Newton's Law of Universal Gravitation with Cavendish's gravitational constant. Assume the two people have masses of 75 and 100 kilograms, respectively, and that they are 5 meters apart. The force of gravitation between them is:

$$F = \frac{G m_1 m_2}{r^2}$$

$$F = \frac{(6.67 \times 10^{-11} \text{ Nm}^2/\text{kg}^2)(75 \text{ kg})(100 \text{ kg})}{(5 \text{ m})^2}$$

$$F = 2.00 \times 10^{-8} \text{ N}$$

Although it is small, there is still a force!

Conclusion

Newton's Law of Universal Gravitation grew in importance as scientists realized its utility in predicting the orbits of the planets and other bodies in space. In 1705, Sir Edmund Halley, after studying comets in great detail, predicted correctly that the famous comet of 1682 would return 76 years later, in December of 1758. Halley had used Newton's Law to predict the behavior of the comet orbiting the sun. With the advent of Cavendish's accurate value for the gravitational constant, scientists were able to use Newton's law for even more purposes. In 1845, John Couch Adams and Urbain Le Verrier predicted the existence of a new, yet unseen, planet based on small discrepancies between predictions for and observations of the position of Uranus. In 1846, the German astronomer Johann Galle confirmed their predictions and officially discovered the new planet, Neptune.

While Newton's Law of Universal Gravitation remains very useful today, Albert Einstein demonstrated in 1915 that the law was only approximately correct, and that it fails to work when gravitation becomes extremely strong. Nonetheless, Newton's gravitational constant plays an important role in Einstein's alternative to Newton's Law, the Theory of General Relativity. The value of G has been the subject of great debate even in recent years, and scientists are still struggling to determine a very accurate value for this most elusive of fundamental physical constants.

Key Concepts for this chapter

▶ Though the mechanisms of gravitational force are still a mystery, physicists have been able to effectively describe the influence of gravity on objects.

▶ Newton's mathematical model describing gravitational attraction paved the way for other scientists to build toward an understanding of the relationships between mass, acceleration, and the force of attraction.

▶ Using the Law of Universal Gravitation, it is possible to predict the behavior of objects under the influence of gravitational force.

▶ According to the Inverse Square Law, as the distance between two objects doubles, the force of gravity between those two objects decreases by a factor of four.

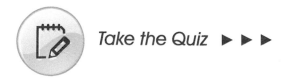 *Take the Quiz* ▶ ▶ ▶

Gravity Quiz

1. The Law of Universal Gravitation was the result of the work of

   A) Henry Cavendish.

   B) Isaac Newton.

   C) Albert Einstein

   D) Robert Hooke.

2. According to the Law of Universal Gravitation, the force of gravity between two objects is directly proportional to

   A) the product of the masses of the objects.

   B) the mass of the earth.

   C) the distance between the objects

   D) the temperature of the objects.

3. According to the Law of Universal Gravitation, the force of gravity between two objects is inversely proportional to

   A) the product of the masses of the objects

   B) the mass of the earth.

   C) the distance between the objects.

   D) the square of the distance between the objects.

4. Henry Cavendish measured the mass of the earth by

   A) determining the value of the gravitational constant.

   B) comparing Earth's orbit to those of other planets.

   C) calculating the amount of water the earth would displace.

   D) estimating the volume and density of the earth

5. The experimental apparatus used by Henry Cavendish to determine the value of the gravitational constant was called the

   A) triple-beam balance

   B) torsion balance.

   C) balance beam.

   D) analytical balance.

6. The force of gravity between two 100-kg masses separated by one meter is approximately

   A) 6.7 newtons

   B) 0.00000067 newtons.

   C) 0.000067 newtons.

   D) 0.0067 newtons.

7. The force of gravity between the earth and an average human is approximately

   A) 67 newtons.

   B) 670 newtons.

   C) 6700 newtons.

   D) 6.7 newtons.

8. Astronomers inferred the existence of which planet using Newton's Law of Universal Gravitation?

   A) Neptune

   B) Jupiter

   C) Uranus

   D) Saturn

9. The twentieth-century theory that made modifications to Newton's Law of Universal Gravitation was

   A) Quantum Theory.

   B) the Theory of Special Relativity

   C) the Theory of General Relativity.

   D) the Theory of Statistical Mechanics.

10. Using the Law of Universal Gravitation, a scientist could predict

   A) the location of a planet in the solar system.

   B) the mass of a planet's moon.

   C) all of the choices

   D) the force with which a comet would collide with earth.

Answers and feedback can be found on Page 257

Light I: Particle or Wave?

by Nathaniel Stites, MS

> Did you know that scientists and philosophers debated for centuries about whether light traveled in waves or particles? Finally in the 20th century, one of science's "most beautiful experiments" seemed to confirm the wave-like nature of light, until it was further refined some 100 years later.

Module Summary

For centuries, controversy over whether light is made of particles or waves abounded. This module traces the controversy over time, from Isaac Newton's "corpuscle" (particle) theory, which prevailed for centuries, to Thomas Young's groundbreaking *double slit* experiment, which provided evidence that light traveled in waves.

Terms you should know:

beam = a ray or shaft of light from a source

particle = a tiny piece of matter

phenomenon = a fact or event that can be observed

Early theories

For as long as the human imagination has sought to make meaning of the world, we have recognized light as essential to our existence. Whether to a prehistoric child warming herself by the light of a fire in a cave, or to a modern child afraid to go to sleep without the lights on, light has always given comfort and reassurance.

The earliest documented theories of light came from the ancient Greeks. Aristotle believed that light was some kind of disturbance in the air, one of his four "elements" that composed matter. Centuries later, Lucretius, who, like Democritus before him, believed that matter consisted of indivisible "atoms," thought that light must be a particle given off by the sun. In the 10th century CE, the Middle Eastern mathematician Alhazen developed a theory that all objects radiate their own light. Alhazen's theory was contrary to earlier theories proposing that we could see because our eyes emitted light to illuminate the objects around us.

In the 17th century, two distinct models emerged from France to explain the phenomenon of light. The French philosopher and mathematician Rene Descartes believed that an invisible substance, which he called the *plenum*, permeated the universe. Much like Aristotle, he believed that light was a disturbance that traveled through the plenum, like a wave that travels through water. Pierre Gassendi, a contemporary of Descartes, challenged this theory, asserting that light was made up of discrete particles.

Particles vs. waves

Figure 1: Seemingly "broken" straws in a glass of water: the result of the refraction of light.

While this controversy developed between rival French philosophers, two of the leading English scientists of the 17th century took up the particles-versus-waves battle. Isaac Newton, after seriously considering both models, ultimately decided that light was made up of particles (though he called them *corpuscles*). Robert Hooke, already a rival of Newton's and the scientist who would identify and name the cell in 1655, was a proponent of the wave theory (see our Cells module). Unlike many before them, these two scientists based their theories on observations of light's behaviors: reflection and refraction. Reflection, as from a mirror, was a well-known occurrence, but refraction, the now familiar phenomenon by which an object partially submerged in water appears to be "broken," was not well understood at the time.

Proponents of the particle theory of light pointed to reflection as evidence that light consists of individual particles that bounce off of objects, much like billiard balls. Newton believed that refraction could be explained by his laws of motion, with particles of light as the objects in motion. As light particles approached the boundary between two materials of different densities, such as air and water, the increased gravitational force of the denser material would cause the particles to change direction, Newton believed (see our Density module).

Newton's particle theory was also based partly on his observations of how the wave phenomenon diffraction related to sound. He understood that sound traveled through the air in waves, meaning sound could travel around corners and obstacles, thus a person in another room can be heard through a doorway. Since light was unable to bend around corners or obstacles, Newton believed that light could not diffract. He therefore supposed light was not a wave.

Hooke and others – most notably the Dutch scientist Christian Huygens – believed that refraction occurred because light waves slowed down as they entered a denser medium such as water and changed their direction as a result. These wave theorists believed, like Descartes, that light must travel through some material that permeates space. Huygens dubbed this medium the *aether*.

Because of Newton's fame and reputation, many scientists of the 17th and 18th centuries subscribed to the view that light was a particle. The wave theory of light, however, would receive a major boost at the beginning of the 19th century from an English scientist named Thomas Young.

> ## Comprehension Checkpoint
>
> Scientists who believed that light was made of particles pointed to
>
> _____ as evidence to support their ideas.
>
> **A)** reflection
> **B)** wave theory

On November 24, 1803, Thomas Young stood before the Royal Society of London to present the results of a groundbreaking experiment. Young had devised a simple scheme to see if light demonstrated a behavior particular to waves: interference. To understand this concept, imagine two waves traveling toward each other on a string, as shown in Figure 2:

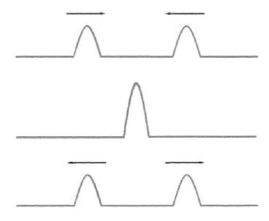

Figure 2: Traveling wave pulses interfering constructively.

When the waves reach the same part of the string at the same time, as shown in the middle of the diagram, they will add together and create one wave with double the amplitude (height) of the original waves. This adding together of waves is known as *constructive interference* because the waves combine to construct a new, bigger wave.

Another possible scenario is shown in Figure 3:

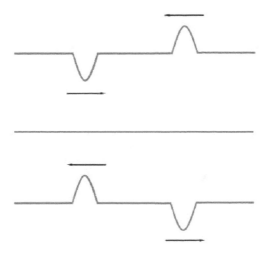

Figure 3: Traveling wave pulses interfering destructively.

Here, the two waves approaching each other have equal and opposite amplitudes. When they pass each other (middle of the diagram), they completely cancel each other out. This canceling effect is known as *destructive interference* because the waves temporarily disappear as they pass.

Beam splitting: Young's "Double Slit" experiment

Thomas Young recognized that if light behaved like a wave it would be possible to create patterns of constructive and destructive interference using light. In 1801 he devised an experiment that would force two beams of light to travel different distances before interfering with each other when they reached a screen. To accomplish this, Young set up a mirror to direct a thin beam of sunlight into a darkened room (and an assistant to make sure the mirror aimed the sun's light properly!). Young split the beam in two by placing a very thin card edgewise in the beam, as shown in the figure below.

Figure 4: Illustration and schematic diagram of Young's experiment. The edge of the card splits the light into two beams. When the beams meet at the screen, they will have traveled different distances as they bend around the edge of the card. This leads to constructive and destructive interference, depending on whether the beams are in phase or out of phase in particular spots. Where constructive interference occurs, the path difference is an integer multiple of a wavelength (or is zero, as shown earlier), and the intensity of the light hitting the screen is at a maximum. Dark spots appear on the screen where destructive interference occurs, which is the result of a path difference that is equal to one half-wavelength of the light or an integer multiple thereof.

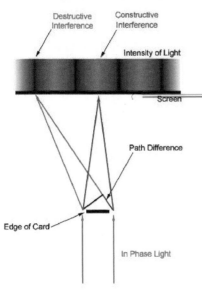

When the two beams of light shone on a screen, Young observed a very interesting pattern of light and dark "fringes" where the two beams interfered with each other constructively and destructively. Bright fringes appeared where the intensity of the light hitting the screen was highest, and dark fringes appeared where the intensity was zero. Where the two beams of light were exactly "in phase" (see Figure 5), they interfered constructively and created light that was brighter than either beam by itself. Where the beams of light were exactly "out of phase," they interfered destructively to produce a dark spot where the total light intensity was zero.

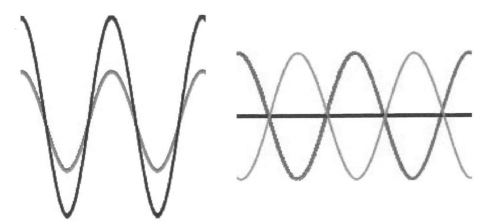

Figure 5: In-phase and out-of-phase waves. Left: The two waves are "in phase," and the combination of these waves (shown in black) is a wave with double the amplitude of the each original wave. Right: The two waves are "out of phase," and the result (shown in black) is a wave of zero amplitude.

To understand the pattern of fringes in Young's experiment, let's examine the movement of two waves in more detail. Imagine starting with two waves that are perfectly in phase, as shown in Figure 6:

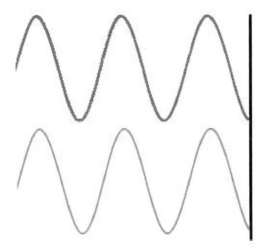

Figure 6: Two waves that are in phase upon reaching the screen at the right side of the figure.

If one wave travels a greater distance than the other, the peaks and troughs of the waves will become offset from one another and they may be out of phase when they reach their destination, as shown in Figure 7.

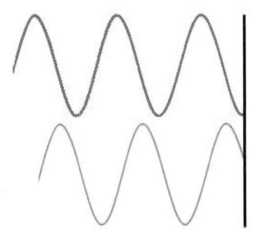

Figure 7: Two waves that have traveled different distances and are out of phase upon reaching the screen at the right side of the figure.

If the difference in distance traveled by the two waves is even greater, they will reach a point where the peak of one wave aligns with the trough of the other. Finally, if the wave that travels farther follows a path that is exactly one wavelength longer than the path the other wave follows (or two or three or any integer multiple longer), then their peaks will again align and they will arrive at their destination in phase, as shown in Figure 8.

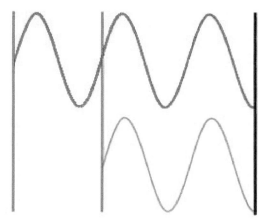

Figure 8: Two waves that have traveled different distances yet are in phase when they reach the screen at the right side of the figure. The additional distance traveled by the red wave (indicated by the vertical green lines) is exactly equal to one wavelength, so the waves arrive at their destination in phase with each other even though they have traveled different distances.

Young realized that the bright spots on his screen occurred where the difference in the length of the path traveled by the beams of light was an integer multiple of the wavelength of the light. The waves that met at this spot were perfectly in phase and had formed a bright spot because the peaks and troughs aligned with each other.

At the spots where there was no light at all, the difference in path lengths was a multiple of exactly one half-wavelength, so the two waves were completely out of phase and interfered destructively, as seen in Figure 9.

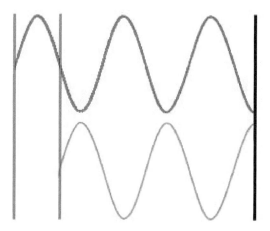

Figure 9: Two waves that have traveled different distances and are perfectly out of phase when they reach the screen at right. The additional distance traveled by the red wave (indicated by the vertical green lines) is exactly equal to one half-wavelength, so the waves arrive at their destination out of phase and interfere destructively.

Through this experiment (often called Young's "Double Slit" experiment, and voted by *The New York Times* in 2002 as science's 5th most beautiful experiment – see the News & Events link under Resources in the online version of this module), Young demonstrated with certainty the wave-like nature of light. His experiment answered Newton's charge that light could not bend around corners or obstacles because, when it bent around the edge of the card, it had.

Physicists now know that waves will go around obstacles – a process referred to as *diffraction* – but only if the size of the obstacle is comparable to the size, or wavelength, of the wave. The card that Young used in his apparatus was very thin – only about as thick as the wavelength of the light he was using it to divide, so the light did, indeed, bend around the card.

Comprehension Checkpoint

In Young's experiment with two beams of light traveling toward each other, bright spots appeared on the screen when

A) the peaks and troughs of the wavelengths aligned with each other.

B) the peaks and troughs of the wavelengths offset each other.

Light theory in the 19th century and beyond

In the face of this compelling evidence, nineteenth-century scientists had to concede that light was a wave. This happened slowly, though, hampered by Newton's reputation and the legacy of his corpuscular theory. Yet, once it did take root, the idea of light as a wave paved the way for the nineteenth-century Scottish physicist James Clerk Maxwell to devise an elegant description of light as a wave, which unified two rapidly developing concepts of physics into one complete theory. It was this description that set the stage for a discovery that would arise 100 years later, when a young German-born patent clerk by the name of Albert Einstein would show that the conception of light as a wave was not entirely correct and thereby revolutionize scientific thinking of the twentieth century.

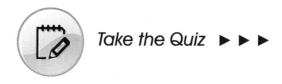

Take the Quiz ▶ ▶ ▶

Light I Quiz

1. "Refraction" of light occurs when

   A) light bends around corners or obstacles.

   B) light waves add together to make a new wave with larger amplitude.

   C) light bounces off a surface.

   D) light changes direction due to a change in speed.

2. "Diffraction" of light occurs when

   A) light bounces off a surface.

   B) light waves add together to make a wave with larger amplitude.

   C) light bends around corners or obstacles.

   D) light changes direction when passing from one material into another.

3. For diffraction of a wave to occur,

   A) the wave must be traveling from a less dense to a denser material.

   B) the wave must be traveling slower than the speed of light in a vacuum.

   C) the wave must be a sound wave.

   D) the wave must encounter an obstacle that is comparable in size to the wavelength of the wave.

4. "Constructive" and "destructive" interference refer to the phenomenon of

   A) waves traveling different distances.

   B) waves changing direction when entering a new material.

   C) waves bending around obstacles.

   D) waves adding together or canceling each other out when they are superimposed.

5. Young found that bright and dark spots appeared on the screen because of

   A) holes in a piece of paper.

   B) spectral lines.

   C) bright and dark lights shining on the screen.

   D) constructive and destructive interference.

6. Constructive interference occurs when the difference in path lengths traveled by two light rays is

   A) exactly zero.

   B) zero or an integer multiple of the wavelength of the light.

   C) anything other than zero.

   D) an integer multiple of the half-wavelength of the light.

7. Destructive interference occurs when the difference in path lengths traveled by two light rays is

   A) exactly zero.

   B) anything other than zero.

   C) zero or an integer multiple of the wavelength of the light.

   D) an integer multiple of the half-wavelength of the light.

Answers and feedback can be found on Page 258

Light and Electromagnetism

by Nathaniel Stites, MS

Did you know that visible light is no different in its form from microwaves, radio waves, or X-rays? Throughout the 19th century, scientists dedicated themselves to the study of electricity and magnetism. James Clerk Maxwell unified these two ideas in his theory of "electromagnetism" and demonstrated that light was just another form of electromagnetic radiation.

Module Summary

The study of electricity and magnetism were artfully united in John Clerk Maxwell's theory of electromagnetism. This module explores the experimental connection between electricity and magnetism, beginning with the work of Oersted, Ampere, and Faraday. The module gives an overview of the electromagnetic nature of light and its properties, as predicted by Maxwell's mathematical model.

Terms you should know:

current = flow of electricity
magnetism = forces of attraction or repulsion between objects
wave = a motion of rising and falling in curves; undulation

In 1873, seventy years after Thomas Young presented his experimental results on the nature of light (see our Light I: Particle or Wave? module), a Scottish physicist named James Clerk Maxwell published a theory that accounted for the physical origins of light. Throughout the 19th century, many of science's greatest minds dedicated themselves to the study of two exciting new ideas: electricity and magnetism. Maxwell's work synthesized these two ideas, which had previously been considered separate phenomena. His new theory was aptly named a theory of "electromagnetism."

Early experiments in electricity and magnetism

The earliest experimental connection between electricity and magnetism came in the 1820s from the work of the Danish physicist Hans Christian Oersted. Oersted discovered that a wire carrying electric current could deflect the needle of a magnetic compass. This planted the seed for Andre-Marie Ampere, a French physicist, to demonstrate that two current-carrying wires would interact with each other due to the magnetic field that they generated.

Ampere found that two long, straight wires carrying current in the same direction would attract each other, and two wires carrying current in opposite directions would repel each other. Ultimately, Ampere formulated a general expression – called Ampere's Law – for determining the magnetic field created by any distribution of electric currents. (Animations of this attraction/repulsion are available through the online version of this module.)

Ampere's important contributions to magnetism and electricity led other scientists to conduct experiments that probed the relationship between these two cutting-edge areas of nineteenth century physics. For example, in 1831, Michael Faraday discovered that a change in the magnetic field passing through a loop of wire creates a current in the wire.

Faraday, an English physicist with almost no formal mathematical training, had observed that passing a bar magnet through a coil of wire created an electric current. Similarly, moving a coil of wire in the vicinity of a stationary magnet also produced electric current. Faraday hypothesized that somehow the magnet "induced" the current in the wire, and named the phenomenon "induction." Faraday's name is still associated with this idea, in the form of "Faraday's Law," which, put simply, says that *a changing magnetic field produces an electric field*. A demonstration of Faraday's inductor can be accessed through the online version of this module.

Today, the principle behind Faraday's Law is at work in electrical generators. Using some mechanical source of energy (such as a hand crank, a windmill, the force of falling water, or steam from boiling water) to spin a turbine, magnets inside the generator spin next to a large coil of wire. As the magnets spin, the magnetic field that passes through the wire loop changes. This changing "magnetic flux" establishes an "induced" current in the wire and mechanical energy becomes electrical energy. A virtual example of a simple electrical generator in which a magnet spins within a coil of wire generating an electric current can be accessed through the online version of this module.

Over 40 years after Faraday, James Clerk Maxwell, based on little more than an intuitive feeling for the symmetry of physical laws, speculated that the converse of Faraday's Law must also be true: a changing electric field produces a magnetic field. When Maxwell took the work of Ampere and Faraday and incorporated his new idea, he was able to derive a set of equations (originally there were twenty equations, but now they have been simplified to just four) that completely unified the concepts of electric and magnetic fields into one mathematical model. To learn more about the math behind the equations, be sure to follow the links under "Further Exploration" in our Resources section in the online version of this module.

Comprehension Checkpoint

Which of the following describes an "induced" current?

A) A magnetic compass placed near an electrical wire produces a current.

B) Mechanical energy becomes electrical energy.

After developing his now-famous equations, Maxwell and other physicists began exploring their implications and testing their predictions. One prediction that came from Maxwell's equations was that a charge moving back and forth in a periodic fashion would create an oscillating electric field. This electric field would then set up a periodically changing magnetic field, which in turn would cause the original electric field to continue its oscillation, and so on. This mutual vibration allowed the electric and magnetic fields to travel through space in the form of an "electromagnetic wave," as shown below in Figure 1. A movie version of an electromagnetic wave is also available through the online version of this module.

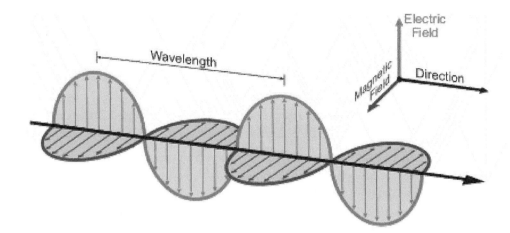

Figure 1: An electromagnetic wave.

Because this new mathematical model of electromagnetism described a wave, physicists were able to imagine that electromagnetic radiation could take on the properties of waves. Thus, just like all waves, Maxwell's electromagnetic waves could have a range of wavelengths and corresponding frequencies (see our Wave Motion module for more information on waves). This range of wavelengths is now known as the "electromagnetic spectrum." Maxwell's theory also predicted that all of the waves in the spectrum travel at a characteristic speed of approximately 300,000,000 meters per second. Maxwell was able to calculate this speed from his equations in the following way:

$$c = \frac{1}{\sqrt{\varepsilon_0 \mu_0}} = 2.998 \times 10^8 \ m/s$$

where

c = speed of the electromagnetic wave

ε_0 = permittivity of free space ($8.854 \times 10^{-12} \ F/m$)

μ_0 = permeability of free space ($4\pi \times 10^{-7} \ N/A^2$)

Maxwell's calculation of the speed of an electromagnetic wave included two important constants: the permittivity and permeability of free space. The permittivity of free space is also known as the "electric constant" and describes the strength of the electrical force between two charged particles in a vacuum. The permeability of free space is the magnetic analogue of the electric constant. It describes the strength of the magnetic force on an object in a magnetic field. Thus, the speed of an electromagnetic wave comes directly from a fundamental consideration of electricity and magnetism.

When Maxwell calculated this speed, he realized that it was extremely close to the measured value for the speed of light, which had been known for centuries from detailed astronomical observations. After Maxwell's equations became widely known, the Polish-American physicist Albert Michelson made a very precise measurement of the speed of light that was in extremely close agreement with Maxwell's predicted value. This was too much for Maxwell to accept as coincidence, and led him to the realization that light was an electromagnetic wave and thus part of the electromagnetic spectrum.

Comprehension Checkpoint

All electromagnetic waves travel at approximately

A) the speed of light.

B) half the speed of light.

The Electromagnetic Spectrum

As scientists and engineers began to explore the implications of Maxwell's theory, they performed experiments that verified the existence of the different regions, or groups of wavelengths, of the electromagnetic spectrum. As practical uses for these regions of the spectrum developed, they acquired now-familiar names, like "radio waves, and "X-rays." The longest wavelength waves predicted by Maxwell's theory are longer than 1 meter, and this band of the electromagnetic spectrum is known as radio waves. The shortest wavelength electromagnetic waves are called gamma rays, and have wavelengths shorter than 10 picometers (1 trillion times shorter than radio waves).

Between these two extremes lies a tiny band of wavelengths ranging from 400 to 700 nanometers. Electromagnetic radiation in this range is what we call "light," but it is no different in form from radio waves, gamma rays, or any of the other electromagnetic waves we now know exist. The only thing unique about this portion of the electromagnetic spectrum is that the majority of the radiation produced by the sun and hitting the surface of the planet Earth falls into this range.

Because humans evolved on Earth in the presence of the sun, it is no accident that our own biological instruments for receiving electromagnetic radiation – our eyes – evolved to detect this range of wavelengths. Other organisms have evolved sensory organs that are attuned to different parts of the spectrum. For example, the eyes of bees and other insects are sensitive to the ultraviolet portion of the spectrum (not coincidentally, many flowers reflect ultraviolet light), and these insects use UV radiation to see. However, since the sun emits primarily electromagnetic waves in the "visible" light region, most organisms have evolved to use this radiation instead of radio or gamma or other waves. For example, plants use this region of the electromagnetic spectrum in photosynthesis. For more information about the different regions of the electromagnetic spectrum, visit the interactive Electromagnetic Spectrum page in the online version of this module.

The impact of Maxwell's work

Maxwell's elegant equations not only unified the concepts of electricity and magnetism, they also put the familiar and much-studied phenomenon of light into a context that allowed scientists to understand its origin and behaviors. Maxwell appeared to have established conclusively that light behaves like a wave, but interestingly enough he also planted the seed of an idea that would lead to an entirely different view of light. It would be another thirty years before a young Austrian physicist named Albert Einstein would cultivate that seed, and in doing so spark the growth of a revolution in our understanding of how the universe is put together.

Key Concepts for this chapter

▶ In the mid 1800s, scientists including Andre Ampere and Michael Faraday noted a connection between electricity and magnetism and carried out a series of experiments that showed how they interact.

▶ James Clerk Maxwell built on the work of Faraday and developed a single set of equations defining both electricity and magnetism; unifying the concepts into one theory of electromagnetism.

▶ We now know that the electromagnetic spectrum is made up of a series of waves of varying wavelength, and visible light is just one small portion of this spectrum.

Take the Quiz ▶ ▶ ▶

Light and Electromagnetism Quiz

1. Two parallel wires carrying current in the same direction will

    A) repel each other.

    B) emit visible light.

    C) attract each other.

    D) not interact.

2. Two parallel wires carrying current in the opposite direction will

    A) repel each other.

    B) emit visible light.

    C) attract each other.

    D) not interact.

3. "Induction" is a term to describe

    A) the creation of a magnetic field from a changing electric field.

    B) the emission of radio waves from the sun.

    C) the force between two current-carrying wires.

    D) the creation of an electric field from a changing magnetic field.

4. The speed of light is closest to

    A) 3,000,000,000 m/s.

    B) 300,000,000 m/s.

    C) 30,000,000 m/s.

    D) 3,000,000 m/s.

5. The shortest wavelength portion of the electromagnetic spectrum is known as

    A) infrared.

    B) gamma rays.

    C) ultraviolet.

    D) radio waves.

6. The longest wavelength portion of the electromagnetic spectrum is known as

    A) ultraviolet.

    B) radio waves.

    C) infrared.

    D) gamma rays.

7. The region of the electromagnetic spectrum where humans can detect electromagnetic radiation is

    A) infrared.

    B) visible.

    C) x-ray.

    D) ultraviolet.

8. The theory of electromagnetism was first devised by

    A) Hans Christian Oersted.

    B) Michael Faraday.

    C) Thomas Young.

    D) James Clerk Maxwell.

9. The region of the electromagnetic spectrum where the sun radiates the majority of its energy is

    A) ultraviolet.

    B) visible.

    C) infrared.

    D) microwave.

10. One piece of evidence that convinced Maxwell that light was electromagnetic radiation was

    A) a moving magnetic field can generate light.

    B) the measured speed of light was close to Maxwell's calculated speed.

    C) the speed of light is the same as the speed of sound.

    D) light can generate electrical currents.

Answers and feedback can be found on Page 260

Earth Structure:
A Virtual Journey to the Center of the Earth

by Anne Egger, PhD

Did you know that although earthquakes can be very destructive, they provide a wealth of information about Earth's interior? Miners, geologists, and others have always wondered what lies below the surface of Earth, but heat and pressure make it impossible to explore deep into its interior. However, seismic waves produced by earthquakes reveal the structure and composition of our planet.

Module Summary

Earth's interior structure is composed of layers that vary by composition and behavior. Using principles of physics like gravity and wave motion, this module explains how scientists have determined Earth's deep structure. Different types of seismic waves are discussed. The module details both compositional and mechanical layers of Earth.

Terms you should know:

boundary = a line or limit that divides one area from another

dense = compact, packed close together, having a high mass in relation to volume

wave = a motion of rising and falling in curves; undulation

The deepest places on Earth are in South Africa, where mining companies have excavated 3.5 km into Earth to extract gold. No one has seen deeper into Earth than the South African miners because the heat and pressure felt at these depths prevents humans from going much deeper. Yet Earth's radius is 6,370 km – how do we begin to know what is below the thin skin of the earth when we cannot see it?

Evidence about Earth's interior

Isaac Newton was one of the first scientists to theorize about the structure of Earth. Based on his studies of the force of gravity, Newton calculated the average density of Earth and found it to be more than twice the density of the rocks near the surface. From these results, Newton realized that the interior of Earth had to be much denser than the surface rocks. His findings excluded the possibility of a cavernous, fiery underworld inhabited by the dead, but still left many questions unanswered. Where does the denser material begin? How does the composition differ from surface rocks?

Volcanic vents like Shiprock occasionally bring up pieces of Earth from as deep as 150 km, but these rocks are rare, and we have little hope of taking Jules Verne's *Journey to the Center of the Earth*. Instead, much of our knowledge about the internal structure of the earth comes from remote observations – specifically, from observations of earthquakes.

Earthquakes can be extremely destructive for humans, but they provide a wealth of information about Earth's interior. This is because every earthquake sends out an array of seismic waves in all directions, similar to the way that throwing a stone into a pond sends out waves through the water. Observing the behavior of these seismic waves as they travel through the earth gives us insight into the materials the waves move through.

Comprehension Checkpoint

Our knowledge about the internal structure of Earth comes mainly from

A) earthquakes.

B) deep mine shafts.

Seismic waves

An earthquake occurs when rocks in a fault zone suddenly slip past each other, releasing stress that has built up over time. The slippage releases seismic energy, which is dissipated through two kinds of waves, P-waves and S-waves. The distinction between these two waves is easy to picture with a stretched-out slinky. If you push on one end of a slinky, a compression wave passes through the slinky parallel to its length. If instead you move one end of the slinky up and down rapidly, a "ripple" wave moves through the slinky. The compression waves are P-waves, and the ripple waves are S-waves. (You can view videos of P- and S-waves in the online version of this module.)

Both kinds of waves can reflect off of boundaries between different materials: they can also refract, or bend, when they cross a boundary into a different material. But the two types of waves behave differently depending on the composition of the material they are passing through. One of the biggest differences is that S-waves cannot travel through liquids whereas P-waves can. We feel the arrival of the P- and S-waves at a given location as a ground-shaking earthquake.

If Earth were the same composition all the way through its interior, seismic waves would radiate outward from their source (an earthquake) and behave exactly as other waves behave – taking longer to travel further and dying out in velocity and strength with distance, a process called attenuation (see Figure 1).

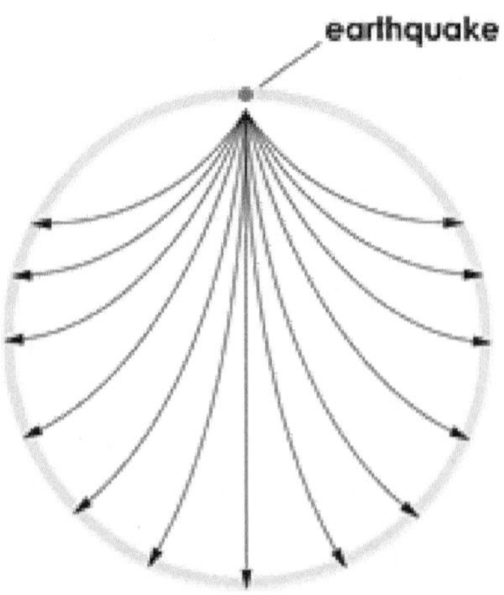

Figure 1: Seismic waves in an Earth of the same composition.

As early as 132 CE, the Chinese had built instruments to measure the ground shaking associated with earthquakes. The first modern seismographs, however, weren't built until the 1880s, when British seismologists in Japan designed them to record local earthquakes. It wasn't long before those seismologists recognized that they were also recording earthquakes occurring thousands of kilometers away.

The Moho

Andrija Mohorovičić was a Croatian scientist who recognized the importance of establishing a network of seismometers. Though his scientific career had begun in meteorology, he shifted his research pursuits to seismology around 1900, and installed several of the most advanced seismometers around central Europe in 1908. His timing was fortuitous, as a large earthquake occurred in the Kupa Valley in October 1909, which Mohorovičić felt at his home in Zagreb, Croatia. He made careful observations of the arrivals of P- and S-waves at his newly-installed stations, and noticed that P-waves measured more than 200 km away from an earthquake's epicenter arrived with higher velocities than those within a 200 km radius. Although these results ran counter to the concept of attenuation, they could be explained if the waves that arrived with faster velocities traveled through a medium that allowed them to speed up, having encountered a structural boundary at depth.

This recognition allowed Mohorovičić to define the first major boundary within Earth's interior – the boundary between the crust, which forms the surface of Earth, and a denser layer below, called the mantle (Mohorovičić, 1910). Seismic waves travel faster in the mantle than they do in the crust because it is composed of denser material. Thus, stations further away from the source of an earthquake received waves that had made part of their journey through the denser rocks of the mantle. The waves that reached the closer stations stayed within the crust the entire time. Although the official name of the crust–mantle boundary is the Mohorovičić Discontinuity, in honor of its discoverer, it is usually called the Moho.

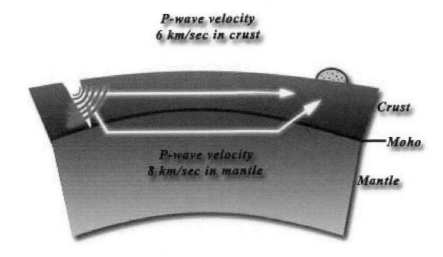

Figure 2: The Moho.

Another observation made by seismologists was the fact that P-waves die out about 105 degrees away from an earthquake, and then reappear about 140 degrees away, arriving much later than expected. This region that lacks P-waves is called the P-wave shadow zone (Figure 3). S-waves, on the other hand, die out completely around 105 degrees from the earthquake (Figure 3). Remember that S-waves are unable to travel through liquid. The S-wave shadow zone indicates that there is a liquid layer deep within Earth that stops all S-waves but not the P-waves.

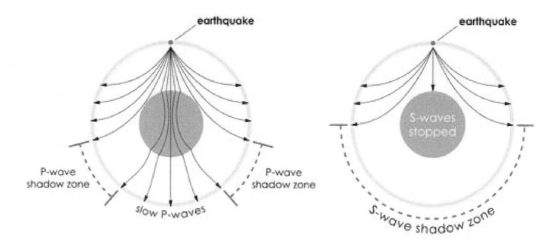

Figure 3: *The P-wave and S-wave shadow zones.*

In 1914, Beno Gutenberg, a German seismologist, used these shadow zones to calculate the size of another layer inside of the earth, called its core. He defined a sharp core-mantle boundary at a depth of 2,900 km, where P-waves were refracted and slowed and S-waves were stopped.

Comprehension Checkpoint

Scientists figured out that there is a liquid layer deep wthin Earth by observing

- **A)** when there is an earthquake, S-waves – which cannot travel through liquid – die out at 105 degrees.
- **B)** ponds of water have waves after an earthquake.

The layers of Earth

On the basis of these and other observations, geophysicists have created a cross-section of Earth. The early seismological studies previously discussed led to definitions of compositional boundaries; for example, imagine oil floating on top of water – they are two different materials, so there is a compositional boundary between them.

Later studies highlighted mechanical boundaries, which are defined on the basis of how materials act, not on their composition. Water and oil have the same mechanical properties – they are both liquids. On the other hand, water and ice have the same composition, but water is a fluid with far different mechanical properties than solid ice.

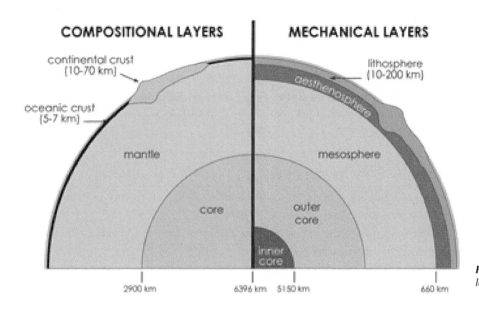

COMPOSITIONAL LAYERS   **MECHANICAL LAYERS**

continental crust
[10-70 km]

oceanic crust
[5-7 km]

mantle

core

lithosphere
[10-200 km]

asthenosphere

mesosphere

outer
core

inner
core

2900 km   6396 km   5150 km   660 km

Figure 4: Compositional and mechanical layers of Earth's structure.

Compositional layers

There are two major types of crust: crust that makes up the ocean floors and crust that makes up the continents. Oceanic crust is composed entirely of basalt extruded at mid-ocean ridges, resulting in a thin (~ 5 km), relatively dense crust (~3.0 g/cm3). Continental crust, on the other hand, is made primarily of less dense rock such as granite (~2.7 g/cm3). It is much thicker than oceanic crust, ranging from 15 to 70 km. At the base of the crust is the Moho, below which is the mantle, which contains rocks made of a denser material called peridotite (~3.4 g/cm3). This compositional change is predicted by the behavior of seismic waves and it is confirmed in the few samples of rocks from the mantle that we do have.

At the core–mantle boundary, composition changes again. Seismic waves suggest this material is of a very high density (10–13 g/cm3), which can only correspond to a composition of metals rather than rock. The presence of a magnetic field around Earth also indicates a molten metallic core. Unlike the crust and the mantle, we don't have any samples of the core to look at, and thus there is some controversy about its exact composition. Most scientists, however, believe that iron is the main constituent. These compositional layers are shown in Figure 4.

Comprehension Checkpoint

The crust, mantle, and core are defined as compositional layers of Earth because

A) they are made of different things.

B) they behave differently.

Mechanical layers

The compositional divisions of Earth were understood decades before the development of the theory of plate tectonics – the idea that Earth's surface consists of large plates that move (see our Plate Tectonics I module). By the 1970s, however, geologists began to realize that the plates had to be thicker than just the crust, or they would break apart as they moved. In fact, plates consist of the crust acting together with the uppermost part of the mantle; this rigid layer is called the lithosphere and it ranges in thickness from about 10 to 200 km. Rigid lithospheric plates "float" on a layer called the asthenosphere that flows like a very viscous fluid, like Silly Putty®. It is important to note that although the asthenosphere can flow, it is not a liquid, and thus both S- and P-waves can travel through it. At a depth of around 660 km, the pressure becomes so great that the mantle can no longer flow, and this solid part of the mantle is called the mesosphere. The lithospheric mantle, asthenosphere, and mesosphere all share the same composition (that of peridotite), but their mechanical properties are significantly different. Geologists often refer to the asthenosphere as the jelly in between two pieces of bread: the lithosphere and mesosphere.

The core is also subdivided into an inner and outer core. The outer core is liquid molten metal (and able to stop S-waves) while the inner core is solid. (Because the composition of the core is different than that of the mantle, it is possible for the core to remain a liquid at much higher pressures than peridotite.) The distinction between the inner and outer core was made in 1936 by Inge Lehmann, a Danish seismologist, after improvements in seismographs in the 1920s made it possible to "see" previously undetectable seismic waves within the P-wave shadow zone. These faint waves indicated that they had been refracted again within the core when they hit the boundary between the inner and outer core. The mechanical layers of Earth are also shown in Figure 4, in comparison to the compositional layers.

Our picture of the interior of Earth becomes clearer as imaging techniques improve. Seismic tomography is a relatively new technique that uses seismic waves to measure very slight temperature variations throughout the mantle. Because waves move faster through cold material and slower through hot material, the images they receive help scientists "see" the process of convection in the mantle (see our Plates, Plate Boundaries, and Driving Forces module). These and other images offer a virtual journey into the center of Earth.

Key Concepts for this chapter

▶ Our knowledge about the structure Earth's interior comes from studying how different types of seismic waves, created by earthquakes, travel through Earth.

▶ Earth is composed of multiple layers, which can be defined either by composition or by mechanical properties.

▶ The crust, mantle, and core are defined by differences in composition.

▶ The lithosphere, asthenosphere, mesosphere, and outer and inner cores are defined by differences in mechanical properties.

Take the Quiz ▶ ▶ ▶

Earth Structure Quiz

1. The Moho is the boundary between
   A) the inner core and the outer core.
   B) the lithosphere and the asthenosphere.
   C) the crust and the mantle.
   D) the mantle and the core.

2. Earthquakes are useful for studying Earth's interior because
   A) each earthquake produces an array of seismic waves.
   B) they happen below the surface of the Earth.
   C) they release stress that has been stored.
   D) earthquakes are extremely destructive.

3. Both S-waves and P-waves can travel easily through liquids.
   A) True
   B) False

4. Although we don't have any samples of the core, most scientists agree that its main constituent is
   A) basalt.
   B) iron.
   C) granite.
   D) peridotite.

5. Continental crust is _____ than oceanic crust.
   A) thinner and more dense
   B) thinner and less dense
   C) thicker and more dense
   D) thicker and less dense

6. When seismic waves hit a boundary with a different material, they might
   A) refract.
   B) reflect.
   C) change velocity.
   D) all of the choices

7. What does the S-wave shadow zone indicate about Earth's interior?
   A) The mantle is denser than the crust.
   B) The core is made of iron.
   C) The mantle is liquid.
   D) The outer core is liquid.

8. Tectonic plates consist of the lithosphere, which is made up of the crust and the uppermost mantle.
   A) True
   B) False

9. How do we know that Earth is not the same composition all the way through?
   A) Seismic waves attenuate with distance.
   B) Seismic waves do not arrive uniformly all over Earth.
   C) There are two types of seismic waves, S- and P-waves.
   D) Where the mantle is exposed, it looks very different.

Answers and feedback can be found on Page 262

The Composition of Earth's Atmosphere

by Anne Egger, PhD

Did you know that without the atmosphere, Earth's surface would be covered with meteor craters and life on this planet would be non-existent? Protecting us from meteorites, regulating temperature, and providing the air we breathe are only some of the ways that the atmosphere makes Earth the home it is.

Module Summary

Earth's atmosphere contains many components that can be measured in different ways. This module describes these different components and shows how temperature and pressure change with altitude. The scientific developments that led to an understanding of these concepts are discussed.

Terms you should know:

ozone = a form of oxygen, O_3, produced by the reaction of sunlight with O_2

pressure = the application of force; the weight of air in the atmosphere

surface = the outside or external part; the topside face of something

The fact that the moon's surface is covered with meteorite impact craters is obvious to us today. Though the moon is not far from us, impact craters are few and far between on Earth. As it turns out, Earth has received just as many incoming meteorites as the moon, but the presence of the atmosphere has determined the fate of many of them. Small meteorites burn up in the atmosphere before ever reaching Earth. Those that do hit the surface and create an impact crater are lost to us in a different way – the craters are quickly eroded by weather generated in the atmosphere, and the evidence is washed away. The moon, on the other hand, has no atmosphere, and thus every meteor aimed at the moon hits it, and the craters have remained essentially unchanged for 4 billion years.

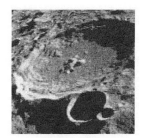

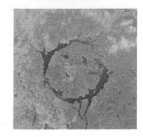

Figure 1: *Craters on the far side of the moon (top) and Manicouagan crater in Quebec (bottom).*

The early Greeks considered "air" to be one of four elementary substances; along with earth, fire, and water, air was viewed as a fundamental component of the universe. By the early 1800s, however, scientists such as John Dalton recognized that the atmosphere was in fact composed of several chemically distinct gases, which he was able to separate and determine the relative amounts of within the lower atmosphere. He was easily able to discern the major components of the atmosphere: nitrogen, oxygen, and a small amount of something incombustible, later shown to be argon.

The development of the spectrometer in the 1920s allowed scientists to find gases that existed in much smaller concentrations in the atmosphere, such as ozone and carbon dioxide. The concentrations of these gases, while small, varied widely from place to place. In fact, atmospheric gases are often divided up into the major, constant components and the highly variable components, as listed below:

Table 1: *Constant Components. Proportions remain the same over time and location.*

Nitrogen (N_2)	78.08%
Oxygen (O_2)	20.95%
Argon (Ar)	0.93%
Neon, Helium, Krypton	0.0001%

Table 2: *Variable Components. Amounts vary over time and location.*

Carbon dioxide (CO_2)	0.038%
Water vapor (H_2O)	0-4%
Methane (CH_4)	*trace*
Sulfur dioxide (SO_2)	*trace*
Ozone (O_3)	*trace*
Nitrogen oxides (NO, NO_2, N_2O)	*trace*

Although both nitrogen and oxygen are essential to human life on the planet, they have little effect on weather and other atmospheric processes. The variable components, which make up far less than 1% of the atmosphere, have a much greater influence on both short-term weather and long-term climate. For example, variations in water vapor in the atmosphere are familiar to us as relative humidity. Water vapor, CO_2, CH, N_2O, and SO_2 all have an important property: They absorb heat emitted by Earth and thus warm the atmosphere, creating what we call the "greenhouse effect." Without these so-called greenhouse gases, the Earth's surface would be about 30 degrees Celsius cooler – too cold for life to exist as we know it. Though the greenhouse effect is sometimes portrayed as a bad thing, trace amounts of gases like CO_2 warm our planet's atmosphere enough to sustain life. Global warming, on the other hand, is a separate process that can be caused by increased amounts of greenhouse gases in the atmosphere.

In addition to gases, the atmosphere also contains particulate matter such as dust, volcanic ash, rain, and snow. These are, of course, highly variable and are generally less persistent than gas concentrations, but they can sometimes remain in the atmosphere for relatively long periods of time. Volcanic ash from the 1991 eruption of Mt. Pinatubo in the Philippines, for example, darkened skies around the globe for over a year.

Though the major components of the atmosphere vary little today, they have changed dramatically over Earth's history, about 4.6 billion years. The early atmosphere was hardly the life-sustaining blanket of air that it is today; most geologists believe that the main constituents then were nitrogen gas and carbon dioxide, but no free oxygen. In fact, there is no evidence for free oxygen in the atmosphere until about 2 billion years ago, when photosynthesizing bacteria evolved and began taking in atmospheric carbon dioxide and releasing oxygen. The amount of oxygen in the atmosphere has risen steadily from 0% 2 billion years ago to about 21% today.

Comprehension Checkpoint

Nitrogen and oxygen, which make up more than 99% of Earth's atmosphere, have a bigger influence on climate than other components of the atmosphere.

A) True

B) False

Measuring the atmosphere

We now have continuous satellite monitoring of the atmosphere and Doppler radar to tell us whether or not we will experience rain anytime soon; however, atmospheric measurements used to be few and far between. Today, measurements such as temperature and pressure not only help us predict the weather, but also help us look at long-term changes in global climate (see our Temperature module). The first atmospheric scientists were less concerned with weather prediction, however, and more interested in the composition and structure of the atmosphere.

The two most important instruments for taking measurements in Earth's atmosphere were developed hundreds of years ago: Galileo is credited with inventing the thermometer in 1593, and Evangelista Torricelli invented the barometer in 1643. With these two instruments, temperature and pressure could be recorded at any time and at any place. Of course, the earliest pressure and temperature measurements were taken at Earth's surface. It was a hundred years before the thermometer and barometer went aloft.

While many people are familiar with Ben Franklin's kite and key experiment that tested lightning for the presence of electricity, few realize that kites were the main vehicle for obtaining atmospheric measurements above Earth's surface. Throughout the 18th and 19th centuries, kite-mounted instruments collected pressure, temperature, and humidity readings; unfortunately, scientists could only reach up to an altitude of about 3 km with this technique.

Figure 2: Scientist launches a radiosonde. Instruments for collecting data are in the white and orange box.

Unmanned balloons were able to take measurements at higher altitudes than kites, but because they were simply released with no passengers and no strings attached, they had to be retrieved in order to obtain the data that had been collected. This changed with the development of the *radiosonde*, an unmanned balloon capable of achieving high altitudes, in the early 1930s. The radiosonde included a radio transmitter among its many instruments, allowing data to be transmitted as it was being collected so that the balloons no longer needed to be retrieved. A radiosonde network was developed in the United States in 1937, and continues to this day under the auspices of the National Weather Service.

Comprehension Checkpoint

What was the advantage of the *radiosonde* over earlier data collection instruments?

A) The radiosonde was easy to retrieve.

B) The radiosonde did not need to be retrieved.

Temperature in the atmosphere

Through examination of measurements collected by radiosonde and aircraft (and later by rockets), scientists became aware that the atmosphere is not uniform. Many people had long recognized that temperature decreased with altitude – if you've ever hiked up a tall mountain, you might learn to bring a jacket to wear at the top even when it is warm at the base – but it wasn't until the early 1900s that radiosondes revealed a layer, about 18 km above the surface, where temperature abruptly changed and began to increase with altitude. The discovery of this reversal led to division of the atmosphere into layers based on their thermal properties.

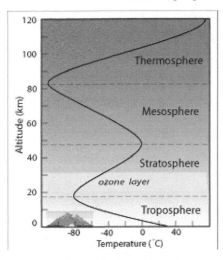

Figure 3: *This graph shows how temperature varies with altitude in earth's atmosphere.*

The lowermost 12 to 18 km of the atmosphere, called the *troposphere*, is where all weather occurs – clouds form and precipitation falls, wind blows, humidity varies from place to place, and the atmosphere interacts with the surface below. Within the troposphere, temperature decreases with altitude at a rate of about 6.5° C per kilometer. At 8,856 m high, Mt. Everest still reaches less than halfway through the troposphere. Assuming a sea level temperature of 26° C (80° F), that means the temperature on the summit of Everest would be around -31° C (-24° F)! In fact, temperature at Everest's summit averages -36° C, whereas temperatures in New Delhi (in nearby India), at an elevation of 233 m, average about 28° C.

At the uppermost boundary of the troposphere, air temperature reaches about -100° C and then begins to increase with altitude. This layer of increasing temperature is called the *stratosphere*. The cause of the temperature reversal is a layer of concentrated ozone. Ozone's ability to absorb incoming ultraviolet (UV) radiation from the sun had been recognized in 1881, but the existence of the ozone layer at an altitude of 20 to 50 km was not postulated until the 1920s. By absorbing UV rays, the ozone layer both warms the air around it and protects us on the surface from the harmful short-wavelength radiation that can cause skin cancer.

It is important to recognize the difference between the ozone layer in the stratosphere and ozone present in trace amounts in the troposphere. Stratospheric ozone is produced when energy from the sun breaks apart O_2 gas molecules into O atoms; these O atoms then bond with other O_2 molecules to form O_3, ozone. This process was first described in 1930 by Sydney Chapman, a geophysicist who synthesized many of the known facts about the ozone layer. Tropospheric ozone, on the other hand, is a pollutant produced when emissions from fossil-fuel burning interact with sunlight.

Above the stratosphere, temperature begins to drop again in the next layer of the atmosphere called the *mesosphere*, as seen in the previous figure. This temperature decrease results from the rapidly decreasing density of the air at this altitude. Finally, at the outer reaches of Earth's atmosphere, the intense, unfiltered radiation from the sun causes molecules like O_2 and N_2 to break apart into ions. The release of energy from these reactions actually causes the temperature to rise again in the *thermosphere*, the outermost layer. The thermosphere extends to about 500 km above Earth's surface, still a few hundred kilometers below the altitude of most orbiting satellites.

Comprehension Checkpoint

All weather, including clouds, wind, and precipitation, occurs in the

A) troposphere.

B) stratosphere.

Pressure in the atmosphere

Atmospheric pressure can be imagined as the weight of the overlying column of air. Unlike temperature, pressure decreases exponentially with altitude. Traces of the atmosphere can be detected as far as 500 km above Earth's surface, but 80% of the atmosphere's mass is contained within the 18 km closest to the surface. Atmospheric pressure is generally measured in millibars (mb); this unit of measurement is equivalent to 1 gram per centimeter squared (1 g/cm^2). Other units are occasionally used, such as bars, atmospheres, or millimeters of mercury. The correspondence between these units is shown in the table below.

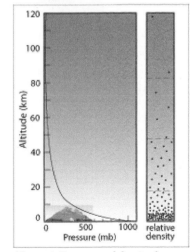

Figure 4: Pressure and density decrease rapidly with altitude.

bars		millibars		atmo-spheres		millibars of mercury
1.013 bar	=	1013 mb	=	1 atm	=	760 mm Hg

Table 3: Correspondence of atmospheric measurement units.

At sea level, pressure ranges from about 960 to 1,050 mb, with an average of 1,013 mb. At the top of Mt. Everest, pressure is as low as 300 mb. Because gas pressure is related to density, this low pressure means that there are approximately one-third as many gas molecules inhaled per breath on top of Mt. Everest as at sea level – which is why climbers experience ever more severe shortness of breath the higher they go, as less oxygen is inhaled with every breath.

Though other planets host atmospheres, the presence of free oxygen and water vapor makes our atmosphere unique as far as we know. These components both encouraged and protected life on Earth as it developed, not only by providing oxygen for respiration, but by shielding organisms from harmful UV rays and by incinerating small meteors before they hit the surface. Additionally, the composition and structure of this unique resource are important keys to understanding circulation in the atmosphere, biogeochemical cycling of nutrients, short-term local weather patterns, and long-term global climate changes.

Key Concepts for this chapter

► Earth's atmosphere is made up of a combination of gases. The major components of nitrogen, oxygen, and argon remain constant over time and space, while trace components like CO_2 and water vapor vary considerably over both space and time.

► The atmosphere is divided into the thermosphere, mesosphere, stratosphere, and troposphere, and the boundaries between these layers are defined by changes in temperature gradients.

► Pressure decreases exponentially with altitude in the atmosphere.

► Our knowledge about the atmosphere has developed based on data from a variety of sources, including direct measurements from balloons and aircraft as well as remote measurements from satellites.

Take the Quiz ► ► ►

The Composition of Earth's Atmosphere Quiz

1. Which of the following is NOT a major component of the atmosphere?

   A) argon

   B) ozone

   C) oxygen

   D) nitrogen

2. Why does atmospheric temperature increase with altitude in the stratosphere?

   A) because it is under a lot of pressure

   B) because is it less dense than the troposphere

   C) because it is closer to the sun

   D) because of the presence of the ozone layer

3. In the troposphere, temperature _____ with altitude.

   A) changes randomly

   B) stays the same

   C) decreases

   D) increases

4. Earth is the only known planet with an atmosphere.

   A) True

   B) False

5. The outermost layer of the atmosphere is called the

   A) thermosphere.

   B) mesosphere.

   C) stratosphere.

   D) troposphere.

6. Atmospheric pressure remains a constant 1,013 mb at sea level.

   A) True

   B) False

7. Carbon dioxide and water vapor are both _____, acting to warm the atmosphere.

   A) major components

   B) highly variable

   C) minor components

   D) greenhouse gases

8. Pressure decreases rapidly with altitude because the air becomes

   A) warmer.

   B) colder.

   C) less dense.

   D) rich in ozone.

9. Why does the atmosphere help sustain and protect life on the earth's surface?

   A) Oxygen is a major component of the atmosphere.

   B) Greenhouse gases warm the air near the surface by 30° C.

   C) The ozone layer shields us from harmful UV radiation.

   D) all of the choices

Answers and feedback can be found on Page 264

The Origins of Plate Tectonic Theory

by Anne Egger, PhD

Did you know that fossils of sea creatures are found on Earth's highest mountain peaks? Scientists used to think that the Earth contracted as it cooled after it formed, forcing mountains up like wrinkles. Now we understand that plate tectonics explains why these mountains are there, why there are sea organisms on top of those mountains, and why the continents of the world look like a super-sized jigsaw puzzle.

Module Summary

The theory of continental drift was the first step toward plate tectonic theory, which became the foundation upon which modern geology is built. This module describes how the work of Alfred Wegener, Harry Hess, and others led to our understanding of plate tectonics. It explains plate tectonics as the driving force behind ongoing changes on Earth.

Terms you should know:

drift = to float; to be carried along by a current

ridge = a raised strip along a surface

seafloor = the bottom surface of the ocean

The Himalayas are often referred to as the "roof of the world" because they host the highest peaks on Earth, most famously Mt. Everest at 8,848 meters above sea level. But the rock that caps Mt. Everest is limestone, a type of rock that forms at the bottom of warm, shallow seas and is composed primarily of fossilized marine creatures, everything from plankton to clams and fish. For years, geologists struggled to explain how the remains of tiny sea organisms could exist at the top of a mountain range.

Into the 1900s, many scientists believed that as Earth cooled after its formation, the planet's surface contracted and wrinkled like the skin of an apple, subjected to the sun and drying out over time. The contraction theory, independently proposed by two prominent scientists in the late 1800s and early 1900s, implied that mountain ranges like the Himalayas were forced up by the wrinkling process. This theory assumed that all of the features on Earth had formed during one cooling event and that the planet was relatively static, changing little as the cooling (and wrinkling) slowed to a halt over millions of years.

Alfred Wegener, a German geophysicist and meteorologist, was not satisfied by this explanation. His ideas drew on the widely recognized fact that Africa and South America appeared to fit together like jigsaw puzzle pieces. He collected paleoclimate data, or information about what the climate was like in the geologic past as recorded in rocks, from the continents on both sides of the Atlantic (Figure 1). He recognized that belts of coal, which forms in tropical regions, crossed from North America in Europe and Asia, far north of the modern tropics. He also found evidence that an ice sheet had once advanced from southern Africa and India (see Figure 1), a phenomenon that was impossible to explain in the modern arrangement of the continents.

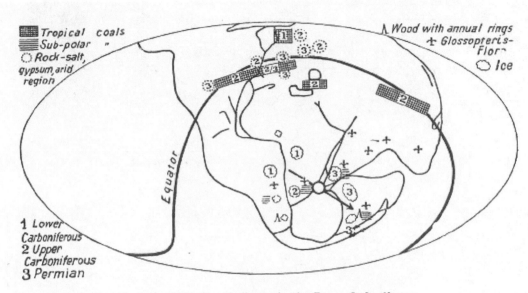

FIG. 17.—Evidences of climate in the Permo-Carboniferous.

Figure 1: Wegener's map of paleoclimate data from his 1915 publication, showing the continents joined together and the bands of similar rock types that crossed the oceans (Wegener, 1924).

To explain these data, Wegener proposed the theory of continental drift in his book T*he Origins of the Continents and the Oceans,* published in German in 1915 and in English in 1924 (Wegener, 1924). His theory stated that all of the continents had originally been joined together during the time period called the Carboniferous (now known to be about 300–360 million years ago) in a supercontinent called Pangaea (see Figure 2 for his depiction). By the Eocene (about 50 million years ago), when new fossil species were present that were not as widely distributed, the continents as we know them today had broken apart and were far enough apart that species could not easily migrate from one to the other (see Figure 3 for his depiction).

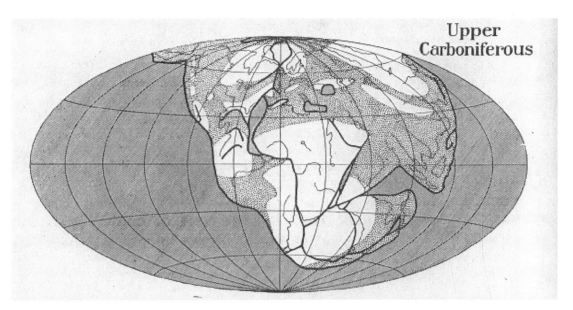

Figure 2: Wegener's depiction of Pangaea (Wegener, 1924). The dotted areas would have been warm, shallow seas. Wegener provided the present-day outlines and the rivers for the purpose of identification only.

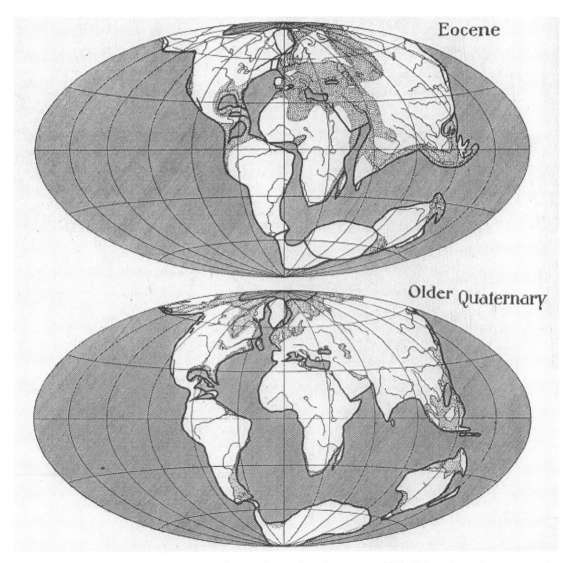

Figure 3: Additional images from Wegener's publication showing how the continents "drifted" through time (Wegener, 1924).

Driving the drift

When Wegener's book was translated into English, French, Spanish, and Russian in 1924, he was widely ridiculed for his suggestion that the continents had moved. One of the main problems with his theory was that he did not propose a driving mechanism for the motion of the continents. What was the force that moved the continents? Where did it come from? How much force was needed to move a continent?

The driving mechanism, an important key to the continental drift theory, lay out of reach until the 1960s. Wegener had made his claims based on data from the continents, but the oceans cover 70% of Earth's surface – a vast area hidden from his view under kilometers of water. But the First and Second World Wars brought major technical and scientific developments that allowed scientists to (1) map the ocean floor and (2) measure the magnetism of seafloor rocks in detail. These two sets of data provided geologists with additional evidence for the process of continental drift.

> ## Comprehension Checkpoint
>
> Why wasn't Wegener's theory of continental drift widely accepted at first?
>
> **A)** Wegener did not propose a driving force behind continental drift.
>
> **B)** The continents of the world did not look as if they could have fit together.

Mapping the ocean floor

Before the 1920s, the crust below the seas was thought to be flat and featureless. During World War I, however, ships equipped with sonar began to produce data about the topography of the seafloor. These sonar maps showed the seafloor to be anything but featureless – instead, the ocean floor hosted valleys deeper than the Grand Canyon, mountain chains rivaling the Andes both in length and height, as well as vast, flat plains.

Most surprising to scientists, a long ridge was found to run down the middle of the Atlantic Ocean, rising 1 to 2 km above the surrounding ocean floor and paralleling the continental coasts on both sides. Similar features, called "mid-ocean ridges" by their discoverers, were mapped in the eastern Pacific Ocean and the western Indian Ocean. Based on the fact that they were parallel to the edges of the continents, the ridges had something to do with continental drift, but what?

In a 1962 paper entitled "History of Ocean Basins," Harry Hess, a geologist at Princeton University, proposed that the mid-ocean ridges marked regions where hot magma rose close to the surface (Hess, 1962). Further, he suggested that the extrusion of magma at the ridges pushed the ocean floor away from the ridges like a conveyor belt. In deep trenches like those found off the coast of South America and Japan, the spreading ocean floor was forced down below the thick continents in regions he called subduction zones. Hess's theory of "seafloor spreading" offered a compelling driving mechanism for Wegener's continental drift, but it needed more proof.

Comprehension Checkpoint

Ocean floors around the world

   A) are mostly flat with some random ridges and valleys.

   B) have deep valleys and ridges that parallel continental coasts.

Seafloor magnetism

The same year that Hess proposed his theory, the US Navy published a report that summarized their findings concerning seafloor magnetism. During World War II, ships dragged magnetometers, which are devices to measure magnetism, in order to locate submarines. The magnetometers were on and measuring at all times while the ships traveled back and forth across the Atlantic and Pacific, and they found a lot more than submarines. When Navy scientists examined the data, they found bands of alternating strong and weak magnetism in the rocks of the seafloor (see Figure 4).

Figure 4: An example of magnetic data collected by ship across the Juan de Fuca ridge off the coast of Washington state. Gammas are a unit of magnetic force.

The magnetism was caused by the presence of magnetic minerals in the rocks, primarily one called magnetite, which is common in the basalt that makes up the rocks of the ocean floor. When magma cools and crystallizes, the magnetite crystals are locked into alignment with Earth's magnetic field like the needle of a compass (see our Earth Structure module).

The existence of Earth's magnetic field had been known since ancient times, but only after World War II did scientists realize that the magnetic field is not constant – it fluctuates in intensity and frequently reverses itself. Today we consider the field to have "normal" polarity, and our compass needles point to the north. But at various times in the past, the polarity has been reversed – any compass needles would have instead pointed to the South Pole. This phenomenon of magnetic reversals had previously been observed in continental rocks, and was clearly the case for oceanic rocks as well. The basalt on the ocean floor preserved paleomagnetic reversals: evidence that Earth's magnetic field had flipped from normal to reversed many times throughout geologic history.

Proof of seafloor spreading

In 1963, Fred Vine and Drummond Matthews, two British geologists, joined the topographic map of the Mid-Atlantic Ridge with the symmetric bands of magnetism on the seafloor (Vine and Matthews, 1963). Where the navy ships mapped strong magnetism, rocks showed normal polarity; where they mapped bands of weak magnetism, the rocks showed reversed polarity. The bands not only paralleled the mid-ocean ridges, but were patterned symmetrically about the crest of those ridges (see Figure 5 for an example).

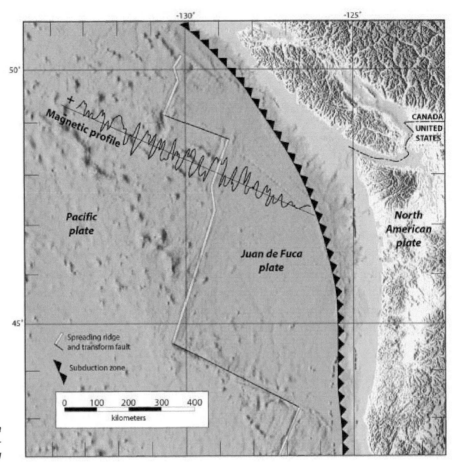

Figure 5: The magnetic profile shown in Figure 4 combined with topography and the location of the spreading ridge.

At the crests, the magnetism was strong; therefore, the polarity was normal. But moving in either direction away from the ridge, the magnetism would drop suddenly at about the same distance from the crest – the polarity was reversed. Continue away from the ridge in both directions, and magnetism would suddenly be strong again – back into rocks with normal polarity. The symmetry suggested that magma was rising at the ridges and cooling to lock in the magnetic field at the time, then being pushed away from the ridge in both directions, preserving a record of paleomagnetic reversals and the generation of new crust over time (see the Mid-Ocean Ridges concept simulation available through the online version of this module).

These strongly patterned paleomagnetic reversals recorded on the seafloor provided the necessary proof of Hess's seafloor spreading. Specifically, they proved that new crust was continuously being generated at the mid-ocean ridges, where magma cooled and magnetite crystals "locked in" according to the orientation of Earth's magnetic field at that time. The continents no longer had to "drift" to their present locations – they could be driven by slow and steady magma "conveyor belts" that originated at the mid-ocean ridges.

The work of Hess, Vine, and Matthews resulted in a new map of Earth that highlighted the features of the ocean floor, one that included plate boundaries in addition to coastlines. Plate boundaries could be drawn at mid-oceanic ridges and subduction zones (see Figure 6).

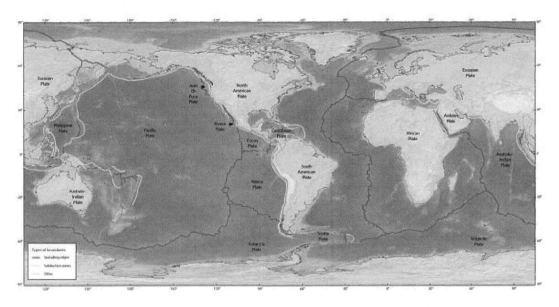

Figure 6: Red lines indicate spreading ridges; yellow lines indicate subduction zones. Light blue lines don't fit either category.

Comprehension Checkpoint

Magnetic stripes on the seafloor are evidence for

A) constant addition of magma to the crust at mid-ocean ridges.

B) drifting of continents through the crust.

Ongoing evidence for plate tectonics

Today, much of the evidence concerning plate tectonics is acquired with satellite technology. Through use of the global positioning system (GPS) and other satellite-based data collection techniques, scientists can directly measure the velocity (or speed and direction of movement) of plates on Earth's surface. Speeds range from 10 to 100 mm per year, confirming the long-held belief that plates move at a slow but constant rate (see our module on Linear Equations for more detail on how to calculate rates of plate movement).

The Himalayas, as it turns out, started forming about 40 million years ago when the Indian Plate collided head-on with the Eurasian Plate, shoving and folding rocks that had formed below sea level into lofty peaks. Because the Indian Plate is still moving northward, the Himalayas are still rising at a rate of about 1 cm per year. We no longer need to invoke a shrinking, wrinkled Earth to explain the marine fossils at the top of these tall mountains; it is the process of plate tectonics that continues to lift seafloor rocks to the sky.

Earth is incredibly dynamic – mountain chains build and erode away, volcanoes erupt and go extinct, seas advance and recede – and these changes are all a result of the processes of plate tectonics. Before Wegener, few had conceived of such a world. His continental drift theory was the first step in the development of plate tectonic theory, the foundation upon which modern geology is built.

Key Concepts for this chapter

▶ The idea that continents can move was proposed by Wegener in 1915 on the basis of fossil evidence, the way in which coastlines seemed to fit together, and other features, but it was not widely accepted at the time.

▶ Evidence that led to the development of plate tectonic theory in the 1960s came primarily from new data from the sea floor, including topography and the magnetism of rocks.

▶ Seafloor spreading was proposed as a mechanism to drive the movement of the continents on the basis of symmetrical patterns of reversed and normal magnetic rocks on the sea floor.

References

Hess, H. H., 1962, "History Of Ocean Basins," in Engel, A. E. J., James, H. L., and Leonard, B. F., eds., *Petrologic Studies: A volume in honor of A.F. Buddington*: Boulder, CO, Geological Society of America, p. 599-620.

Vine, F. J., and Matthews, D. H., 1963, "Magnetic Anomalies Over Oceanic Ridges": *Nature*, v. 199, no. 4897, p. 947-949.

Wegener, A., 1924, *The origin of continents and oceans (Entstehung der Kontinente und Ozeane)*, Methuen & Co.

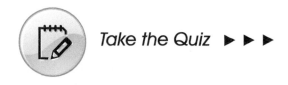 *Take the Quiz* ▶ ▶ ▶

Module Name Quiz

1. The contraction theory implied that Earth's features formed through the process of

   A) magma upwelling.

   B) seafloor spreading.

   C) cooling and contracting.

   D) continental drift.

2. What data did Wegener use to prove that the continents had once been joined together?

   A) seafloor topography

   B) magnetic stripes

   C) magma

   D) paleoclimate data

3. Although Wegener proposed his continental drift theory in 1915, it was not widely accepted until the 1960s. Why not?

   A) Wegener's book was not read outside of Germany.

   B) Continental drift still did not explain the presence of marine fossils in the Himalayas.

   C) Wegener had not proposed a driving force for the movement of the continents.

   D) Wegener had looked only at South America and Africa.

4. Who proposed the theory of seafloor spreading based on maps of the ocean floor?

   A) Alfred Wegener

   B) Harry Hess

   C) a British geologist

   D) Vine and Matthews

5. Why was the mapping of the ocean floor such an important step in the development of plate tectonic theory?

   A) The features mapped on the ocean floor disproved continental drift.

   B) The ocean floor had tracks from the continents

   C) Most plate boundaries are under the ocean.

   D) Nobody had known how deep the oceans were.

6. Earth's magnetic field is constant.

   A) True

   B) False

7. Which feature on the ocean floor caused Hess to suggest the presence of subduction zones?

   A) flat plains

   B) magnetic stripes

   C) deep trenches

   D) mid-ocean ridges

8. When did the Pangaean supercontinent begin to break up?

   A) 1915

   B) in the 1960s

   C) 200 million years ago

   D) billions of years ago

9. Vine and Matthews are considered to have discovered the final proof for seafloor spreading. What were they able to show based on magnetic bands?

   A) Seafloor rocks contain magnetite.

   B) New crust is being generated at mid-ocean ridges.

   C) Mid-ocean ridges and subduction zones are plate boundaries.

   D) Earth's magnetic field had reversed in the past.

10. Plate tectonic theory fundamentally altered how geologists view the earth. The biggest difference in the new theory was that Earth

    A) is contracting.

    B) is dynamic, constantly changing.

    C) has numerous features on the ocean floor.

    D) has a magnetic field that fluctuates.

Answers and feedback can be found on Page 266

Plates, Plate Boundaries, and Driving Forces

by Anne Egger, PhD

Did you know that earthquakes and volcanic eruptions do not happen in random places? Both are concentrated along the boundaries of tectonic plates and provide evidence for the theory of plate tectonics. Earth is a dynamic planet, and nowhere is this more evident than along the plate boundaries.

Module Summary

Earthquakes and volcanoes can reveal a lot about plate boundaries. This module looks at the nature of tectonic plates and discusses the different boundary types that exist between them – convergent, divergent, and transform. Forces that drive the push and pull of these landmasses are explored.

Terms you should know:

boundary = a line or limit that divides one area from another

buoyant = able to float

dense = compact, packed close together, having a high mass in relation to volume

By 1962, the idea that pieces of the Earth's surface moved around no longer seemed radical. The concepts of continental drift and seafloor spreading had revolutionized geology (see our module The Origins of Plate Tectonic Theory), and scientists excitedly began to revise their interpretations of existing data into a comprehensive theory of plate tectonics. For example, geologists had long recognized that earthquakes are not randomly distributed on the Earth (see Figure 1).

In fact, earthquakes are concentrated along the plate boundaries drawn by Harry Hess along mid-ocean ridges and subduction zones. Not all earthquakes occur at the same depth, however. Where Hess had postulated that the rocks of the ocean floor were diving down into subduction zones, earthquakes occur at shallow depths of 0 to 33 km below the surface near the trenches and at depths of almost 700 km below the surface further inland (illustrated in Figure 1 by different shaded circles). On the other hand, only shallow earthquakes (depths of 0 to 33 km, shown in red in the online version of Figure 1) are recorded at the spreading ridges. These data helped geologists draw more detailed cross-sections showing that plates are thin at spreading ridges, and that subduction extends long distances, taking plates deep beneath the continents.

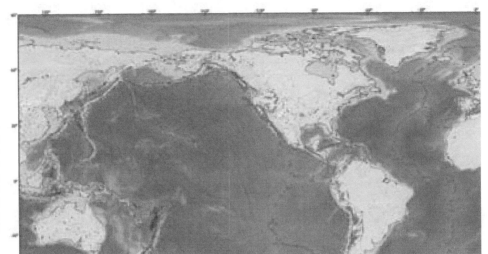

Figure 1: Map showing earthquakes from 2003-2011 with magnitude greater than 3. Colors indicate depth of hypocenter, or origin of the earthquake: red is 0-33 km, yellow is 33-100 km, green is 100-400 km, and blue is >400 km depth. Data are from the Advanced National Seismic System.

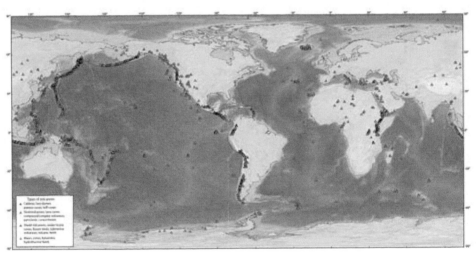

Figure 2: Map showing volcanoes that have been active in the last 10,000 years. Colored triangles indicate different volcano types: red triangles are primarily calderas, green triangles are stratovolcanoes, blue triangles are shield volcanoes and fissure vents. Data are from the Smithsonian Institution, Global Volcanism Program.

Similar to earthquakes, volcanoes are located preferentially on or near plate boundaries (see Figure 2). Also similar to earthquakes, different kinds of volcanoes occur along different types of plate boundaries. Most of the volcanic eruptions that make the news, such as the 1980 Mount St. Helens eruption, take place near subduction zones. This type of volcano is represented by green triangles in Figure 2 (view large, color versions of images online at www.visionlearning.com). These devastating, explosive eruptions reflect the composition of the magma – it is extremely viscous, or thick and resistant to flow, and thus results in tall, steep-sided volcanoes. In contrast, the volcanic eruptions that occur along spreading ridges are much gentler, in part because most of these eruptions occur under 2 to 3 kilometers of water, but also because the magma is far less viscous. This type of volcano is represented by blue triangles in Figure 2.

Plate boundaries

These observations about the distribution of earthquakes and volcanoes helped geologists define the processes that occur at spreading ridges and subduction zones. In addition, they helped scientists recognize that there are other types of plate boundaries. In general, plate boundaries are the scene of much geologic action – earthquakes, volcanoes, and dramatic topography such as mountain ranges like the Himalayas are all concentrated where two or more plates meet along a boundary.

There are three major ways that plates interact along boundaries: (1) they can move away from each other (diverge), (2) they can move toward each other (converge), or (3) they can move past each other, parallel to the boundary (transform). Each of these interactions produces a different and characteristic pattern of earthquakes, volcanic activity, and topography. The results of these interactions also depend on the type of crust involved, and there are two types of crust: oceanic and continental. Continental crust is thick and buoyant; oceanic crust is thin, dense, and forms at mid-ocean ridges.

Divergent boundaries

The most common divergent boundaries are the mid-ocean ridges that launched the plate tectonics revolution, and the Mid-Atlantic Ridge is a classic example (see Figure 3). Shallow earthquakes and minor, basaltic lava flows characterize divergent boundaries at mid-ocean ridges. The seafloor at the ridges is higher than the surrounding plain because the rocks are hot and thus less dense and more buoyant, riding higher in the underlying mantle. As the rocks move away from the spreading center, they cool and become more dense and less buoyant. Spreading has been occurring along the Mid-Atlantic Ridge for 180 million years, resulting in a large ocean basin – the Atlantic Ocean.

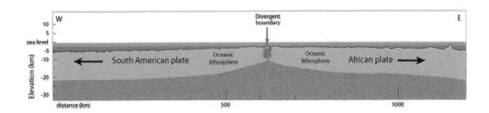

Figure 3: Cross-section of the Mid-Atlantic Ridge near latitude 14° S. Blue triangle represents the location of fissure volcanoes. Colored circles represent earthquakes, color-coded by depth (see Figure 1 for key).

Comprehension Checkpoint

Divergent boundaries are most common

A) in the middle of oceans.

B) in the middle of continents.

Convergent boundaries

Convergent boundaries are the most geologically active, with different features depending on the type of crust involved. The activity that takes place at convergent boundaries depends on the type of crust involved, as explained next.

Oceanic meets continental

These are the subduction zones first imagined by Hess, where dense oceanic crust is diving beneath more buoyant continental crust. These boundaries are characterized by: (a) a very deep ocean trench next to a high continental mountain range, (b) large numbers

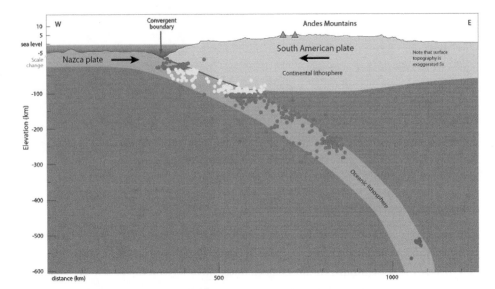

Figure 4: Cross-section of the South American subduction zone near latitude 22° S. Green triangles represent the locations of stratovolcanoes. Colored circles represent earthquakes, color-coded by depth (see Figure 1 for key).

of earthquakes that progress from shallow to deep, and (c) large numbers of intermediate composition volcanoes (see Figure 4). The Andes owe their existence to a subduction zone on the western edge of the South American plate; in fact, this type of boundary is often called an Andean boundary since it is the primary example.

Oceanic meets more oceanic

Where two plates converge along a boundary where the crust on both sides is oceanic, a subduction zone also occurs, but the result is slightly different than an Andean margin. Since the densities of the two plates are similar, it is usually the plate with the older oceanic crust that is subducted because that crust is colder and denser. Earthquakes progress from shallow to deep moving away from the trench like in the oceanic–continental convergence, and volcanoes form an island arc, like the mountain range along the Tonga trench in the western Pacific (see Figure 5).

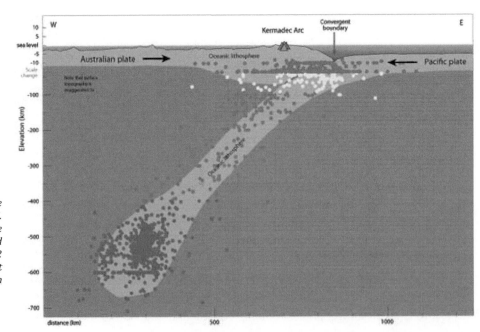

Figure 5: Cross-section of the Tonga trench near latitude 21° S. Colored triangles represent the location of volcanoes, color-coded by type of volcano (see Figure 2 for key). Colored circles represent earthquakes, color-coded by depth (see Figure 1 for key).

Continental meets more continental

When two pieces of continental crust converge, the result is a great pileup of continental material. Both pieces of crust are buoyant and are not easily subducted. Continental convergence is exemplified by the Himalayan mountain range, where the Indian plate runs into the Asian plate (see Figure 6). Numerous shallow earthquakes occur, but there is very little volcanism.

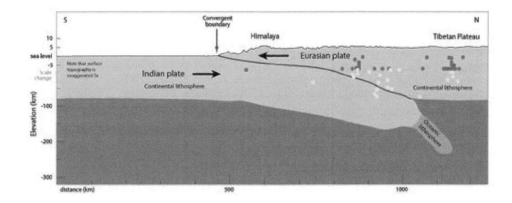

Figure 6: Cross-section of the Himalayas along 88° E longitude. Colored circles represent earthquakes, color-coded by depth (see Figure 1 for key).

Comprehension Checkpoint

Along convergent plate boundaries there are always big volcanoes.

A) True

B) False

Transform boundaries

Most boundaries are either convergent or divergent, but transform boundaries occur in a few places to accommodate lateral motion, where plates move horizontally past one another. This type of boundary is very rare on continents, but they are dramatic where they do occur. For example, the San Andreas Fault in California is a continental transform boundary. Along this boundary, frequent, shallow earthquakes occur (like the famous 1906 and 1989 San Francisco earthquakes), but there is little associated volcanic activity or topographic relief (see Figure 7). The Alpine Fault in New Zealand is very similar. Most transform boundaries occur not on land, however, but in short segments along mid-ocean ridges.

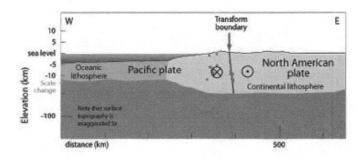

Figure 7: Cross-section of the San Andreas Fault in California near latitude 36° N. Colored circles represent earthquakes, color-coded by depth (see Figure 1 for key).

A few boundaries defy simple classification and are referred to as "plate boundary zones." For example, a complicated earthquake pattern is produced by a wide, poorly understood plate boundary zone between the Eurasian and African plates in the Mediterranean region.

Geologic activity away from plate boundaries

The plate boundaries described above account for the vast majority of seismic and volcanic activity on Earth. The more data that began to fit into the plate tectonics scheme, however, the more the exceptions stood out. What could account for Hawaii, for example, a scene of long-lived volcanic activity in the middle of the Pacific plate where there is no subduction or spreading to generate magma?

There had to be something else. In 1963, J. Tuzo Wilson, a Canadian geophysicist, theorized that the mantle contained immobile hotspots, thin plumes of hot magma that acted like Bunsen burners as plates moved over them (Wilson, 1963). The Hawaiian Islands form a long, linear chain, with ongoing volcanic eruptions on the island of Hawaii and extinct, highly eroded volcanic islands to the northwest. According to Wilson's hotspot theory, the chain of islands represents the northwestward motion of the Pacific plate over a mantle plume.

One important implication of Wilson's theory was that because hotspots were stationary, hotspot tracks could be used to trace plate motion history. For example, the track of the Hawaiian chain continues to the northwest as an underwater chain of progressively older, no longer active volcanoes. Once the volcanic eruptions stop, ocean waves begin to take their toll, eroding the islands down to just below sea level, at which point they are called seamounts. The islands and seamounts associated with the Hawaiian hotspot provide a history of motion for the Pacific plate, which appears to have taken an eastward turn around 42 million years ago (see Figure 10). Other hotspot tracks around the world can be used in a similar manner to reconstruct a global plate tectonic history.

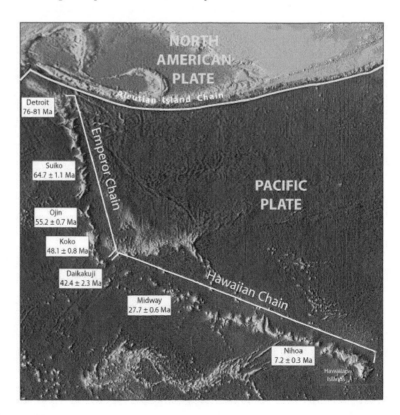

Figure 10: Ages of the seamounts and volcanoes in the Hawaii-Emperor chain, suggesting that the Pacific plate changes its direction of motion about 42 million years ago.

What are the driving forces?

Hotspots added further proof to confirm that plates move constantly and steadily. Ironically, however, the question that incited ridicule for Wegener continues to launch heated debate today: What ultimately drives plate motion? Plates are constantly shifting and rearranging themselves in response to each other. Eventually, a new Pangaea (or single supercontinent) will form, break apart, and form again on Earth. What keeps these plates moving?

Hess assumed that mantle convection was the main driving force – hot, less dense material rises along mid-ocean ridges, cools, and subsides at subduction zones, and the plates "ride" these convection cells (see our Density module for more information). Though there is little doubt that convection does occur in the mantle, current modeling suggests that it is not so simple. Many geologists argue that the force of convection is not enough to push enormous lithospheric plates like the North American plate. They suggest instead that gravity is the main driving force: Cold, dense oceanic crust sinks at subduction zones, pulling the rest of the plate with it. According to this theory, magmatic intrusions at spreading ridges are passive – the magma merely fills a hole created by pulling two plates apart.

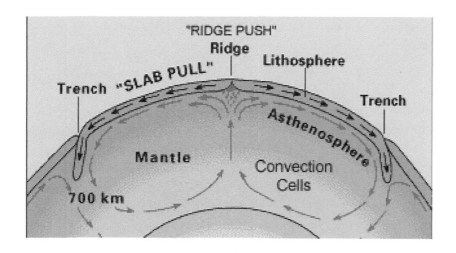

Figure 11: "Ridge push" and "slab pull" are both ways that gravity can act to keep a plate in motion. Note that arrows on convection cells and overlying plate are going in the same direction. Figure modified from This Dynamic Earth, a publication from the US Geological Survey.

Undoubtedly, gravity and convection both supply energy to keep plates moving. Their relative contributions, however, are a matter of debate and ongoing research.

The strength of plate tectonic theory lies in its ability to explain everything about the processes we see both in the geologic record and in the present. Our understanding of the subtleties continues to evolve as we learn more about our planet, but plate tectonics is truly the foundation upon which the science of geology is built.

Key Concepts for this chapter

▶ Earthquakes and volcanoes occur primarily along plate boundaries; the frequency and type of events vary with the type of boundary.

▶ Plates interact with one another at boundaries in one of three ways: they diverge, converge, or slide past one another.

▶ Plates are made up of two types of crust – oceanic and continental; oceanic crust is thinner and denser that continental crust. A single plate can have both continental and oceanic crust.

▶ Gravity and mantle convection are two driving forces for the movement of plates.

 *Take the Quiz* ▶ ▶ ▶

Plates, Plate Boundaries, and Driving Forces Quiz

1. Most earthquakes are located

   A) on oceanic crust.

   B) in the ocean.

   C) along plate boundaries.

   D) on continental crust.

2. Which of the three main boundary types is least common?

   A) transform

   B) divergent

   C) convergent

   D) They are all equally common.

3. Earthquakes along divergent boundaries occur only at shallow depths of 0 to 33 km below the earth's surface.

   A) True

   B) False

4. Why are we able to measure past plate motion using hotspots?

   A) Hotspots are unaffected by gravity, which drives plate motion.

   B) Hotspots only erupt when a plate moves.

   C) Hotspots are relatively stationary, whereas plates move.

   D) Hotspots only erupt every 1,000 years.

5. The driving forces behind plate tectonics, a subject that plagued Wegener, continue to be a matter of debate today. Which of the following is NOT a possible cause of plate motion?

   A) mantle upwelling

   B) earthquake activity

   C) convection

   D) gravity

6. The Himalayas occur along a convergent boundary where

   A) oceanic crust meets oceanic crust.

   B) transform motion occurs.

   C) continental crust meets continental crust.

   D) continental crust meets oceanic crust.

7. When oceanic crust meets oceanic crust along a convergent boundary, which plate is most likely to be subducted?

   A) the plate with the oldest crust

   B) the plate with the biggest continent

   C) the plate with an island arc

   D) the plate with the youngest crust

8. The San Andreas Fault in California is an example of what kind of boundary?

   A) transform

   B) convergent

   C) divergent

   D) plate boundary zone

9. Why did the distribution of earthquakes and volcanoes help confirm plate tectonic theory?

   A) Neither earthquakes nor volcanoes had been studied much before plate tectonics.

   B) Earthquakes and volcanoes were different along different types of boundaries.

   C) Both earthquakes and volcanoes were distributed randomly.

   D) Earthquakes and volcanoes were the same along all of the plate boundaries.

Continue on next page ▶ ▶ ▶

10. Continental crust is _____ than oceanic crust.

   A) more explosive

   B) less buoyant

   C) thinner and denser

   D) thicker and less dense

Answers and feedback can be found on Page 268

Carbon Chemistry: An Introduction

by Anthony Carpi, PhD

Did you know that organic chemicals make up all the life forms we know of? Organic chemistry, defined by the carbon–hydrogen bond, is at the foundation of life. Because of the unique properties of the carbon atom, it can bond with other atoms in many different ways, resulting in millions of different organic molecules.

Module Summary

The chemical basis of all living organisms is linked to the way that carbon bonds with other atoms. This introduction to organic chemistry explains the many ways that carbon and hydrogen form bonds. Basic hydrocarbon nomenclature is described, including alkanes, alkenes, alkynes, and isomers. Functional groups of atoms within organic molecules are discussed.

Terms you should know:

bonding = the act of linking two atoms together
formula = an expression of the composition of a chemical compound using symbols
property = a characteristic; an attribute

To understand life as we know it, we must first understand a little bit of organic chemistry. Organic molecules contain both carbon and hydrogen. Though many organic chemicals also contain other elements, it is the carbon-hydrogen bond that defines them as organic. Organic chemistry defines life. Just as there are millions of different types of living organisms on this planet, there are millions of different organic molecules, each with different chemical and physical properties. There are organic chemicals that make up your hair, your skin, your fingernails, and so on. The diversity of organic chemicals is due to the versatility of the carbon atom. Why is carbon such a special element? Let's look at its chemistry in a little more detail.

The uniqueness of carbon

Carbon (C) appears in the second row of the periodic table and has four bonding electrons in its valence shell (see our Periodic Table module for more information). Similar to other non-metals, carbon needs eight electrons to satisfy its valence shell. Carbon therefore forms four bonds with other atoms (each bond consisting of one of carbon's electrons and one of the bonding atom's electrons). Every valence electron participates in bonding; thus, a carbon atom's bonds will be distributed evenly over the atom's surface. These bonds form a tetrahedron (a pyramid with a spike at the top), as illustrated below:

Carbon forms 4 bonds

Organic chemicals get their diversity from the many different ways carbon can bond to other atoms. The simplest organic chemicals, called hydrocarbons, contain only carbon and hydrogen atoms; the simplest hydrocarbon (called methane) contains a single carbon atom bonded to four hydrogen atoms:

Methane – a carbon atom
bonded to 4 hydrogen atoms

But carbon can bond to other carbon atoms in addition to hydrogen, as illustrated in the molecule ethane below:

Ethane – a carbon-car-
bon bond

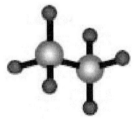

In fact, the uniqueness of carbon comes from the fact that it can bond to itself in many different ways. Carbon atoms can form long chains:

Hexane – a
6-carbon chain

branched chains:

Isohexane – a
branched-carbon
chain

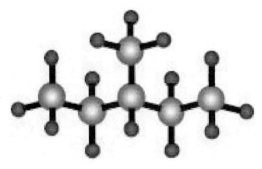

rings:

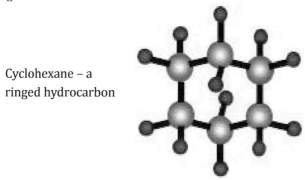

Cyclohexane – a ringed hydrocarbon

There appears to be almost no limit to the number of different structures that carbon can form. To add to the complexity of organic chemistry, neighboring carbon atoms can form double and triple bonds in addition to single carbon-carbon bonds:

Single bonding   **Double bonding**   **Triple bonding**

Keep in mind that each carbon atom forms four bonds. As the number of bonds between any two carbon atoms increases, the number of hydrogen atoms in the molecule decreases (as can be seen in the figures above).

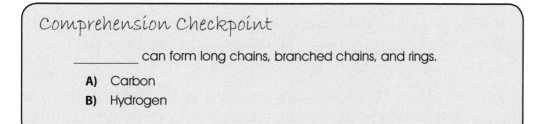

Comprehension Checkpoint

_____ can form long chains, branched chains, and rings.

A) Carbon
B) Hydrogen

Simple hydrocarbons

The simplest hydrocarbons are those that contain only carbon and hydrogen. These simple hydrocarbons come in three varieties depending on the type of carbon-carbon bonds that occur in the molecule.

Alkanes

Alkanes are the first class of simple hydrocarbons and contain only carbon-carbon single bonds. The alkanes are named by combining a prefix that describes the number of carbon atoms in the molecule with the root ending "ane". The names and prefixes for the first ten alkanes are given in the following table.

Carbon Atoms	Prefix	Alkane name	Chemical Formula	Structural Formula
1	Meth	Methane	CH_4	CH_4
2	Eth	Ethane	C_2H_6	CH_3CH_3
3	Prop	Propane	C_3H_8	$CH_3CH_2CH_3$
4	But	Butane	C_4H_{10}	$CH_3CH_2CH_2CH_3$
5	Pent	Pentane	C_5H_{12}	$CH_3CH_2CH_2CH_2CH_3$
6	Hex	Hexane	C_6H_{14}	...
7	Hept	Heptane	C_7H_{16}	
8	Oct	Octane	C_8H_{18}	
9	Non	Nonane	C_9H_{20}	
10	Dec	Decane	$C_{10}H_{22}$	

The chemical formula for any alkane is given by the expression $CnH2n+2$. The structural formula, shown for the first five alkanes in the table, shows each carbon atom and the elements that are attached to it. This structural formula is important when we begin to discuss more complex hydrocarbons. The simple alkanes share many properties in common. All enter into combustion reactions with oxygen to produce carbon dioxide and water vapor. In other words, many alkanes are flammable. This makes them good fuels. For example, methane is the principle component of natural gas, and butane is common lighter fluid.

$$CH_4 \quad + \quad 2O_2 \quad \rightarrow \quad CO_2 \quad + \quad 2H_2O$$

The chemical reaction between a fuel (for example wood) and an oxidizing agent.

Alkenes

Ethene

The second class of simple hydrocarbons, the alkenes, consists of molecules that contain at least one double-bonded carbon pair. Alkenes follow the same naming convention used for alkanes. A prefix (to describe the number of carbon atoms) is combined with the ending "ene" to denote an alkene. Ethene, for example is the two-carbon molecule that contains one double bond. The chemical formula for the simple alkenes follows the expression $CnH2n$. Because one of the carbon pairs is double bonded, simple alkenes have two fewer hydrogen atoms than alkanes.

Alkynes

Alkynes are the third class of simple hydrocarbons and are molecules that contain at least one triple-bonded carbon pair. Like the alkanes and alkenes, alkynes are named by combining a prefix with the ending "yne" to denote the triple bond. The chemical formula for the simple alkynes follows the expression CnH2n-2.

Ethyne

Comprehension Checkpoint

The simplest hydrocarbons are called

A) alkanes.

B) alkynes.

Isomers

Because carbon can bond in so many different ways, a single molecule can have different bonding configurations. Consider the two molecules illustrated here:

C_6H_{14}

$$CH_3CH_2CH_2CH_2CH_2CH_3$$

C_6H_{14}

$$CH_3$$
$$|$$
$$CH_3CH_2CHCH_2CH_3$$

Both molecules have identical chemical formulas (shown in the left column); however, their structural formulas (and thus some chemical properties) are different. These two molecules are called isomers. Isomers are molecules that have the same chemical formula but different structural formulas.

Comprehension Checkpoint

When molecules have the same number and types of atoms, they must have the same structure.

A) True

B) False

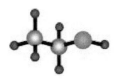

Ethanol

In addition to carbon and hydrogen, hydrocarbons can also contain other elements. In fact, many common groups of atoms can occur within organic molecules, these groups of atoms are called functional groups. One good example is the hydroxyl functional group. The hydroxyl group consists of a single oxygen atom bound to a single hydrogen atom (-OH). The group of hydrocarbons that contain a hydroxyl functional group is called alcohols. The alcohols are named in a similar fashion to the simple hydrocarbons, a prefix is attached to a root ending (in this case "anol") that designates the alcohol. The existence of the functional group completely changes the chemical properties of the molecule. Ethane, the two-carbon alkane, is a gas at room temperature; ethanol, the two-carbon alcohol, is a liquid.

Ethanol, common drinking alcohol, is the active ingredient in "alcoholic" beverages such as beer and wine.

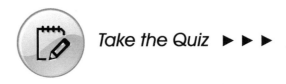

Take the Quiz ▶ ▶ ▶

Carbon Chemistry Quiz

1. Organic chemistry is broadly defined as
   A) the chemistry of the compounds that contain carbon and hydrogen.
   B) the chemistry of metallic compounds.
   C) the chemistry of substances produced by living organisms.
   D) all of the choices

2. Which of the following is the simplest alkane?
   A) ethane
   B) ethene
   C) ethyne
   D) methane

3. The group of simple organic molecules that contain only C and H are called:
   A) carbon
   B) hydrocarbons
   C) hydrogens
   D) hydronium

4. A compound containing only carbon and hydrogen and that has no double bonds is called an
   A) alkane
   B) alkene
   C) alkyne
   D) isomer

5. C_4H_6 is the chemical formula for
   A) butene.
   B) butyne.
   C) ethane.
   D) propyne.

6. An alkene with seven carbon atoms has the formula
   A) C_7H_{12}
   B) C_7H_{13}
   C) C_7H_{14}
   D) C_7H_{16}

7. Compounds with the same chemical formula but different structures are called
   A) hydrogens.
   B) isomers.
   C) isotopes.
   D) all of the above

8. Alcohols contain what functional group?
   A) an alkyl group
   B) carboxyl group
   C) hydroxyl group
   D) none of the choices

9. What is the name of the compound with the formula $CH_3CH_2CH_3$?
   A) ethane
   B) methane
   C) pentane
   D) propane

Answers and feedback can be found on Page 270

DNA I: The Genetic Material

by Nathan Lents, PhD

Did you know that one of the most important discoveries in biology was made while a British army medical officer was trying to develop a vaccine for pneumonia after World War I? Although a vaccine for pneumonia still does not exist, Frederick Griffith discovered "transformation." This means that organisms can be genetically reprogrammed into a slightly different version of themselves.

Module Summary

This module is the first in a series that discusses the discovery, structure, and function of DNA. Key experiments are discussed: from Griffith's discovery of genetic "transformation" to Avery, MacLeod, and McCarty's determination of the "transforming agent" to confirmation by Hershey and Chase of DNA rather than protein as the genetic material.

Terms you should know:

cell = the basic structural unit of all living things

heredity = the passing of genetic traits from parent to offspring

strain = (noun) a group of closely related organisms; a distinct variety

Consider yourself. You are an adult human, or nearly so, composed of hundreds of different types of cells. Each of these cell types has a different structure and function which together make up you as an individual. Millions of chemical reactions are taking place inside these cells, all carefully coordinated and timed. Yet, you started life as one single cell, a zygote, the result of the fusion of a sperm and an egg. How does all this remarkable complexity come about? Just what is it that you inherit that gives you your father's eyes and your mother's hair color? These questions had perplexed scientists and non-scientists alike for thousands of years, and they were addressed through a series of very clever experiments in the early part of the 20th century.

The chemical basis of heredity

In the mid 19th century, Gregor Mendel completed his now classic experiments on genetics (see our Mendel and Inheritance module). Mendel proposed that the "characters" that

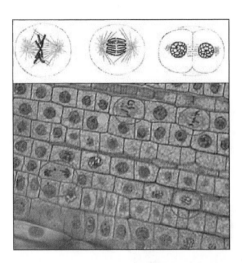

Figure 1: Microscopic view of chromosomes lining up (red circles at top) and separating (red circles at bottom) during mitosis (cell division) in an onion root tip.

controlled inheritance exhibited certain patterns of behavior. Specifically, they seemed to operate in pairs and separated independently during reproduction. The work that Mendel did established some trustworthy rules and properties about genetics and heredity, but no one had any idea what Mendel's "characters" were and how features were passed from generation to generation. Scientists were convinced that the basis of genetics and heredity could be found somewhere in the chemistry of our cells.

In the early 1900s, scientists began to focus on a recently discovered structure in cells called *chromosomes* (named by Walther Flemming from the Greek words for "colored bodies" because they selectively absorbed a red dye that Flemming used to color cells). Curiously, chromosomes seemed to behave in a manner similar to Mendel's "characters." Specifically, they were seen to line up randomly, separate, and then segregate from each other just prior to cell division, reminiscent of Mendel's Laws of Independent Assortment and Segregation (Figure 1). Gradually, scientists began to suspect a connection between chromosomes and heredity.

DNA or Protein?

While biologists were becoming convinced that chromosomes were the physical seat of genetics and inheritance, chemists were claiming that these structures were made of both protein and DNA. So, which was the genetic molecule housing all the hereditary information? Many scientists of the day actually thought it was protein because there are 20 different amino acids for building a protein polymer, while DNA polymers are made of only four nucleotide bases.

Consider it this way: The genetic molecule works like a language for storing information consisting of words that are made of individual "letters." The "language" of the DNA polymer would only have four different "letters" to work with (the four nucleotide bases), while "protein language" would have twenty possible letters – the 20 different amino acids. Imagine making a language using only four letters! Thus, because it offers far more complexity, most scientists in the early 20th century believed that protein was the component of chromosomes that housed the genetic information. Regarding the DNA, they thought that perhaps it acted as structural support for the chromosomes, like the frame of a house.

Griffith discovers "transformation"

Clarification came during the First World War. During the war, hundreds of thousands of servicemen died from pneumonia, a lung infection caused by the bacterium *Streptococcus pneumoniae*. In the early 1920s, a young British army medical officer named Frederick Griffith began studying *Streptococcus pneumoniae* in his laboratory in the hopes of developing a vaccine against it. As so often happens in scientific research, Griffith never found what he was looking for (there is still no vaccine for pneumonia), but instead, he made one of the most important discoveries in the field of biology: a phenomenon he called "transformation."

Dr. Griffith had isolated two strains of *S. pneumoniae,* one of which was pathogenic (meaning it causes sickness or death, in this case, pneumonia), and one which was innocu-

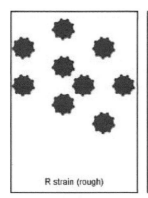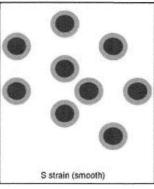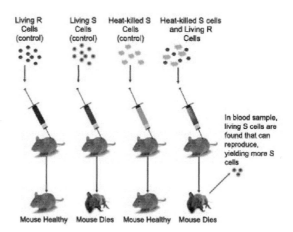

Figure 2: Cartoon depictions of the rough (harmless) and smooth (pathogenic) strains of S. pneumoniae.

Figure 3: Illustration of F. Griffith's discovery of transformation in S. pneumoniae *using mice.*

ous, or harmless. The pathogenic strain looked smooth under a microscope due to a protective coat surrounding the bacteria, and so he named this strain S, for smooth. The harmless strain of *S. pneumoniae* lacked the protective coat and appeared rough under a microscope, so he named it R, for rough (Figure 2).

Dr. Griffith observed that if he injected some of the S strain of *S. pneumoniae* into mice, they would get sick with the symptoms of pneumonia and die, while mice injected with the R strain did not become sick. Next, Griffith noticed that if he applied heat to the S strain of bacteria, then injected them into mice, the mice would no longer get sick and die. He thus hypothesized that excessive heat kills the bacteria, something that other scientists, including Louis Pasteur, had already shown with other types of bacteria.

However, Dr. Griffith didn't stop there – he decided to try something: He mixed living R bacteria (which are not pathogenic) with heat-killed S bacteria, and then he injected the mixture into mice. Surprisingly, the mice got pneumonia infections and eventually died (Figure 3).

Dr. Griffith examined samples from these sick mice and saw living S bacteria. This meant that either the S bacteria came back to life, an unlikely scenario, or the live R strain was somehow "transformed" into the S strain. Thus, after repeating this experiment many times, Dr. Griffith named this phenomenon "transformation." This discovery was significant because it showed that organisms can somehow be genetically "re-programmed" into a slightly different version of themselves. One strain of bacteria, in this case the R strain of *S. pneumoniae*, can be changed into something else, presumably because of the transfer of genetic material from a donor, in this case the heat-killed S strain.

Scientists around the world began repeating this experiment, but in slightly different ways, trying to discover exactly what was happening. It became clear that, when the S bacteria are killed by heat, they break open and many substances are released. Something in this mixture can be absorbed by living bacteria, leading to a genetic transformation. But because the mixture contains protein, RNA, DNA, lipids, and carbohydrates, the question remained – which molecule is the "transforming agent"?

Avery, MacLeod, and McCarty discover the transforming agent

This question was examined in several ways, most famously by three scientists working at The Rockefeller Institute (now Rockefeller University) in New York: Oswald Avery, Colin MacLeod, and Maclyn McCarty. These scientists did almost exactly what Griffith did in his experiments but with the following changes. First, after heat-killing the S strain of bacteria, the mixture was separated into six test tubes. Thus, each of the test tubes would contain the unknown "transforming agent." A different enzyme was then added to each tube except one – the control – which received nothing. To the other five tubes, one of the following enzymes was added: RNase, an enzyme that destroys RNA; protease, an enzyme that destroys protein; DNase, an enzyme that destroys DNA; lipase, an enzyme that destroys lipids; or a combination of enzymes that break down carbohydrates.

The theory behind this experiment was that if the "transforming agent" was, for example, protein, the transforming agent would be destroyed in the test tube containing protease, but not the others. Thus, whatever the transforming agents was, the liquid in one of the tubes would no longer be able to transform the *S. pneumonia* strains. When they did this, the result was both dramatic and clear. The liquid from the tubes that received RNase, protease, lipase, and the carbohydrate-digesting enzymes was still able to transform the R strain of pneumonia into the S strain. However, the liquid that was treated with DNase completely lost the ability to transform the bacteria (Figure 4).

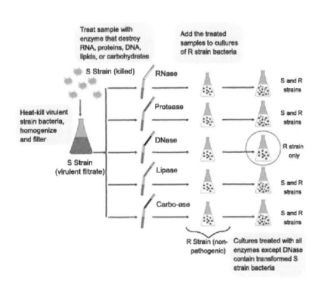

Figure 4: Illustration of the classic experiment by Avery, MacLeod, and McCarty demonstrating that DNA is capable of transforming harmless R strain S. pneumoniae *into the pathogenic S strain.*

Thus, it was apparent that the "transforming agent" in the liquid was DNA. To further demonstrate this, the scientists took liquid extracted from heat-killed *S. pneumoniae* (S strain) and subjected it to extensive preparation and purification, isolating only the pure DNA from the mixture. This pure DNA was also able to transform the R strain into the S strain and generate pathogenic *S. pneumoniae*. These results provided powerful evidence that DNA, and not protein, was actually the genetic material inside of living cells.

Comprehension Checkpoint

Which agent transformed one strain of bacteria into another?

A) RNA

B) DNA

Hershey and Chase further investigate DNA vs. protein

Despite this very clear result, some scientists remained skeptical and continued to think that proteins were likely the genetic molecule. Eight years after the famous Avery, MacLeod, and McCarty experiment was published, two scientists named Alfred Hershey and Martha Chase performed an entirely different type of genetic experiment. For their experimental system, they selected an extremely small virus called a *bacteriophage* (or just *phage*), which only infects bacterial cells. At that time, scientists knew that when these phage infect a bacterial cell, they somehow "reprogram" the bacterium to transform itself into a factory for producing more phage. They also knew that the phage itself does not enter the bacterium during an infection. Rather, a small amount of material is injected into the bacteria and this material must contain all of the information necessary to build more phages. Thus, this injected substance is the genetic material of the phage.

Hershey and Chase designed a very simple experiment to determine which molecule, DNA or protein, acted as the genetic material in phages. To do this, they made use of a technique called radioactive labeling. In radioactive labeling, a radioactive isotope of a certain atom is used and can be followed by tracking the radioactivity (radioactivity is very easily detected by laboratory instruments, even back in the 1940s, and remains a very common tool in scientific research). So, what Hershey and Chase did was to grow two batches of phage in their laboratory. One batch was grown in the presence of radioactive phosphorous. The element phosphorous is present in large amounts in DNA, but is not present in the proteins of bacteria and phage. Thus, this batch of phage would have radio-labeled DNA. The second batch of phage was grown in the presence of radioactive sulfur. Sulfur is an element that is often found in proteins, but never in DNA. Thus, the second batch of phage would have radio-labeled proteins.

Then, Hershey and Chase used these two batches of phage separately to infect bacteria and then measured where the radioactivity ended up. What they observed was that only those bacteria infected by phage with radio-labeled DNA became radioactive, bacteria infected by phage with radio-labeled protein did not. Thus Hershey and Chase concluded that it is DNA, and not protein, that is injected into the bacteria during phage infection and this DNA must be the genetic material that reprograms the bacteria.

Comprehension Checkpoint

Hershey and Chase used radioactive phosphorus in their experiment because

A) phosphorous is found in the DNA but not proteins of bacteria and phage.

B) phosphorous would show up in radio-labeled proteins of phages.

Taken together, these experiments represented strong evidence that DNA is the genetic material. Other scientists later confirmed these result in many different kinds of experiments, including showing that eukaryotic, and even human cells can be "transformed" by the injection of DNA. The result of these findings was to convince the scientific and lay communities that the molecule of heredity is indeed DNA. It turns out that the initial instincts of many scientists were exactly backward: They assumed that protein was the genetic material of chromosomes and DNA merely provided structure. The opposite turned out to be true. The DNA molecule houses genetic information, and proteins act as the structural framework of chromosomes.

The discovery that DNA was the "transforming agent" and the genetic component of human chromosomes was one of the greatest discoveries of science in the 20th century. However, the mechanism of how DNA codes for genetic information was initially a complete mystery and became the focus of intense scientific study (see our DNA II module). Still today, the study of how DNA functions comprises an entire discipline of science called molecular biology. Originally an offshoot of biochemistry, the field of molecular biology joins biologists, chemists, anthropologists, forensic scientists, geneticists, botanists, and many others who are working to shed light onto the immense complexity of DNA, the so-called blueprint of life.

Key Concepts for this chapter

▶ It required numerous experiments by many scientists to determine that DNA, and not protein, is the genetic material on which life is built.

▶ DNA can be "transformed," or genetically re-programmed, into a slightly different version of itself.

Take the Quiz ▶ ▶ ▶

DNA I Quiz

1. In the late 19th and early 20th century, most scientists believed that _____ was the genetic material because it offers more potential complexity.

   A) carbohydrate

   B) protein

   C) DNA

   D) lipid

2. Frederick Griffith made his important observations about "transformation" while attempting to develop a vaccine against which pathogenic organism?

   A) *E. coli*

   B) bacteriophage

   C) HIV

   D) *S. pneumoniae*

3. When Frederick Griffith coined the term, "transformation," this was in reference to the genetic re-programming of _____ .

   A) strains of bacteria

   B) laboratory mice

   C) patients with pneumonia

   D) bacteriophages

4. In the famous Avery, MacLeod, and McCarty experiment, the tube that was treated with _____ resulted in the destruction of the "transforming material."

   A) lipase

   B) RNase

   C) DNase

   D) protease

5. The Hershey and Chase experiment served as powerful independent confirmation that DNA was indeed the genetic material. They made their discovery using which type of organism?

   A) *S. pneumoniae*

   B) mice

   C) strains of bacteria

   D) bacteriophage

6. As determined by Frederick Griffith, when DNA is "transformed"

   A) its structure completely changes.

   B) it produces a slightly different organism.

   C) its structure does not change at all.

   D) it produces a pathogenic organism.

7. After Griffith's results were made known, scientists all over the world began to repeat his experiment in slightly different ways. Which statement best explains why that happened?

   A) The scientific community did not trust Griffiths' results.

   B) Scientists wanted to build on and extend his research.

   C) Scientists in different countries were competing to prove Griffith wrong.

   D) Scientists wanted to create new forms of *S. pneumoniae*.

Answers and feedback can be found on Page 272

DNA II: The Structure of DNA

by Nathan Lents, PhD

Did you know that the precise combinations of just four nitrogen bases form the billions of nucleotides that make up our own unique DNA molecules? The information stored in the base sequence of a single DNA strand stores all of the genetic information in your body and gives us our individual genetic traits.

Module Summary

Exploration of the structure of DNA sheds light on fascinating properties of the molecule. This module, the second in a series, highlights major discoveries, from the parts of a nucleotide – the building blocks of DNA – to the double helix structure of the DNA molecule. The module describes scientific developments that led to an understanding of the mechanism by which DNA replicates itself.

Terms you should know:

pair (noun) = a set of two; two similar things that form a unit; two similar things that are used together

pair (verb) = to arrange in a set of two; to become grouped together with one other similar thing

strand = a long, thin piece of something; a length of something thin like string

Look around you. Most objects you are familiar with will eventually fall into ruin if not constantly maintained: a car will eventually rust and fall to pieces; a house will spring leaks in the roof and fall to the ground; even mountain ranges are eroded by wind and rain. Yet, life on Earth continues to flourish. Your children are no weaker or more likely to fall to pieces than you are. This is because living things have a fascinating and somewhat unique ability to reproduce and make "copies" of themselves. To do this, they must first copy their genetic material, their DNA (see our DNA I module for more information). And it is the unique chemical properties of DNA that allow it to generate copies of itself. As we all know, living things do eventually age and deteriorate, much like the old house and rusty car, but by making copies of our DNA and passing it to our offspring, life continues.

Scientists first began to investigate the unique chemical properties of DNA long before the structure of the molecule was understood, and even before DNA was discovered to be the genetic material. In the late 1800s, J. Friedrich Miescher, a Swiss chemist working in Germany, was studying white blood cells (leukocytes). Because white blood cells are the principal component of pus, Miescher would go to the nearby hospital and collect pus from used bandages. He found that the nucleus of these cells was rich in a then-unknown substance that contained several elements, among them phosphorous and nitrogen. He called this substance "nuclein" because it was found in the nucleus of the cells. We now know that Miescher's "nuclein" (later renamed nucleic acid, for its acidic chemical properties) contained DNA.

In the early 1900s, the Lithuanian-American biochemist Phoebus Levene, probed deeper into the chemical composition of nucleic acid and was able to further purify the material. Although Levene was not the first scientist to successfully purify DNA, he was uniquely qualified to correctly determine its composition – he had extensive expertise in the area of carbohydrate and sugar chemistry. When Levene analyzed the chemical properties of nucleic acid, he discovered that DNA was abundant in three things: five-carbon sugars (pentoses), phosphate (as Miescher had previously found), and nitrogen bases. Thus, Levene correctly deduced that the DNA molecule was made of smaller molecules linked together, and these smaller molecules, which he named nucleotides, were made of three parts – a five-carbon sugar, a phosphate group (PO4), and one of four possible nitrogen bases – adenine, cytosine, guanine, or thymine (often abbreviated A, C, G, and T).

Levene was correct in identifying the three parts of a nucleotide, and determining that nucleotides were linked together to make DNA; however, in 1928, he also incorrectly proposed that one of each of the four nucleotides was linked together in a small circular molecule and that these "tetranucleotides" were the basis of DNA (Levene and London,1928) (Figure 1).

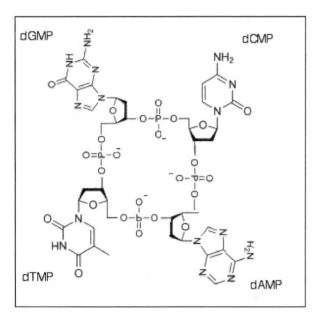

Figure 1: *Phoebus Levene incorrectly hypothesized that DNA was made of circular "tetranucleotides."*

Because he thought DNA was a simple circular structure, Levene rejected the notion that it could be the genetic material and sided firmly with those who believed that proteins contained the genetic code of organisms. However, much later, in the 1940s, Austrian-American scientist Erwin Chargaff reported that DNA from various species of life forms had different amounts of the four nucleotides (Vischer and Chargaff,1948). This strongly argued against Levene's hypothesis that DNA was simply a circular tetranucleotide, and scientists began to propose other possible structures of the DNA molecule. Despite what he got wrong, Levene's contributions to our understanding of the DNA molecule were substantial.

Thanks to the work of Levene and several others, the chemical structure of the individual nucleotides was established by the early 1910s. Figure 2 shows diagrams of the three parts of a nucleotide.

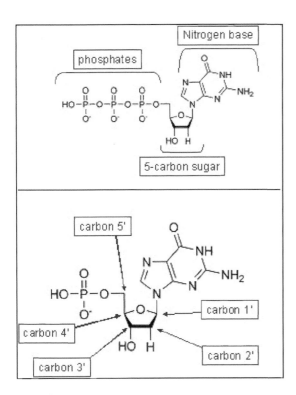

Figure 2: A nucleotide. The five-carbon sugar deoxyribose forms the center of the molecule. Attached to carbon #1 is the nitrogen base, and attached to carbon #5 is the phosphate group (there may be 1, 2, or 3 phosphates in a nucleotide)

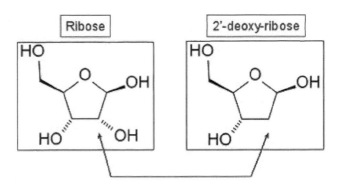

Figure 3: Ribose vs. Deoxyribose. These two pentoses, or five carbon sugars, differ only in the presence of an oxygen on ribose at the #2 carbon. At the #2 carbon of deoxyribose, a H exists in place of the ⁻OH group on ribose; however, lone hydrogens are often omitted from drawings of organic molecules, as above.

The sugar deoxyribose gets its name because when it was discovered (by Levene), it was found to lack one oxygen atom when compared to another sugar he discovered called ribose (Figure 3).

The oxygen missing from deoxyribose is on carbon #2, thus the full name of the sugar is 2'-deoxyribose. (In biochemistry, the carbons in sugar groups are often numbered with the "prime" symbol (as in 2'), to clarify that the carbon referred to is in the sugar and not another part of the molecule.)

Levene correctly deduced the connections between the nucleotides, and the chemical name for these connections are "phosphodiester bonds." These bonds are often casually referred to as "5' to 3' connections" because a phosphate molecule (PO_4) serves as the bridge between the 5' carbon of one nucleotide and the 3'carbon of the next (Figure 4).

Although Levene originally thought that four nucleotides were connected together in a circular molecule, we now know that the individual nucleotides are connected to form a very long linear structure (Figure 5).

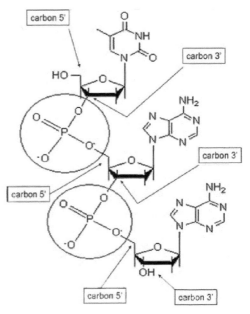

Figure 4: Phosphodiester bonds. Nucleotides are connected to one another through a phosphate group that is connected to the 5' carbon of one nucleotide and the 3' nucleotide of another.

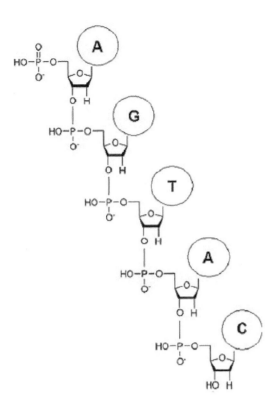

Figure 5: *A chain of nucleotides. As shown in this linear drawing, the sugar and phosphate groups connect in a long chain. This is referred to as the "sugar-phosphate backbone," while the nitrogen bases are attached to the backbone.*

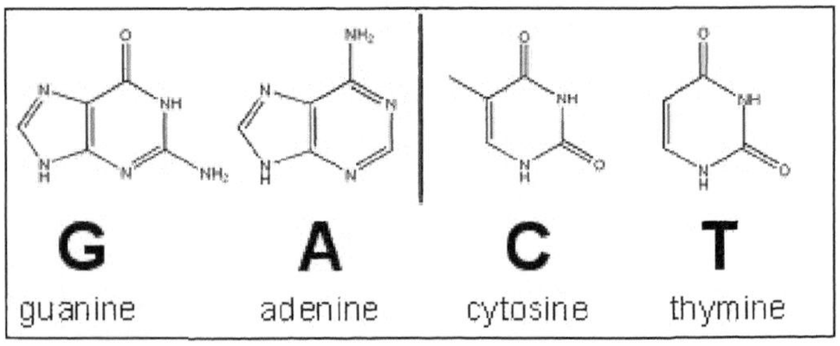

Figure 6: *The nitrogen bases. Shown here are the four different nitrogen bases found in DNA nucleotides. Note that guanine and adenine, the purines, have two rings, while cytosine and thymine, the pyrimidines, have only one ring.*

The four nucleotides of DNA are grouped into two "families" based on their chemical structure: the purines, adenine and guanine, have a structure with two rings; and the pyrimidines, cytosine and thymine, have only one ring (Figure 6).

Thus, the strands of DNA inside our cells are polymers of repeating units of nucleotides. It is the precise order, or sequence, of the billions of nucleotides – As, Cs, Gs, and Ts – that make up our own unique DNA molecules and give us our individual genetic traits.

Comprehension Checkpoint

Nucleotides are

A) smaller molecules that link together to form a DNA molecule.

B) the scientific name for white blood cells.

The discovery of the double helix

Once the building blocks of DNA were fully understood, by the late 1940s and early 1950s, scientists began to study the larger structure of DNA by taking X-ray diffraction pictures of purified DNA molecules. However, the pictures they took were not consistent with a simple linear strand of nucleotides, as depicted in Figure 5. Instead, the pictures argued that DNA is even more complex and has a very regular and symmetrical shape.

A number of scientists began to propose possible structures for the DNA molecule based on this research. Because the pictures argued for a symmetrical shape and chemical evidence argued that DNA was a polymer of nucleotides, many scientists thought that multiple strands wrapped around each other, like a braid or a rope. In fact, Linus Pauling, a prominent American scientist, had envisioned that DNA might be a triple helix – three strands of nucleotides wrapping around each other. Pauling, who would later win a Nobel Prize for correctly deducing the "alpha-helix" structure of proteins, even published a paper proposing a triple helix model of DNA in 1953 (Pauling and Corey,1953). Pauling's practice of building models of molecular structures caught on with many biochemists of the day, and this time period has been referred to as the era of model building.

Several variants of a helix-shaped DNA were proposed by other scientists. In 1951, the English molecular biologists Francis Crick and James Watson had published their own incorrect version of a triple helix model. However, the diffraction pictures at the time were all relatively poor quality and resolution. As the technique was further refined, a brilliant chemist named Rosalind Franklin (Figure 7), working at King's College in England, was able to take much higher-resolution X-ray diffraction pictures.

Figure 7: Rosalind Franklin (25 July 1920 - 16 April 1958), a chemist who made vital contributions to the understanding of the fine molecular structures of DNA and RNA. Franklin is best known for her work on X-ray diffraction images of DNA, which James Watson and Frances Crick used to formulate their 1953 hypothesis about the structure of DNA.

Franklin's high quality pictures confirmed that DNA is actually a double helix – two strands wrapped around each other. However, the first double-stranded molecule built by Watson and Crick had the sugar–phosphate backbones of two strands wrapped around each other and the nitrogen bases pointing outward. It was Rosalind Franklin who pointed out the error in this model. She reminded Watson and Crick that the nitrogen bases are not very soluble in water and thus they would not be pointed outward where they would be surrounded by nearby water molecules in the cell. Instead, she argued, the sugars and phosphates, which are soluble in water, would be pointed outwards, towards the water, and the nitrogen bases would likely be tucked into the interior of the molecule, away from the water molecules, and perhaps interacting with each other.

Comprehension Checkpoint

The double helix structure of DNA was confirmed by

A) Linus Pauling's models of DNA molecules.

B) Rosalind Franklin's X-ray diffraction images of DNA.

Chargaff's Law

This was a vital piece of advice for Watson and Crick, leading them to take their model apart and begin to build a new one. This time, they built the double helix with the sugar–phosphate backbones on the outside of the helix and the nitrogen bases facing inward. They realized that the nitrogen bases of the two strands would now be in proximity of one another and would likely interact. A crucial piece of evidence that helped them figure this out came from Erwin Chargaff's studies. In addition to demonstrating that different organisms had different amounts of the four nitrogen bases of DNA, in 1951, Chargaff also reported that the amount of adenine (A) always equals the amount of thymine (T) and the amount of cytosine (C) always equals the amount of guanine (G). This is now known as "Chargaff's law."

With Chargaff's law in mind, Watson and Crick had a revelation. They reasoned that if the molecule is double-stranded, perhaps every time that an A was on one strand of the molecule, a T appears in the complementary position on the opposite strand (and vice versa); further, every time a C was on one side, a G would be on the other. This would explain why

Chargaff's law held true. But, there was one problem. The nitrogen bases did not "fit together" in this configuration. Franklin had taken very good pictures of the DNA molecule that demonstrated that it was a tightly packed, narrow structure. When large molecules interact tightly, the smaller constituent molecules that closely pack together must be "complementary" like two inter-locking pieces of a puzzle. For example, a negative charge will be closely associated with a positive charge, etc. Watson and Crick knew that their model wasn't quite right, because the nitrogen bases were not fitting together very well.

Comprehension Checkpoint

"Chargaff's Law" has to do with

A) the role of sugar and phosphates.

B) the pairing of the four nitrogen bases.

Anti-parallel configuration of DNA strands

The final revelation that allowed Watson and Crick to complete their model came in a moment described as "a stroke of inspiration" when Watson realized that the nucleotides would fit together if one was "upside down" relative to the other. (According to Watson, he saw this possibility as he sat across a small table from Crick, both of them working with small models of nucleotides.) This upside down orientation would occur if the two strands that wrap around each other are not pointed in the same direction, but in opposite directions. Thus, these two strands are said to be anti-parallel, like the traffic on a two-lane highway (Figure 8).

Suddenly, everything made sense! With the two strands wrapping around each other in an anti-parallel configuration, Watson and Crick were able to fit the strands very close together, as Franklin's picture shows them to be, and the structure is regular and symmetrical. Most importantly, the nitrogen bases fit perfectly together through a type of chemical attraction called a hydrogen bond. Hydrogen bonds hold the two strands together stably, but not permanently. Specifically, an adenine–thymine "base pair" has two hydrogen bonds and a cytosine–guanine base pair has three hydrogen bonds. (See Figure 8 at left.)

Given this anti-parallel structure, to distinguish the two strands of DNA, scientists say that one strand is oriented "5' to 3' " and the other strand is "3' to 5'." This is

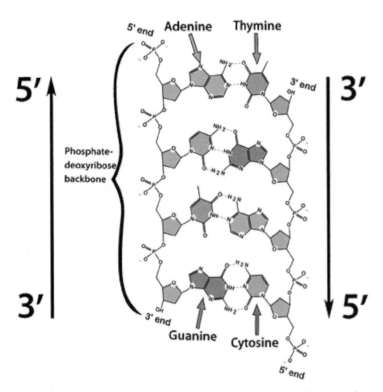

Figure 8: Antiparallel nature of the DNA double helix. Notice how the sugar-phosphate backbone is on the outside of the "ladder" while the bases point inward. Notice also how the orientation of the two strands is "antiparallel" and thus look upside down compared to each other. This is most easily seen by looking at the pentose sugars (outside columns).

in reference to the 5'-3' connections in the phosphate–sugar backbone. The machinery of the cell also uses this orientation to select which direction to read the genetic information contained in the nucleotide sequence. Imagine trying to read an English sentence going from right to left. This would make no sense because the proper direction of reading English is left to right. Similarly, the DNA code must be read in the correct direction, which is 5' to 3'.

The beauty of the double-stranded anti-parallel configuration is found in the complementary base pairing according to Chargaff's law. If we know the sequence of nucleotides on one strand, we can accurately predict the nucleotides on the other. An adenine on one side of the DNA molecule would be paired with a thymine on the other side, and so on. Thus, if the two strands are separated, we could look at either strand and know exactly what was on the complementary strand. In fact, this is precisely what happens during DNA replication: the DNA double helix is pried apart or "unzipped" and both of the single strands then serve as copy templates for synthesizing a new strand. The result is two new DNA double helixes, both of which are identical to each other and to the original strand (Figure 9).

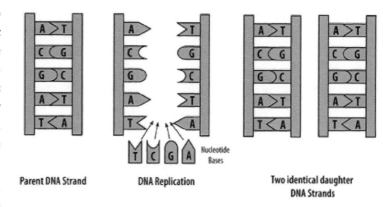

Figure 9: *Schematic of DNA replication method proposed by Watson and Crick. In this model, the two strands of the original DNA molecule are first pried apart. Then, complementary nucleotides (A with T, G with C, etc.) are added opposite of both of the original strands. The result is two DNA molecules, both identical to the original strand (and thus to each other), and both with one old strand and one new strand.*

Once Watson and Crick had built the correct model, all could see that the anti-parallel configuration and the hydrogen bond base-pairing allowed this simple and effective means of DNA self-replication. In fact, the final sentence of their 1953 research article announcing the structure of DNA was, "It has not escaped our notice that the specific pairing we have postulated immediately suggests a possible copying mechanism for the genetic material." Watson and Crick published their model of DNA in the journal *Nature* in 1953, a model which earned them the Nobel Prize in 1962.

There has been much debate about whether Rosalind Franklin, as a rare female scientist in the 1950s, received enough credit for her crucial contributions to this important discovery. Unfortunately, she died from ovarian cancer just five years after the model was built and Nobel Prizes are not given posthumously. In the 1950s, scientists were not aware of the cancer risks involved with repeated X-ray exposure and did not properly protect themselves from the radiation given off by these instruments. Thus, it is conceivable that Franklin's premature death was a direct result of her dedication to scientific research and her pursuit of the structure of the DNA molecule.

Comprehension Checkpoint

From the sequence of nucleotides on one DNA strand, we can predict

A) the sequence of nucleotides on the other strand.

B) how many times a DNA strand will replicate itself.

But how does DNA store information?

With the discovery of the structure of DNA, a number of fascinating properties of the molecule were revealed. Not only can the molecule replicate itself, but the information stored in the base sequence of a single DNA strand stores all of the genetic information in your body. Think of the phone numbers stored in your cell phone. Each digit by itself means nothing. But when strung together in a precise sequence (e.g., 6-4-6-5-5-7-4-5-0-4), these numbers form a code for contacting another specific telephone. The same is true for DNA. The bases T, C, A and G mean nothing by themselves. However, a long sequence such as ATGGCTAGCTCGATCGTACGT...can form the code for building an important molecule in your body. This molecule may then perform a function in your body that allows your heart to beat, your stomach to digest, your muscle to flex, or your brain to think. Thus, because these sequences of nucleotides provide the information for the cell to build proteins and other molecules, DNA is often called the "blueprint of life." How this blueprint is actually used by cells to build other molecules is explored in additional modules.

Key Concepts for this chapter

▶ DNA consist of two strands of repeating units called nucleotides; each nucleotide is made up of a five-carbon sugar, a phosphate group, and a nitrogen base.

▶ The specific sequence of the four different nucleotides that make up an organism's DNA gives that organism its own unique genetic traits.

▶ The four nitrogen bases are complementary – adenine is complementary to thymine, cytosine is complementary to guanine – and the pairs form hydrogen bonds when the 5'/3' ends of their attached sugar–phosphate groups are oriented anti-parallel to one another.

References

Levene PA, London EJ. "On the Structure of Thymonucleic Acid." *Science.* 1928 Dec 7;68(1771):572-573.

Vischer E, Chargaff E. "The composition of the pentose nucleic acids of yeast and pancreas." *J Biol Chem.* 1948 Nov;176(2):715-34.

Linus Pauling and Robert B. Corey "A Proposed Structure For The Nucleic Acids" *Proc Natl Acad Sci U S A.* 1953 February; 39(2): 84-97.

Watson JD, Crick FH (April 1953). "Molecular structure of nucleic acids; a structure for deoxyribose nucleic acid". *Nature* 171 (4356): 737-8.

R. Franklin and R. G. Gosling: Molecular Configuration in Sodium Thymonucleate, *Nature* (1953) volume 171 pages 740-741.

Maddox, B. 2003. *Rosalind Franklin: The Dark Lady of DNA.* Harper Perennial. ISBN 0-060-98508-9.

Watson, J. D. (1968) *The Double Helix: A Personal Account of the Discovery of the Structure of DNA.* New York: Atheneum.

Take the Quiz ▶ ▶ ▶

DNA II Quiz

1. What are the building blocks of DNA?

    A) amino acids

    B) proteins

    C) helices

    D) nucleotides

2. What are the three "parts" of a nucleotide?

    A) nuclein, helix, and amino acid

    B) protein, DNA, sugar

    C) sugar, phosphate, nitrogen base

    D) adenine, thymine, cytosine

3. Whose work showed that all living things have different amounts of each of the four nucleotides, and disproved Phoebus Leven's hypothesis of the "tetra-nucleotide" structure of DNA?

    A) Erwin Chargaff

    B) J. Friedrich Miescher

    C) Rosalind Franklin

    D) James Watson

4. Why was Rosalind Franklin's famous X-ray diffraction picture of DNA so important?

    A) It showed that DNA has a triple helix.

    B) It helped to reveal the molecular structure of DNA.

    C) It showed that there are more than four nucleotides that make up DNA.

    D) It proved that Watson and Crick's original model was correct.

5. What forms the "bridge" connecting two nucleotides within a single strand of the DNA polymer?

    A) phosphate

    B) electrons

    C) cytosine

    D) hydrogen bonds

6. DNA is typically double stranded. Which of the following statements about the two strands of DNA is NOT correct?

    A) The two strands are oriented in opposite directions (anti-parallel)

    B) The two strands are held together by hydrogen bonds.

    C) The phosphate groups are pointed "inwards" toward the center of the molecule.

    D) The two strands twist around each other.

7. When they announced their proposed structure of DNA, Watson and Crick noted that, "It has not escaped our notice that the specific pairing we have postulated immediately suggests a possible copying mechanism for the genetic material." What did they mean by this?

    A) The twisting nature of the molecule would make it very easy to copy. **B)** Because A always base-pairs with T, phosphates would always bond with the sugars.

    C) Hydrogen bonding is much weaker than covalent bonding, so the molecule could be easily taken apart and re-built when necessary.

    D) If the two strands of DNA were separated, both separate strands could be used as templates for copying the other strand, according to the complementary base pairing.

Answers and feedback can be found on Page 274

The Discovery and Structure of Cells

by Carl Shuster, MS

Did you know that human cells range from 1/12,000 of an inch to over 39 inches long? Cells can vary widely depending on their function. In fact, there are hundreds of different types of cells in the human body alone. These basic building blocks of all living things share certain features and are just as "alive" as you are.

In this module

The cell is the basic structural unit of life. This module discusses the different types of cells that exist and the structures they are composed of. It also explores the relationship between cell structure and function. A brief history of modern cell theory is provided.

Terms you should know:

function = special purpose; designated action

membrane = layer of molecules that form the boundary of a cell, or a structure within a cell

structure = a physical form; the arrangement of parts; the way something is built

In 1655, the English scientist Robert Hooke made an observation that would change basic biological theory and research forever. While examining a dried section of cork tree with a crude light microscope, he observed small chambers and named them cells. Within a decade, researchers had determined that cells were not empty but instead were filled with a watery substance called cytoplasm.

Over the next 175 years, research led to the formation of the cell theory, first proposed by the German botanist Matthias Jacob Schleiden and the German physiologist Theodore Schwann in 1838 and formalized by the German researcher Rudolf Virchow in 1858. In its modern form, this theorem has four basic parts:

1. The cell is the basic structural and functional unit of life; all organisms are composed of cells.

2. All cells are produced by the division of preexisting cells (in other words, through reproduction). Each cell contains genetic material that is passed down during this process.

3. All basic chemical and physiological functions – for example, repair, growth, movement, immunity, communication, and digestion – are carried out inside of cells.

4. The activities of cells depends on the activities of subcellular structures within the cell (these subcellular structures include organelles, the plasma membrane, and, if present, the nucleus).

The cell theory leads to two very important generalities about cells and life as a whole:

A. Cells are alive. The individual cells of your organs are just as "alive" as you are, even though they cannot live independently. This means cells can take energy (which, depending on the cell type, can be in the form of light, sugar, or other compounds) and building materials (proteins, carbohydrates and fats), and use these to repair themselves and make new generations of cells (reproduction).

B. The characteristics and needs of an organism are in reality the characteristics and needs of the cells that make up the organism. For example, you need water because your cells need water.

What's in a cell?

Most of the activities of a cell (repair, reproduction, etc.) are carried out via the production of proteins. Proteins are large molecules that are made by specific organelles within the cell using the instructions contained within its genetic material.

Cytology is the study of cells, and cytologists are scientists that study cells. Cytologists have discovered that all cells are similar. They are all composed chiefly of molecules containing carbon, hydrogen, oxygen, nitrogen, phosphorus, and sulfur. Although many non-living structures also contain these elements, cells are different in their organization and maintenance of a boundary, their ability to regulate their own activity, and their controlled metabolism.

Figure 1: The plasma membrane, shown above, forms the outer boundary and barrier of a cell. The membrane protects the contents of the cell. The bulk of the membrane is made of the phospholipid bilayer. Cholesterol is also found in animal cell membranes to increase the fluidity of the membrane and prevent freezing of cells at low temperatures. Transmembrane proteins are proteins that are embedded in the membrane and may also have carbohydrates attached. These transmembrane proteins perform many important cellular functions, such as communication between cells, and can be used to form channels in the membrane that allow certain molecules in and out of the cell.

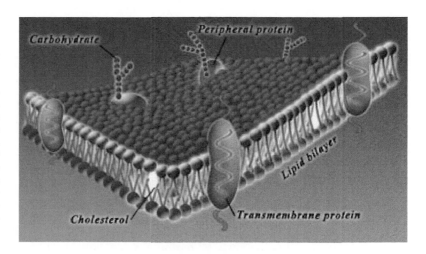

Cell similarities

All cells contain three basic features:

1. A plasma membrane consisting of a phospholipid bilayer, which is a fatty membrane that houses the cell. This membrane contains several structures that allow the cell to perform necessary tasks - for example, channels that allow substances to move in and out of the cell, antigens that allow the cell to be recognized by other cells, and proteins that allow cells to attach to each other.

2. A cytoplasm containing cytosol and organelles. Cytosol is a fluid consisting mostly of water and dissolved nutrients, wastes, ions, proteins, and other molecules. Organelles are small structures suspended in the cytosol. The organelles carry out the basic functions of the cell, including reproduction, metabolism, and protein synthesis (see our module Cellular Organelles I).

3. Genetic material (DNA and RNA), which carries the instructions for the production of proteins.

Comprehension Checkpoint

_____ controls the movement of substances into and out of cells.

A) The plasma membrane

B) Cytoplasm

Cell differences

Apart from these three similarities, cell structure and form are very diverse and are therefore difficult to generalize. Some cells are single, independent units and spend their entire existence as individual cells (these are the single-celled organisms such as amoebas and bacteria). Other cells are part of multicellular organisms and cannot survive alone.

One major difference among cells is the presence or absence of a nucleus, which is a subcellular structure that contains the genetic material. *Prokaryotic* cells (which include bacteria) lack a nucleus, whereas *eukaryotic* cells (which include protozoan, animal, and plant cells) contain a nucleus.

There are other major differences in cell structure and function between different types of organisms. For example:

• The cells of autotrophic organisms (most plants and some protozoans), which can produce their own food, contain an organelle called the chloroplast that contains chlorophyll and allows the cell to produce glucose using light energy in the process known as photosynthesis (see our Photosynthesis I module).

• The cells of plants, protists, and fungi are surrounded by a cell wall composed mostly of the carbohydrate cellulose; the cell wall helps these cells maintain their shape. Animal cells lack a cell wall but instead have a cytoskeleton, a network of long fibrous protein strands that attach to the inner surface of the plasma membrane and help them maintain shape (see our Cellular Membranes I module).

There are even major differences in cells within the same organism, reflecting the different functions the cells serve within the organism. For example, the human body consists of trillions of cells, including some 200 different cell types that vary greatly in size, shape, and function. The smallest human cells, sperm cells, are a few micrometers wide (1/12,000 of an inch) whereas the longest cells, the neurons that run from the tip of the big toe to the spinal cord, are over a meter long in an average adult!

Human cells also vary significantly in structure and function. For example:

- Only muscle cells contain myofilaments, protein-containing structures that allow the cells to contract (shorten) and therefore cause movement.

- Specialized cells called photoreceptors within the eye have the ability to detect light. These cells contain special chemicals called pigments that can absorb light, and special organelles that can then turn the absorbed light into electrical current that is sent to the brain and is perceived as vision.

Key Concepts for this chapter

▶ Cells are the basic structural and functional unit of all living things and contain inheritable genetic material.

▶ The activity of a cell is carried out by the sub-cellular structures it possesses.

▶ Cells possess an outer boundary layer, called a cell membrane, cytoplasm, organelles, and genetic material.

▶ There is considerable variety among living cells, including the function of membranes and sub-cellular strucutres, and the different types of functions the cells carry out, such as chemical transport, support, and other functions.

Take the Quiz ▶ ▶ ▶

The Discovery and Structure of Cells Quiz

1. What is the smallest structural unit of living things?

    A) a chromosome

    B) a membrane

    C) the cell

    D) the ribosome

2. What are the three basic features that are common to all cells?

    A) a plasma membrane, RNA, and genetic material

    B) cytoplasm, a plasma membrane, and genetic material

    C) DNA, cytoplasm, and RNA

    D) DNA, RNA, and a plasma membrane

3. What is one major aspect that may differ between different types of cells?

    A) the ability to reproduce

    B) the presence or absence of ribosomes

    C) the presence or absence of the nucleus

    D) the presence or absence of the plasma membrane

4. What is one major difference between animal and plant cells?

    A) the amount of water

    B) the cell membrane

    C) the cell wall

    D) the color

5. Prokaryotic and eukaryotic cells differ in that prokaryotic cells do not have

    A) a plasma membrane.

    B) ribosomes.

    C) a nucleus.

    D) genetic material.

6. The structure of a cell is independent from its function.

    A) True

    B) False

7. The presence of a boundary layer allows a cell to

    A) regulate its metabolism.

    B) reproduce quickly and efficiently.

    C) eliminate waste without contamination.

    D) determine which activities it will perform.

Answers and feedback can be found on Page 276

Theories, Hypotheses, and Laws

by Anthony Carpi, PhD and Anne Egger, PhD

Did you know that the idea of evolution had been part of Western thought for more than 2,000 years before Charles Darwin was born? Like many theories, the theory of evolution was the result of the work of many different scientists working in different disciplines over a period of time.

Theories are not based on one scientist's work but on an accumulation of evidence and ideas from many scientists over time. This module discusses how scientific theories are built and revised. It uses the development of the theory of evolution through natural selection to illustrate how how theories are built through a process of testing, expanding, and refining.

Terms you should know:

data = pieces of information collected through observation and measurement

evidence = support for an idea, opinion, or hypothesis

evolution = genetic change in a plant or animal population over generations

Imagine yourself shopping in a grocery store with a good friend who happens to be a chemist. Struggling to choose between the many different types of tomatoes in front of you, you pick one up, turn to your friend and ask her if she thinks the tomato is organic. Your friend simply chuckles and replies, "Of course it's organic!" without even looking at how the fruit was grown. Why the amused reaction? Your friend is highlighting a simple difference in vocabulary. To a chemist, the term *organic* refers to any compound in which hydrogen is bonded to carbon. Tomatoes (like all plants) are abundant in organic compounds – thus your friend's laughter. In modern agriculture, however, the term *organic* has come to mean food items grown or raised without the use of chemical fertilizers, pesticides, or other additives.

So who is correct? You both are. Both uses of the word are correct, though they mean different things in different contexts. There are, of course, lots of words that have more than one meaning (like *bat*, for example), but multiple meanings can be especially confusing when two meanings convey very different ideas and are specific to one field of study.

Scientific theories

The term *theory* also has two meanings, and this double meaning often leads to confusion. In common language, the term theory generally refers to speculation or a hunch or guess. You might have a theory about why your favorite sports team isn't playing well, or who ate the last cookie from the cookie jar. But these theories do not fit the scientific use of the term. In science, a theory is a well-substantiated and comprehensive set of ideas that explains a phenomenon in nature. A scientific theory is based on large amounts of data and observations that have been collected over time. Scientific theories can be tested and refined by additional research, and they allow scientists to make predictions. Though you may be correct in your hunch, your cookie jar conjecture doesn't fit this more rigorous definition.

All scientific disciplines have well-established, fundamental theories. For example, atomic theory describes the nature of matter and is supported by multiple lines of evidence from the way substances behave and react in the world around us (see our series on Atomic Theory). Plate tectonic theory describes the large scale movement of the outer layer of the Earth and is supported by evidence from studies about earthquakes, magnetic properties of the rocks that make up the seafloor, and the distribution of volcanoes on Earth (see our series on Plate Tectonic Theory). The theory of evolution by natural selection, which describes the mechanism by which inherited traits that affect survivability or reproductive success can cause changes in living organisms over generations, is supported by extensive studies of DNA, fossils, and other types of scientific evidence (see our Charles Darwin series for more information). Each of these major theories guides and informs modern research in those fields, integrating a broad, comprehensive set of ideas.

So how are these fundamental theories developed, and why are they considered so well supported? Let's take a closer look at some of the data and research supporting the theory of natural selection to better see how a theory develops.

Comprehension Checkpoint

A theory is simply an educated guess made by a scientist.

A) True

B) False

The development of a scientific theory: Evolution and natural selection

The theory of evolution by natural selection is sometimes maligned as Charles Darwin's speculation on the origin of modern life forms. However, evolutionary theory is not speculation. While Darwin is rightly credited with first articulating the theory of natural selection, his ideas built on more than a century of scientific research that came before him, and are supported by over a century and a half of research since.

The Fixity Notion: Linnaeus

Research about the origins and diversity of life proliferated in the 18th and 19th centuries. Carolus Linnaeus, a Swedish botanist and the father of modern taxonomy (see our module Taxonomy I for more information), was a devout Christian who believed in the concept of Fixity of Species, an idea based on the biblical story of creation. The Fixity of Species concept said that each species is based on an ideal form that has not changed over time. In the early stages of his career, Linnaeus traveled extensively and collected data on the structural similarities and differences between different species of plants. Noting that some very different plants had similar structures, he began to piece together his landmark work *Systema Naturae* in 1735 (Figure 1). In *Systema*, Linnaeus classified organisms into related groups based on similarities in their physical features. He developed a hierarchical classification system, even drawing relationships between seemingly disparate species (for example, humans, orangutans, and chimpanzees) based on the physical similarities that he observed between these organisms. Linnaeus did not explicitly discuss change in organisms or propose a reason for his hierarchy, but by grouping organisms based on physical characteristics, he suggested that species are related, unintentionally challenging the Fixity notion that each species is created in a unique, ideal form.

The age of Earth: Leclerc and Hutton

Also in the early 1700s, Georges-Louis Leclerc, a French naturalist, and James Hutton, a Scottish geologist, began to develop new ideas about the age of Earth. At the time, many people thought of Earth as 6,000 years old, based on a strict interpretation of the events detailed in the Christian Old Testament by the influential Scottish Archbishop Ussher. By observing other planets and comets in the solar system, Leclerc hypothesized that Earth began as a hot, fiery ball of molten rock, mostly consisting of iron. Using the cooling rate of iron, Leclerc calculated that Earth must therefore be at least 70,000 years old in order to have reached its present temperature.

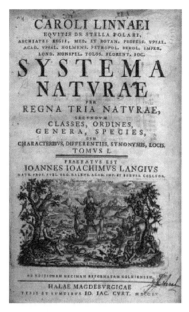

Figure 1: Cover of the 1760 edition of Systema Naturae.

Hutton approached the same topic from a different perspective, gathering observations of the relationships between different rock formations and the rates of modern geological processes near his home in Scotland. He recognized that the relatively slow processes of erosion and sedimentation could not create all of the exposed rock layers in only a few thousand years (see our module The Rock Cycle). Based on his extensive collection of data (just one of his many publications ran to 2,138 pages), Hutton suggested that Earth was far older than human history – hundreds of millions of years old.

While we now know that both Leclerc and Hutton significantly underestimated the age of Earth (by about 4 billion years), their work shattered long-held beliefs and opened a window into research on how life can change over these very long timescales.

Fossil studies lead to the development of a theory of evolution: Cuvier

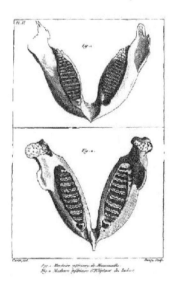

Figure 2: Illustration of an Indian elephant jaw and a mammoth jaw from Cuvier's 1796 paper.

With the age of Earth now extended by Leclerc and Hutton, more researchers began to turn their attention to studying past life. Fossils are the main way to study past life forms, and several key studies on fossils helped in the development of a theory of evolution. In 1795, Georges Cuvier began to work at the National Museum in Paris as a naturalist and anatomist. Through his work, Cuvier became interested in fossils found near Paris, which some claimed were the remains of the elephants that Hannibal rode over the Alps when he invaded Rome in 218 BCE. In studying both the fossils and living species, Cuvier documented different patterns in the dental structure and number of teeth between the fossils and modern elephants (Figure 2) (Horner, 1843). Based on these data, Cuvier hypothesized that the fossil remains were not left by Hannibal, but were from a distinct species of animal that once roamed through Europe and had gone extinct thousands of years earlier: the mammoth. The concept of species extinction had been discussed by a few individuals before Cuvier, but it was in direct opposition to the Fixity of Species concept – if every organism were based on a perfectly adapted, ideal form, how could any cease to exist? That would suggest it was no longer ideal.

While Cuvier's work provided critical evidence of extinction, a key component of evolution, he was highly critical of the idea that species could change over time. As a result of his extensive studies of animal anatomy, Cuvier had developed a holistic view of organisms, stating that the

> number, direction, and shape of the bones that compose each part of an animal's body are always in a necessary relation to all the other parts, in such a way that ... one can infer the whole from any one of them ...

In other words, Cuvier viewed each part of an organism as a unique, essential component of the whole organism. If one part were to change, he believed, the organism could not survive. His skepticism about the ability of organisms to change led him to criticize the whole idea of evolution, and his prominence in France as a scientist played a large role in discouraging the acceptance of the idea in the scientific community.

Studies of invertebrates support a theory of change in species: Lamarck

Jean Baptiste Lamarck was a contemporary of Cuvier's at the National Museum in Paris who studied invertebrates like insects and worms. As Lamarck worked through the museum's large collection of invertebrates, he was impressed by the number and variety of organisms. He became convinced that organisms could, in fact, change through time, stating that

> ...time and favorable conditions are the two principal means which nature has employed in giving existence to all her productions. We know that for her time has no limit, and that consequently she always has it at her disposal.

This was a radical departure from both the fixity concept and Cuvier's ideas, and it built on the long timescale that geologists had recently established. Lamarck proposed that changes that occurred during an organism's lifetime could be passed on to their offspring. This suggests, for example, that a body builder's muscles would be inherited by their children.

As it turned out, the mechanism by which Lamarck proposed that organisms change over time was wrong, and he is now often referred to disparagingly for his "inheritance of acquired characteristics" idea. Yet despite the fact that some of his ideas were discredited, Lamarck established a support for evolutionary theory that others would build on and improve.

Comprehension Checkpoint

To develop theories, scientists most often

A) rely on an accumulation of knowledge developed by many scientists over time.

B) use only their own direct experience and observations.

Rock layers as evidence for evolution: Smith

In the early 1800s, a British geologist and canal surveyor named William Smith added another component to the accumulating evidence for evolution. Smith observed that rock layers exposed in different parts of England bore similarities to one another: these layers (or *strata*) were arranged in a predictable order, and each layer contained distinct groups of fossils. From this series of observations, he developed a hypothesis that specific groups of animals followed one another in a definite sequence through Earth's history, and this sequence could be seen in the rock layers. Smith's hypothesis was based on his knowledge of geological principles, including the Law of Superposition.

The Law of Superposition states that sediments are deposited in a time sequence, with the oldest sediments deposited first, or at the bottom, and newer layers deposited on top. The concept was first expressed by the Persian scientist Avicenna in the 11th century, but was popularized by the Danish scientist Nicolas Steno in the 17th century. Note that the law does not state how sediments are deposited; it simply describes the relationship between the ages of deposited sediments.

Smith backed up his hypothesis with extensive drawings of fossils uncovered during his research (Figure 3), thus allowing other scientists to confirm or dispute his findings. His hypothesis has, in fact, been confirmed by many other scientists and has come to be referred to as the Law of Faunal Succession. His work was critical to the formation of evolutionary theory as it not only confirmed Cuvier's work that organisms have gone extinct, but it also showed that the appearance of life does not date to the birth of the planet. Instead, the fossil record preserves a timeline of the appearance and disappearance of different organisms in the past, and in doing so offers evidence for change in organisms over time.

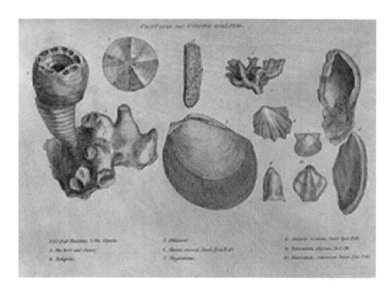

Figure 3: Engraving from William Smith's 1815 monograph on identifying strata by fossils.

The theory of evolution by natural selection: Darwin and Wallace

It was into this world that Charles Darwin entered: Linnaeus had developed a taxonomy of organisms based on their physical relationships, Leclerc and Hutton demonstrated that there was sufficient time in Earth's history for organisms to change, Cuvier showed that species of organisms have gone extinct, Lamarck proposed that organisms change over time, and Smith established a timeline of the appearance and disappearance of different organisms in the geological record.

Charles Darwin collected data during his work as a naturalist on the HMS *Beagle* starting in 1831. He took extensive notes on the geology of the places he visited; he made a major find of fossils of extinct animals in Patagonia and identified an extinct giant ground sloth named *Megatherium*. He experienced an earthquake in Chile that stranded beds of living mussels above water, where they would be preserved for years to come.

Perhaps most famously, he conducted extensive studies of animals on the Galápagos Islands, noting subtle differences in species of mockingbird, tortoise, and finch that were isolated on different islands with different environmental conditions. These subtle differences made the animals highly adapted to their environments.

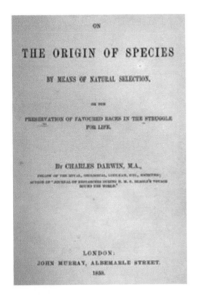

Figure 4: Title page of the 1859 Murray edition of The Origin of Species *by Charles Darwin.*

This broad spectrum of data led Darwin to propose an idea about how organisms change "by means of natural selection" (Figure 4). But this idea was not based only on his work, it was also based on the accumulation of evidence and ideas of many others before him. Because his proposal encompassed and explained many different lines of evidence and previous work, they formed the basis of a new and robust scientific theory regarding change in organisms – the theory of evolution by natural selection.

Darwin's ideas were grounded in evidence and data so compelling that if he had not conceived them, someone else would have. In fact, someone else did. Between 1858 and 1859, Alfred Russel Wallace, a British naturalist, wrote a series of letters to Darwin that independently proposed natural selection as the means for evolutionary change. The letters were presented to the Linnean Society of London, a prominent scientific society at the time (see our module on Scientific Institutions and Societies). This long chain of research highlights that theories are not just the work of one individual. At the same time, however, it often takes the insight and creativity of individuals to put together all of the pieces and propose a new theory. Both Darwin and Wallace were experienced naturalists who were familiar with the work of others. While all of the work leading up to 1830 contributed to the theory of evolution, Darwin's and Wallace's theory changed the way that future research was focused by presenting a comprehensive, well-substantiated set of ideas, thus becoming a fundamental theory of biological research.

Expanding, testing, and refining scientific theories

Genetics and evolution: Mendel and Dobzhansky

Since Darwin and Wallace first published their ideas, extensive research has tested and expanded the theory of evolution by natural selection. Darwin had no concept of genes or DNA or the mechanism by which characteristics were inherited within a species. A contemporary of Darwin's, the Austrian monk Gregor Mendel, first presented his own landmark study *Experiments in Plant Hybridization* in 1865, in which he provided the basic patterns of genetic inheritance, describing which characteristics (and evolutionary changes) can be passed on in organisms (see our Genetics I module for more information). Still, it wasn't until much later that a "gene" was defined as the heritable unit.

In 1937, the Ukrainian born geneticist Theodosius Dobzhansky published *Genetics and the Origin of Species*, a seminal work in which he described genes themselves and demonstrated that it is through mutations in genes that change occurs. The work defined evolution as "a change in the frequency of an allele within a gene pool" (Dobzhansky, 1982). These studies and others in the field of genetics have added to Darwin's work, expanding the scope of the theory.

Evolution under a microscope: Lenski

More recently, Dr. Richard Lenski, a scientist at Michigan State University, isolated a single *Escherichia coli* bacterium in 1989 as the first step of the longest running experimental test of evolutionary theory to date – a true test meant to replicate evolution and natural selection in the lab.

After the single microbe had multiplied, Lenski isolated the offspring into 12 different strains, each in their own glucose-supplied culture, predicting that the genetic make-up of each strain would change over time to become more adapted to their specific culture as predicted by evolutionary theory. These 12 lines have been nurtured for over 40,000 bacterial generations (luckily bacterial generations are much shorter than human generations) and exposed to different selective pressures such as heat, cold, antibiotics, and infection with other microorganisms. Lenski and colleagues have studied dozens of aspects of evolutionary theory with these genetically isolated populations. In 1999, they published a paper that demonstrated that random genetic mutations were common within the populations and highly diverse across different individual bacteria. However, "pivotal" mutations that are associated with beneficial changes in the group are shared by all descendants in a population and are much rarer than random mutations, as predicted by the theory of evolution by natural selection (Papadopoulos et al., 1999).

Punctuated equilibrium: Gould and Eldredge

While established scientific theories like evolution have a wealth of research and evidence supporting them, this does not mean that they cannot be refined as new information or new perspectives on existing data become available. For example, in 1972, biologist Stephen Jay Gould and paleontologist Niles Eldredge took a fresh look at the existing data regarding the timing by which evolutionary change takes place. Gould and Eldredge did not set out to challenge the theory of evolution; rather they used it as a guiding principle and asked more specific questions to add detail and nuance to the theory. This is true of all theories in science: they provide a framework for additional research. At the time, many biologists viewed evolution as occurring gradually, causing small incremental changes in organisms at a relatively steady rate. The idea is referred to as *phyletic gradualism*, and is rooted in the geological concept of uniformitarianism. After reexamining the available data, Gould and Eldredge came to a different explanation, suggesting that evolution consists of long periods of stability that are punctuated by occasional instances of dramatic change – a process they called *punctuated equilibrium*.

Like Darwin before them, their proposal is rooted in evidence and research on evolutionary change, and has been supported by multiple lines of evidence. In fact, punctuated equilibrium is now considered its own theory in evolutionary biology. Punctuated equilibrium is not as broad of a theory as natural selection. In science, some theories are broad and overarching of many concepts, such as the theory of evolution by natural selection; others focus on concepts at a smaller, or more targeted, scale such as punctuated equilibrium. And punctuated equilibrium does not challenge or weaken the concept of natural selection; rather it represents a change in our understanding of the timing by which change occurs in organisms, and a theory within a theory. The theory of evolution by natural selection now includes both gradualism and punctuated equilibrium to describe the rate at which change proceeds.

Hypotheses and Laws: Other scientific concepts

One of the challenges in understanding scientific terms like *theory* is that there is not a precise definition even within the scientific community. Some scientists debate over whether certain proposals merit designation as a hypothesis or theory, and others mistakenly use the terms interchangeably. But there are differences in these terms. A hypothesis is a proposed explanation for an observable phenomenon. Hypotheses, just like theories, are based on observations from research. For example, LeClerc did not hypothesize that Earth had cooled from a molten ball of iron as a random guess; rather he developed this hypothesis based on his observations of information from meteorites.

A scientist often proposes a hypothesis before research confirms it as a way of predicting the outcome of study to help better define the parameters of the research. LeClerc's hypothesis allowed him to use known parameters (the cooling rate of iron) to do additional work. A key component of a formal scientific hypothesis is that it is testable and falsifiable. For example, when Richard Lenski first isolated his 12 strains of bacteria, he likely hypothesized that random mutations would cause differences to appear within a period of time in the different strains of bacteria. But when a hypothesis is generated in science, a scientist will also make an *alternative hypothesis*, an explanation that explains a study if the data do not support the original hypothesis. If the different strains of bacteria in Lenski's work did not diverge over the indicated period of time, perhaps the rate of mutation was slower than first thought.

So you might ask, if theories are so well supported, do they eventually become laws? The answer is no – not because they aren't well-supported, but because theories and laws are two very different things. Laws *describe* phenomena, often mathematically. Theories, however, *explain* phenomena. For example, in 1687 Isaac Newton proposed a Theory of Gravitation, describing gravity as a force of attraction between two objects. As part of this theory, Newton developed a Law of Universal Gravitation that explains how this force operates. This law states that the force of gravity between two objects is inversely proportional to the square of the distance between those objects. Newton's Law does not explain why this is true, but it describes how gravity functions (see our Gravity: Newtonian Relationships module for more detail). In 1916, Albert Einstein developed his theory of general relativity to explain the mechanism by which gravity has its effect. Einstein's work challenges Newton's theory, and has been found after extensive testing and research to more accurately describe the phenomenon of gravity. While Einstein's work has replaced Newton's as the dominant explanation of gravity in modern science, Newton's Law of Universal Gravitation is still used as it reasonably (and more simply) describes the force of gravity under many conditions. Similarly the Law of Faunal Succession developed by William Smith does not explain why organisms follow each other in distinct, predictable ways in the rock layers, but it accurately describes the phenomenon.

Theories, hypotheses, and laws drive scientific progress

Theories, hypotheses, and laws are not simply important components of science, they drive scientific progress. For example, evolutionary biology now stands as a distinct field of science that focuses on the origins and descent of species. Geologists now rely on plate tectonics as a conceptual model and guiding theory when they are studying processes at work in Earth's crust. And physicists refer to atomic theory when they are predicting the existence of sub-atomic particles yet to be discovered. This does not mean that science is "finished," or that all of the important theories have been discovered already. Like evolution, progress in science happens both gradually and in short, dramatic bursts. Both types of progress are critical for creating a robust knowledge base with data as the foundation and scientific theories giving structure to that knowledge.

References

Cook, H., & Bestman, H. D. (2000). A Persistent View: Lamarckian Thought in Early Evolutionary Theories and in Modern Biology. *Perspectives on Science and Christian Faith,* 52, 86-97.

Dobzhansky, T. G. (1982). *Genetics and the Origin of Species*: Columbia University Press.

Gould, S. J. (2002). *The Structure of Evolutionary Theory*: Belknap Press.

Horner, W. E. (1843). Remarks on the Dental System of the Mastodon, with an Account of Some Lower Jaws in Mr. Koch's Collection, St. Louis, Missouri, Where There Is a Solitary Tusk on the Right Side. *Transactions of the American Philosophical Society*, 8, 53-59.

Johnson, S. (2008). *The invention of air: a story of science, faith, revolution, and the birth of America*. New York: Riverhead Books.

Papadopoulos, D., Schneider, D., Meier-Eiss, J., Arber, W., Lenski, R. E., & Blot, M. (1999). Genomic evolution during a 10,000-generation experiment with bacteria (Vol. 96, pp. 3807-3812): *National Acad Sciences.*

Key Concepts for this chapter

▶ A scientific theory is an explanation inferred from multiple lines of evidence for some broad aspect of the natural world and is logical, testable, and predictive.

▶ As new evidence comes to light, or new interpretations of existing data are proposed, theories may be revised and even change; however, they are not tenuous or speculative.

▶ A scientific hypothesis is an inferred explanation of an observation or research finding; while more exploratory in nature than a theory, it is based on existing scientific knowledge.

▶ A scientific law is an expression of a mathematical or descriptive relationship observed in nature.

 *Take the Quiz* ▶ ▶ ▶

Theories, Hypotheses, and Laws Quiz

1. What is the best definition of the term "theory," as it is used in science?

   A) A theory is a guess or hunch about something that has occurred in nature.

   B) A theory is a comprehensive set of ideas explaining a phenomenon in nature.

   C) A theory is based on verifiable laws and can be proven true.

   D) A theory is a hypothesis that uses laws and observation to make an assumption.

2. While speaking to a colleague, a scientist makes the following statement: "I propose that Bald Eagle eggs in northern Maine will have thinner shells than those from birds in southern Alaska due to increased levels of pesticides in the water." This statement is a

   A) theory.

   B) law.

   C) conclusion.

   D) hypothesis.

3. Scientific theories can be tested.

   A) True

   B) False

4. Complete the following sentence so that it is correct: Scientific theories are based on

   A) general assumptions of how systems work.

   B) mathematical principles that can be proven true.

   C) large amounts of data collected over time.

   D) observations from within only one scientific discipline.

5. Why are scientific theories an important part of research and understanding?

   A) Scientific theories allow scientists to make predictions.

   B) Scientific theories allow scientists to ignore data.

   C) Scientific theories determine the work that future scientists can do.

   D) Scientific theories determine the subjects that scientists research.

6. Scientific theories do not change once they have been written down.

   A) True

   B) False

7. Which statement below correctly identifies the difference between laws and theories?

   A) Laws describe phenomena, while theories explain why phenomena exist.

   B) Laws are a statement of fact, while theories are a statement of opinion.

   C) Laws explain why phenomena exist, while theories explain how.

   D) Laws are a prediction of phenomena, while theories are an explanation.

Quiz continues on next page ▶ ▶ ▶

8. Why do scientists develop a hypothesis before conducting research?

A) It gives them direction on how to interpret the results of their research.

B) It helps to predict outcomes and define the parameters of the research.

C) Hypotheses give the researcher an outcome to shape their work around.

D) Hypotheses help a researcher decide which observations to record and ignore.

9. Scientific theories are always broad and cover many concepts.

A) True

B) False

10. Choose the sentence below that is a correct description of scientific theory.

A) Scientific theories in one discipline can influence theories in other disciplines.

B) Theories in one scientific discipline do not affect theories in other disciplines.

C) New scientific theories are always original and do not connect to those that came before.

D) Creativity and insight are not important parts of developing new scientific theories.

Answers and feedback can be found on Page 277

Charles Darwin I: The Origin of Species

by Alfred Rosenberger, PhD

Did you know that the theory of evolution did not begin with Charles Darwin? The idea of evolution was part of Western thought for more than 2,000 years before Darwin changed the world with his legendary book *On the Origin of Species.*

Module Summary

The experiences and observations of Charles Darwin significantly contributed to his theory of evolution through natural selection. This module explores those influences and describes evolution as a force for biological change and diversification. The first in a series, it details how the theory challenged the cultural mindset of the time, including the effect of his major works: *On the Origin of Species by Means of Natural Selection* and *Sexual Selection and the Descent of Man.*

Terms you should know:

origin = source; starting point

species = a distinct variety of animal or plant that breed only among their own kind

naturalist = a person who studies the natural world

Few people have changed the world with the power of an idea. Charles Darwin, the British naturalist who lived during the 1800s, was one of them. While we might equate the idea of evolution with other revolutionary scientific breakthroughs, such as Einstein's general theory of relativity, people seem to care less about what it means to live in a universe where the speed of light is fixed than in a world in which humans descended from hairy apes.

That is a tricky question because of its implications about the very nature of life, humanity, and religion. It is the reason why some greet Darwin's name with a gut-level sense of distrust even though his contributions to our understanding of life are as solidly confirmed as are Einstein's contributions to our understanding of the universe. So, it is no surprise that more people have an inkling – too often wrong – of what is meant by Darwin's concept of natural selection than by the terms of Einstein's famous equation $E = mc^2$.

Darwin's legendary book, *On the Origin of Species by Means of Natural Selection; or, the Preservation of Favoured Races in the Struggle for Life*, is frequently listed as one of the greatest books ever written. The three critical ideas he developed in it are:

- The fact that evolution occurs.

- The theory that natural selection is the driving force or mechanism behind the process of evolution.

- The concept of phylogeny, that all forms of life are related to one another genealogically, through their pedigree or "family's roots."

Darwin began developing these ideas as a result of his experiences during a five-year voyage on the British survey vessel HMS *Beagle*, which sailed around the world on a mapping expedition during the early 1830s. Darwin was on board to work as the ship's naturalist, to record information about the geology, sea life, land animals and plants, and people that the *Beagle* would discover. When he set sail in 1831, Darwin was twenty-two years old, fresh out of college, fascinated with science, and deeply interested in geology and natural history. He was planning to become a clergyman, partly because he thought it would allow him enough free time to pursue his other interests.

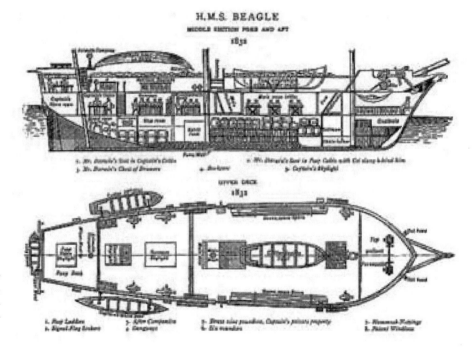

Figure 1: *The HMS* Beagle, *a 90.3 ft, 10 gun brig-sloop of the British Royal Navy. Image courtesy of Special Collections, University of Houston Libraries.*

Comprehension Checkpoint

One of the main ideas of Darwins' book *On the Origins of Species* was that all forms of life share family roots.

A) True

B) False

Ideas about evolution through history

Darwin was keenly aware that the idea of evolution was in the air and was being hotly debated in some circles. Actually, it had been part of Western thought for more than 2,000 years, at least since the Greek philosopher Aristotle proposed there were natural laws that explained how the world came to be. These laws were meant to be alternatives to the usual myths and stories about the origins of the universe and of people that all native cultures seem to generate. Some of Aristotle's proposals were quite specific. He believed, for example, that there were "higher" species and also "lower" species, and the lower ones gave rise to the higher.

As Europe emerged from the Middle Ages, scientists interested in biology considered evolution an idea of historical importance. One of Darwin's own grandfathers, Dr. Erasmus Darwin, had even written extensively about evolution. But what changed the climate of Darwin's times was that the natural sciences were becoming modernized and professionalized, with their own societies, meetings, and publications. This allowed the fuzzy notion of evolution to rise to the level of a scientific hypothesis, which might be proven or disproven by research, evidence, and a method of reasoning.

Evolution vs. fixity

As the mid 1800s approached, the idea of evolution posed a serious challenge to the then-popular view that species were unchanging fixtures of nature. This concept, called the Fixity of Species, was a perspective that European zoologists and botanists adopted as part of their culture, to reflect Western religion and the story of creation as laid out in the Bible. A key feature of the scientific argument for "fixity" was the notion that the structure of each species was based on a model, ideal form. In other words, botanists would make the case that all wild briar roses were supposed to look like replicas of one another because a wild briar rose was meant to be built in a precise, definite way or it would not be a wild briar rose. Why? Because each wild briar rose was a product of God's "perfect" acts of creation. And if each was meant to be perfect, there was no reason for any to change, and no possibility that they ever did.

The fixity idea, however, was not satisfactory to all. Some geologists and zoologists thought that species might actually change over time. In fact, the possibility of evolution being a fundamental feature of nature eventually became the crucial question of 19th century science. One of the reasons why this happened was that fossils were slowly being discovered, some in highly "imperfect" environments that seemed not to follow the logic of creation – such as the occurrence of ocean seashells found buried on the tops of mountains such as the Alps and the Himalayas.

Darwin allowed himself to wonder if species were fixed or prone to evolution. With the intense experience of five years of living and working on the *Beagle*, collecting and describing a vast number and variety of natural history specimens, he developed into a first-rate naturalist – actually, the best in the world. He came to see species differently than those who saw perfec-

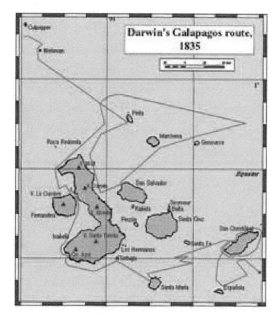

Figure 2: *The* Beagle's *route through the Galapagos in 1835. Red triangles indicate volcanic peaks on the islands. Darwin's observations of differences between animals inhabiting the different islands in the archipelago was instrumental to his development of his theory of evolution.*

tion in them. Darwin did not focus on the sameness of individuals; rather, he thought it was important that individuals, like you and me, vary in spite of the fact that we belong to the same species. He realized that the variations could become the raw material for evolutionary change.

Comprehension Checkpoint

In Darwin's day, most people believed that

A) plants and animals changed in structure over time as they adapt to their environment.

B) each species was based on a perfect model so there was no reason or possibility to change.

Clues to evolution: Birds and fossils

One of the clues that moved Darwin to totally accept the principle of evolution involved a group of small birds called mockingbirds. Mockingbirds are unspectacular animals with a wingspan of about 10 inches. They live in many habitats in North, Central, and South America, from southern Canada to Chile and Argentina. Darwin observed and collected them on the Galapagos, a cluster of small islands off the coast of Ecuador, and sent his specimens back to London for study.

After the voyage, Darwin consulted one of the most experienced ornithologists (bird specialists) in England, John Gould, about their taxonomy (see our Taxonomy I module). Darwin was surprised to learn that he had misclassified some of the birds because it was difficult for him to tell the species apart from the subspecies. The physical traits of mockingbird species and subspecies blended into one another. For Darwin, this meant that the guidelines he had been trained to use to identify and classify animal and plant species, based on the idea that each one ought to have an idealized "perfect" form – Fixity of Species – was an arbitrary rule created by taxonomists, nothing more than an untested assumption. It logically followed that if species were not designed to be a series of perfect individual replicates, then evolutionary change – or "transmutation" of one species into another – was a possibility. Darwin saw immediately that some of Gould's species could have come into existence if one subspecies changed a little bit more than usual, perhaps as it got isolated on a separate island.

A second clue that led Darwin to embrace evolution had to do with fossils. Fossils are formed when an organism dies and its remains become hardened by absorbing minerals from the earth in which they were buried. Thus, fossils are direct evidence of life in the past and have great importance when considering a time-dependent concept such as evolution. In Argentina, Darwin collected fossils of gigantic armor-plated beasts, megatheres, which were unlike anything else anywhere in the world – nearly. Only the tank-like armadillos, which Darwin had also seen in South America, bore any resemblance to them. Considering these extinct and living forms together, Darwin theorized that megatheres and armadillos might be related. He thought they might be part of a large group of South American mammals that had evolved body armor as a protective adaptation. He speculated that an ancient "cousin" of the megatheres might have been the ancestor of the armadillo.

The Galapagos mockingbirds and the Argentine megatheres provided Darwin with two complementary views of evolution. One helped him picture biological change by comparing living animals. The other helped him see it by comparing an extinct species with one that was living. Darwin collected pieces of the evolutionary puzzle during his five years of sailing on the *Beagle*, but to solve the puzzle by putting the pieces together into a basic model for the public to see would take him several more decades of effort. His work was capped by publication of *Origins* in 1859, more than twenty years after he began his voyage on the *Beagle*.

Response to *Origins*

Origins was immediately recognized as a major scientific success. In one of the quirkiest episodes in the history of science, this happened to be the second time that Darwin published his explanation of evolution. A year earlier, Darwin learned that another naturalist, Alfred Russell Wallace, had also thought of evolution by natural selection, and they eventually wrote a joint paper on the subject in order to share the credit. But the Darwin-Wallace essay did not compare with *Origins*, which included examples and reasoning that Darwin developed over a twenty-year period. *Origins* was much more than a statement on the controversial idea of evolution; it laid out a new system of thought, another way of asking scientific questions, assembling scientific evidence, and scientifically testing hypotheses.

Some people were less than happy with the book's publication. Since its central idea was that evolution is an ever-present, unstoppable, fundamental law of nature, *Origins* became an angry flashpoint for those who cared less about the biological history of animals and plants than they cared about the deeper implications of the really big idea it represented – that in the middle 1800s there were new, logically sound, evidence-based ways of looking at life that challenged the religious ways of thinking that had been broadly accepted for centuries.

This makes it all the more interesting that the "Question of Questions" was not at all touched on in *Origins*. Darwin knew all along that this new science of evolutionary biology could be applied to human beings precisely the way he had applied it to mockingbirds and armadillos. Like the mockingbirds, people vary in appearance across countries and continents, and from one island to another. Like the armadillos and megatheres, the skeletons of modern humans closely resemble extinct fossils then being discovered in the Neander Valley of Germany, fossils that would come to be known as Neanderthal man. Darwin said nothing about this in *Origins* for, in his extraordinary thoroughness, he wasn't ready yet. He was also unprepared for the difficult personal battle that would have resulted if he had.

Comprehension Checkpoint

When Darwin's book *On the Origin of Species* was published,

A) it was immediately accepted, by scientists and non-scientists alike, as scientific fact.

B) it made some people angry because the idea of evolution challenged the religious thinking of the day.

About twelve years later, in 1871, Darwin did publish a book specifically about human evolution, *Sexual Selection and the Descent of Man.* By then, the fury against his ideas had died down in England, and evolution was not a hotly contested issue any longer. By then, other highly accomplished scientists had written about people evolving, most notably Thomas Henry Huxley, in *Evidence as to Man's Place in Nature*, which appeared in 1863. The idea was slowly being absorbed by society. But nothing could match Darwin's brilliant thinking about the evolutionary process, so no one could match what Darwin would have to say about the subject of man.

Descent of Man was as much about bringing out the few facts then known about human evolution as it was about the meaning of evolution as a way of thinking about our ethics and personal values. Darwin knew that evolution was one of the most important ideas for the human species to comprehend. He knew that seeing us from an evolutionary perspective was more than peering through a telescope to look back at our own primitive origins. Evolution was also a mirror and a microscope for looking at ourselves as we are today.

Key Concepts for this chapter

▶ Charles Darwin played a key role in supporting and explaining the theory of evolution through natural selection.

▶ Darwin's skills of observation and ability to record data accurately allowed him to create a comprehensive model of the mechanism by which evolution occurs.

▶ The theory of evolution through natural selection explains how all forms of life are related to one another genealogically, and emphasizes that variation within a species is the root for evolutionary change.

Take the Quiz ▶ ▶ ▶

Charles Darwin I Quiz

1. *On the Origin of Species* was written in what decade?

    A) 1830s

    B) 1850s

    C) 1870s

    D) 1890s

2. Which of the following was NOT an important theme of *Origins*?

    A) phylogenetic relationships

    B) natural selection

    C) recapitulation

    D) adaptation

3. Darwin's great work of 1871 about the origins of humans was called

    A) *Evidence of Man's Place in Nature*

    B) *Sexual Selection and the Descent of Man*

    C) *Origins of the Human Species*

    D) *On the Origins of Species by Means of Natural Selection*

4. Nineteenth-century creationists interpreted the individuals of species as exact replicas, whereas Darwin saw them as having variability

    A) True

    B) False

5. One key feature of Darwin's theory of natural selection was that

    A) the structure of every species is based on a model, ideal form.

    B) there is no possibility that species change over time.

    C) members of the same species show variability within a population.

    D) only some species are able to change over time.

6. Why was Darwin's contribution to the theory of evolution so important?

    A) Darwin was able to put his research and observations into a basic model that the public would understand.

    B) Darwin was able to prove to the public that the Fixity of Species concept was not correct.

    C) Darwin was the first person to propose the idea of evolution and the first to publish a paper on the topic.

    D) Darwin was able to travel to places no one had ever seen before and document the organisms that lived there.

7. Which statement best explains why Darwin avoided discussing human beings in *Origins*?

    A) He understood that natural selection does not apply to human beings.

    B) He believed that Fixity of Species explained how humans came to exist.

    C) He had not completed his explanation on how humans had evolved.

    D) He was afraid of the response he would get from religious groups.

Answers and feedback can be found on Page 279

Charles Darwin II: Natural Selection

by Alfred L. Rosenberger, PhD

> Did you know that Darwin's experience with his ten children fueled his thinking about evolution? He theorized that some human behaviors, such as a young child's selfishness, were based upon instincts that were adaptations. These natural differences that always exist among individuals are at the heart of the principle of natural selection as the engine of evolutionary change.

Module Summary

The second in a series discussing the work of Charles Darwin, this module takes a deeper look into the processes that led to Darwin's theory of natural selection and examines specific mechanisms that drive evolutionary change. Key points on which the idea of natural selection rests are outlined. Examples from Darwin's personal life shed light on his thinking about change within a species and the "struggle for existence."

Terms you should know:

population = all individuals of a certain kind of plant or animal that live in a particular habitat

species = a distinct variety of animal or plant that can produce offspring among its kind

bred (past tense and past participle of the verb breed) = mated to ensure offspring of a certain kind to promote certain characteristics

breed (noun) = a group of related plants or animals that share most characteristics, such as a breed of dog

How Charles Darwin came to understand evolution is a fascinating and important story. In our Charles Darwin I module, we focused on how he arrived at an alternative to the idea that each species was uniquely created and unchangeable. Here we look more closely at how Darwin came to propose the mechanism of evolutionary change, which he called "natural selection." Natural selection is the force that promotes changes in a species over generations. It is also the force that produces new species from the changes that accumulate in a population over long periods of time.

Darwin learned the importance of natural selection in bits and pieces as he developed his scientific skills and credentials. He lived during one of the most interesting times, the heyday of Great Britain's Victorian era, from 1809 to 1882, when the sciences, and openness to questioning the status quo, were growing cultural forces. He had a long, productive, brilliant career, and was almost famous even before returning from his five-year voyage around the world on the HMS *Beagle*. Luckily, his correspondence, diaries, and personal workbooks, as well as the writings of his relatives, friends, colleagues, and rivals, document Darwin's adult life extensively. They tell us that every facet of the man reflected his passion for the patterns of evolution, its rules and consequences. Once he fully grasped how it worked, Darwin's life became so steeped in thinking about evolution that today we might call his fascination an obsession.

Darwin builds on the ideas of others

Figure 1: *The title page of Darwin's most famous book,* On the Origin of Species by Means of Natural Selection.

Although we properly credit Darwin with being the founding father of evolutionary theory, one of his own great gifts was being able to spot a good idea and synthesize information from many fields of knowledge. Darwin's success was due, in part, to having learned from others, just as the great physicist Isaac Newton claimed to have stood "on the shoulders of giants."

Thus, to develop the concept of evolution by natural selection Darwin did not have to invent the idea that animals and plants were adapted to their environment, because that was already recognized in the late 1700s. He did not have to buck the Biblical story of a seven-day creation because the father of modern geology, Charles Lyell, had already shown that the earth's history extended over at least millions of years, not the thousands implied by the Bible. Darwin did not even have to come up with the idea of natural selection by himself – it was inspired by someone else! Another Englishman, Thomas Robert Malthus, who was a clergyman and an economist, wrote *Essay on the Principle of Population* in 1798. Malthus argued (from an economic standpoint) that human population growth, if it were not reigned in by disease, starvation, war, and other factors, would naturally expand beyond our capacity to produce the food we need to sustain it. In other words, societies of people also are locked in a "struggle for existence." In his autobiography, Charles Darwin acknowledges this thought as the beginnings of natural selection:

> In October 1838, that is, fifteen months after I had begun my systematic inquiry, I happened to read for amusement Malthus on *Population*, and being well prepared to appreciate the struggle for existence which everywhere goes on from long- continued observation of the habits of animals and plants, it at once struck me that under these circumstances favourable variations would tend to be preserved, and unfavourable ones to be destroyed. The results of this would be the formation of a new species. Here, then I had at last got a theory by which to work.

Charles Darwin, 1876

Comprehension Checkpoint

Darwin is credited as being the first person to recognize that plants and animals adapt to their environment.

A) True

B) False

Darwin learns from research and life experience

After his famous five-year voyage around the world on the Beagle, most of Darwin's life was spent at his home on the outskirts of London, which he used as a base of scientific operations. His efforts involved much more than writing about big ideas like natural selection. He worked hard to build his knowledge of all manners of animals and plants from the ground up, learning lessons from many diverse research projects that were always underway in the Darwin household. Many of them might seem small and trivial, but they left him with enormous insight and they added up to a vast body of experience that earned Darwin a great reputation among the public, as well as among scientists from many different fields. Darwin pioneered studies of barnacles, coral reefs, hybridization between species, orchid fertilization, human origins, animal behavior, and other topics that are now basic to oceanography, botany, genetics, ecology, geology, and psychology.

Figure 2: Down House - Charles Darwin's home and research laboratory.

With his interest in the behaviors of organisms, even Darwin's family life provided lessons about evolution. While he was a doting father to all of his ten children, he also studied them carefully for clues about how nature gave way to nurture. From watching them he theorized that some human behaviors, such as a young child's selfishness, were based upon instincts that were adaptations, while other behaviors were learned, shaped by culture. The death of one of his daughters, Annie, at the age of ten was also a painful reminder to Darwin that all species are captives of their environment and undergo a "struggle for existence" during each generation. Disease was an environmental hazard to all individuals, a potential obstacle to their success. Some individuals were better able to cope with disease than others, just as some are better able to escape predation. Some won and some lost; some grew up and others did not; some lived to have many children while others had few or none. These natural differences that always exist among individuals are at the heart of the principle of natural selection as the engine of evolutionary change.

Figure 3: Annie Darwin (March 2, 1841 to April 23, 1851), the second child and eldest daughter of Charles and Emma Darwin.

Comprehension Checkpoint

In Darwin's family life, he found

A) lessons about evolution as he studied his children's behavior.

B) no connection to his ideas about evolution and the "struggle for survival."

Fundamentals of natural selection

The idea of natural selection rests on several key points:

- More individuals are born to a species in every generation than actually live to reproduce.

- All individuals differ in structure and behavior, and many of these variations are inherited.

- Some individuals have a greater ability to survive and reproduce than do others because their inherited traits are better adapted to the conditions of the environment than the other traits present in different individuals of the same population.

- Because the rate at which offspring are produced in every species is greater than the rate at which the environment can provide food, shelter, and other needs, individuals who carry the advantageous traits will come to outnumber those without them, causing a shift in the common characteristics of the species over time.

That shift is a change, an evolutionary adjustment that takes place across generational time. The process behind it is natural selection. Darwin chose the term because the process works much like "artificial selection," the methods people have long used to produce and maintain the breeds of animals and plants that we live with. Both rely on *differential reproduction* to have an effect. That is, both promote the reproduction of certain members of a population with a desirable set of characteristics. For example, dogs are commonly bred to be protective but not overly aggressive. Eventually, those traits become established as key features of the breed or population.

Figure 4: Dogs with different traits. The collie (left) is frequently used to herd sheep and other livestock. They are bred for their thick coats, which protect them from injury and from intemperate weather while they work, and for their intelligence. The Dalmatian (middle) is similarly intelligent, and is bred for its distinctive black and white coat. The dachshund (right) is a short-legged, elongated dog, originally bred to chase rabbits and other small game living in burrows.

Unlike artificial selection, natural selection is ever present, ongoing, long term, and utterly beyond human control or prediction. After all, there is no telling what new disease might pop up to threaten a population, how severe a drought might be to limit the food supply during a bad summer, or if the predator from the next valley should decide to swim the river and hunt in a new territory just when vulnerable babies are being born. At the same time, there is no telling how well a species can resist the disease, how many nearly starved individuals are able to travel a long distance to the next food-rich plateau, or how clever some individuals might be in protecting their kids from the new carnivore that is tracking them.

Archaeologists have shown that artificial selection of animals and plants has been going on for at least 10,000 years. But Darwin knew that the earth was far older than that - at least millions of years old - thus a lot of change can accumulate in a species through natural selection. In some years, food may be abundant and disease rate low, so the environment exerts less of a "pruning" effect on individuals. A species' total population size may then grow unchecked. However, this means that more individuals who are less fit for lean times will survive, and selective pressure, the forces that shape reproductive success, will be greater when conditions shift. So, it is difficult to tell what types of traits will be favored by natural selection in the long run.

Comprehension Checkpoint

Selective pressure weeds out traits that do not help a species to

A) understand its heritage.

B) survive and reproduce.

The scientific method has its own ways of pruning, as lesser ideas are separated from good ones that explain the data in better ways. The idea of natural selection has survived many tests and challenges as progress in many fields leapt far beyond what was known in Darwin's day. One might have guessed, for example, that the principle of natural selection would fail when we finally learned the basics of heredity decades after *Origin* was published: Darwin didn't have a clue how traits were passed down across the generations. Yet the theory still stands. For every decade that passes, it only becomes stronger as genetics, molecular biology, geology, paleontology, and other disciplines continue to explain phenomena new and old without having to invent another evolutionary mechanism to replace natural selection.

Key Concepts for this chapter

▶ Variation within a species increases the likelihood that at least some members of a population will survive under changed environmental conditions.

▶ The common characteristics of individuals within a population will often change over time, as those with advantageous traits come to be most common or widespread.

▶ While evidence of evolution by natural selection exists, its effects cannot be predicted.

Take the Quiz ▶ ▶ ▶

Charles Darwin II Quiz

1. Ecological adaptations can become widely spread within a wild population by
   A) differential reproduction.
   B) artificial selection.
   C) discretionary breeding.
   D) genetic mutations.

2. The forces that shape reproductive success are called
   A) selective pressures.
   B) adaptations.
   C) population drive.
   D) struggles for existence.

3. The difference between the number of individuals born in a population and the number that actually reproduce suggests that adaptation is at work.
   A) True
   B) False

4. Although we know that natural selection is always there, we can't ____ its effect.
   A) measure
   B) predict
   C) deny
   D) reconstruct

5. Choose the BEST option to complete this sentence: Darwin suggested that the physical characteristics of a population will change over time because
   A) disease will kill off a portion of the population before they are able to reproduce.
   B) those with the traits best suited to the environment will survive to reproduce.
   C) the number of offspring born in a population will increase over time.
   D) physical variation occurs naturally in any given population.

6. When environmental change occurs, those with the traits best suited to the new environment will have the greatest chance of survival.
   A) True
   B) False

7. Why is it impossible to predict how natural selection will effect a population?
   A) It is impossible to know which traits serve certain functions.
   B) It is impossible to know how other factors might affect the population.
   C) It is impossible to tell the individuals within a population apart.
   D) It is impossible to tell how the population will interact with the environment.

Answers and feedback can be found on Page 280

Charles Darwin III: Descent with Modification

by Alfred L. Rosenberger, PhD

Did you know that Charles Darwin preferred the phrase *descent with modification* over the simpler term *evolution*? In his groundbreaking book *On the Origin of Species*, Darwin chose his words very carefully. "Evolution" was used in different ways at the time, and Darwin wanted to convey the important concept that life forms descended from a common ancestor.

Module Summary

Our understanding of the term *evolution* has changed significantly since Darwin's time. This module explains how Darwin's work helped to give evolution the meaning it has today. It details the concept of "descent with modification" that Darwin described with the one figure originally included in *Origin of Species.* The module discusses how this model revolutionized scientific thinking about the similarities and differences between and within species, laying the foundation for our current understanding of biodiversity.

Terms you should know:

adaptations = changes that allow an organism to function better in a particular environment

descent = ancestry or heritage

origin = source, starting point

The first edition of Charles Darwin's groundbreaking book, *On the Origin of Species by Means of Natural Selection*, had only one illustration in it – a picture of a family tree, or descent, also called phylogeny. For the book publisher, this must have been an expensive investment and a somewhat worrying choice. The diagram was printed on oversized paper that had to be unfolded out of the volume to be seen, an expensive printing task. In addition, to have a single drawing in a book was unusual in the middle 1800s because realistic illustrations of plants and animals were considered to be highly artistic. Illustrations were an important selling point of popular books about natural history such as *Origin*, a non-technical work written for the general public to read. Yet, all 1,250 copies of *Origin* sold in a day. For Darwin to have placed only a single picture in the book, he must have considered it crucial to his discussion.

Darwin's single picture was a chart, not a portrait of exotic species or even a map (you can view this chart in the online version of this module). With it, Darwin sought to explain a new concept in science: how various pieces of biology fit together to explain the origins and evolution of species. This involved many details and a lot of ideas. His one drawing was meant to illustrate all of the following:

- How natural selection works over generations to promote structural variation in the physical form or behavior of an organism.

- How these variations accumulate to change a species over time.

- How populations within a species tend to become different from one another.

- How structural change eventually produces new species.

- How several species can arise over time from a single ancestral species.

- How a new genus can evolve from a line of new species.

- How extinction is a natural part of the evolutionary process.

- How all species are actually related to one another.

- How clusters of similar species can form because they have a common origin.

Evolution is a complex, multi-faceted process, and this list is a complex set of ideas to relate. So it is no wonder Darwin focused on producing a graphic to help explain them to the world. He also wrote about five pages explaining how the diagram was to be read.

Darwin chose his words carefully. Here and elsewhere in *Origin* he used a certain phrase – "descent with modification" – over and over again as an expression for "evolution." Why this instead of the simple one-word term "evolution"? Part of the answer must be that evolution was a still a fuzzy concept, and it was Darwin's job to make it clear.

"Evolution" vs. "descent with modification"

At that time, scientists were commonly using the term evolution in discussing physical growth, the changes an individual goes through as one matures. The other meaning of evolution referred to structural change in a species that took place over time, which some, including Darwin, also called *transmutation*. So, there was a reason for his preference for "descent with modification" over "evolution." First, he wanted to make clear that his discussion of evolution dealt with transmutation (modification), not growth and development. Second, Darwin meant to emphasize that the big picture of biological evolution was far more complicated than the image of the fur of a fox transmuting from reddish brown to white as an adaptation to life in the Arctic. It also involved the production of a pedigree that linked species because they are genetically related, through the process of descent.

The concept of phylogenetic descent was a new idea that made Darwin's theories of evolution more sensible than previous proposals that tried to explain certain observations. For many decades before *Origin* appeared, natural scientists had wrestled with a puzzling problem of biodiversity. While taxonomists who classified organisms never intended to find patterns, it was clear to all those who studied taxonomy that there was a "natural order" that grew out of the process of classifying animals and plants (see our Taxonomy module).

Scientists wondered why, when classified, groups of species seemed to form clusters, as if some sort of biodiversity magnet pulled them together and put them in one place. Within clusters, species tended to be similar to one another by different degrees. Surely it was no coincidence that all species of cats are alike, from the alley cat to the lion to the prehistoric saber tooth that roamed the western United States. Chance could not be the reason why dogs, wolves, and coyotes are all variations on the theme of "Dog." Similarly, chance could not explain the similarities and differences of the Galapagos finches that Darwin collected while he was with the *Beagle* expedition. What was behind the repeated pattern of species clusters that was so common in nature?

Comprehension Checkpoint

Darwin preferred the term "descent with modification" over "evolution" because

A) he wanted to prove to the scientific community that he was educated.

B) "evolution" had more than one meaning.

Biodiversity as a staircase: A "macro" view of life

Before Darwin, there was only one available model that naturalists used to explain species' similarities and differences, and that would not work to solve this problem. Scientists had thought that the most important pattern of biodiversity was what they called the *Scale of Nature*. This was the notion that the vast range of living organisms – say, from snail to ant to fish to mouse to monkey to man – was a feature of divine creation meant to highlight our own superiority. Life, they thought, was arranged like a set of stairs, with "lower" forms situated on the bottom and "higher" forms, humans, appearing at the top. This idea can be traced as far back as Aristotle, more than 2,000 years ago, and it was popularized in the 1800s by writers like Robert Chambers. Of course, it was all based on assumption. No evidence was provided to support the model, but it was generally accepted by tradition.

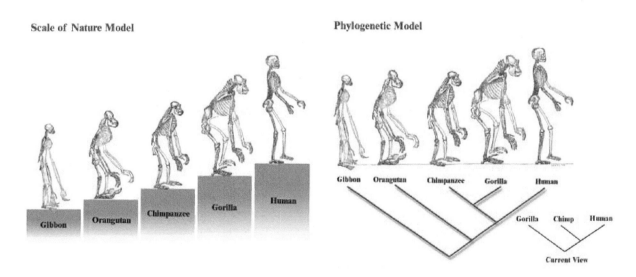

Figure 1: *How the Scale of Nature and Phylogenetic Models interpret the anatomical similarities and differences between apes and humans. The Scale of Nature model assumes a hierarchy of lower and higher organisms, while the Phylogenetic model does not. The current phylogenetic relationship among chimps, gorillas, and humans is different than that believed to be true in Darwin's day and is shown in the lower-right inset.*

The *Scale of Nature*, which was actually more of a "macro" view of life, would not work for Darwin because it did not relate to the clusters of similar species that he had observed. Why would so many types of cats or finches exist? The *Scale of Nature* suggested an unchanging, linear quality to evolution, but that surely could not explain the explosive variety of adaptations that Darwin saw among the finches he found on the Galapagos Islands during the *Beagle* voyage. Darwin observed finches that were adapted to feeding on different things: birds with beaks that were specialized to eat seeds, leaves, insects, or nectar. The list of items could not be interpreted as a scale-like linear climb involving a worse-adapted food source to better-adapted food source, or from poor-food to rich-food.

Comprehension Checkpoint

The _____ model assumes a hierarchy of higher and lower life forms.
- **A)** Scale of Nature
- **B)** Phylogenetic

Biodiversity as a tree: A "micro" view of life

Instead of the macro view offered by the *Scale*, Darwin was focused on a "micro" view of biodiversity: What could explain the small variations distinguishing species that actually resembled one another? He came to see that evolutionary changes on the micro level would add up to the differences that were obvious at the macro level. So, instead of a stairway or ladder as a metaphor for understanding the cluster pattern of biodiversity, Darwin pictured a tree.

This was a brilliant insight. Rather than being arrow-like and linear, a tree has many elements that spread out in different directions. Rather than being static, it is dynamic. It grows over time, just as evolution is embedded in time. It sprouts branches, as if it were generating new varieties and new species. Or, it may have branches that do not subdivide. Some branches grow straight up, parallel to the trunk, while most head off in different directions as they develop, resembling alternative adaptations. Some branches grow into stumps and die out, becoming extinct. Others may grow long and last for generations, thousands of years, tens of thousands of years, and even longer. None of the branches of a tree is judged to be any better than others; none is superior and none is inferior. They are all simply different.

Crucially important is the fact that all the branches of a tree are interconnected. You can trace their origins from their endpoints to the parent shoots from which they grew, just as you might trace the roots of dogs, or cats, or Galapagos finches to their original ancestral species.

The *Origin* tree diagram illustrates how a branching pattern of evolution can produce a greater number of species over time than what was there to begin with. It shows how some lines of species, or lineages, split more frequently than others. It shows that some lineages do not split at all but evolve almost like a column. It shows that extinction is a basic property of descent: Many populations are left behind and do not reach the top because they have died out.

Darwin saw evolution as a

A) branching tree.

B) straight up-and-down ladder.

Darwin's early model

Coming up with this tree-model of evolutionary process and pattern was not easy. In fact, Darwin's personal notebooks reveal how his own understanding grew over the years. In one notebook, which he began writing soon after returning from the *Beagle* expedition, he drew a crude stick-like diagram to show that many species could evolve from a single ancestral species by somehow splitting apart.

This early graphic, shown in Figure 4, is shaped like a cross between a tree and a starburst. It seems as if Darwin was trying to form an idea of how the great diversity of species could come about naturally from a single origin, rather than having each species being specially created. It is a flat image, as if he were drawing the diversity of Galapagos finches on a map of the islands. That, in fact, was key to his figuring out that evolution had occurred on the Galapagos, that is, how the birds had evolved across space. But his 1859 drawing, clearly for the first time, provided the blueprint of evolution though time. It illustrated his notion of *descent with modification*, how natural selection produces change and also a pedigree of connections between species that shows where they came from historically, meaning phylogenetically.

Darwin's finches

To better understand the one illustration that Darwin included in *Origin*, it is helpful to picture the finches that he studied on the Galapagos. What would this diagram look like if he had illustrated it with species of finch? At the bottom of the figure we would see the ancestral finches. As the lines diverge and branch out higher in the diagram, new species of finch would appear, leading to the array of modern birds at the top of the picture. To better illustrate this idea, work your way through "Darwin's Finches," the interactive animation linked through the online version of this module. Additional information about evolutionary descent with modification can be found in the *An Origin of Species* link from PBS found in the Experiment! section under Resources in the online version of this module.

With the tree of life as a metaphor for evolution, Darwin changed the way both scientists and the public view the origin of species. There would no longer be a need to interpret the biodiversity of nature as a ladder or scale, with some species better or worse than others due to the details of their size, fur, and teeth or as measured by their intelligence or ancestry. All are adapted to their specific environments, even though some might not survive. And all, at some level, share a common source of origin.

Key Concepts for this chapter

▶ Darwin's theory of Descent with Modification shows how as organisms reproduce, slight changes create variation, which could lead to new species over time.

▶ Darwin provided the first model that could logically account for biodiversity, explaining lineage and the small variations that distinguish one species from another, similar-looking one.

▶ Darwin's work radically changed thinking regarding the Scale of Nature, a model that suggested that some species were naturally inferior to one another, and showed species evolved in response to environmental pressures, not because of some hierarchy of order.

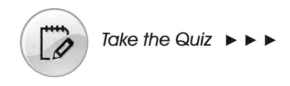 *Take the Quiz* ▶ ▶ ▶

Charles Darwin III Quiz

1. A phylogenetic tree is an illustration of an evolutionary pathway, especially the pedigree or genealogy of an individual species.

   A) True

   B) False

2. Darwin's concept of phylogeny eventually replaced the Creationist's notion of

   A) *Recapitulation.*

   B) *Scale of Nature.*

   C) *Survival of the Fittest.*

   D) *Fixity of Species.*

3. The tree model as an illustration of evolution is more accurate than the ladder model because it

   A) assumes a straight-line direction of change.

   B) reveals that extinction is not possible.

   C) shows how biodiversity can be generated.

   D) shows a hierarchy of animals, from lowest to highest.

4. Before Darwin, one idea that was missing from people's thoughts on evolution was that

   A) all species are linked through their ancestries.

   B) evolution no longer occurs naturally.

   C) adaptation only occurred in the Galapagos.

   D) the term could describe different processes.

5. The key to understanding why some species form clusters of similar organisms is that

   A) they all eat similar foods.

   B) they are made up of closely related individuals.

   C) they are phylogenetic groupings.

   D) they tend to be adapted to similar ecological conditions.

6. Darwin chose to use the term "descent with modification" instead of evolution because evolution

   A) had two meanings at the time, one connected to growth and one connected to change over time.

   B) as a term did not exist in Darwin's time; it was invented in 1932.

   C) was a French word, unfamiliar to Darwin's English audience.

   D) was used by Creationists to explain biodiversity.

7. Which concept gave an explanation for biodiversity and the "natural order" of living things?

   A) descent with modification

   B) natural selection

   C) transmutation

   D) scale of nature

Answers and feedback can be found on Page 281

Mendel and Inheritance

by Natalie Kuldell

Did you know people used to believe that fully formed miniature versions of offspring were contained in sperm cells? Early theories of reproduction were later disproven, but inheritance patterns remained a mystery until Gregor Mendel performed his groundbreaking experiments with pea plants in the 1800s.

Module Summary

This module describes the experiments that resulted in *Mendel's Laws of Inheritance*. A look at specific traits in pea plants over generations shows how Mendel's research methods resulted in an understanding of dominant and recessive genes. Partial dominance is also discussed.

Terms you should know:

breeding = the production of offspring; the propagation of plants or animals by sexual means

experiment = a test or trial carried out under controlled conditions so that specific actions can be performed and the results can be observed

generation = offspring at the same step in the line of descent from a common ancestor

inheritance = the transmission of genetic traits from parent to offspring

Genetics might be one of the oldest scientific pursuits. The Bible tells of Jacob breeding only the goats and sheep with valued coat colors (Genesis 30:32-43), and it's generally believed that dogs were domesticated more than 20,000 years ago by mating wolves with tamer dispositions. However, genetics is also a young science since its founding father, Gregor Mendel, performed his groundbreaking work less than 200 years ago. Mendel's work revealed two fundamental truths: that physical traits are determined by factors (now called genes) passed on by both parents, and that these factors are passed in a predictable pattern from one generation to the next. Mendel's contributions are so profound that his ideas are often referred to as *Mendel's Laws of Inheritance*.

Figure 1: *Sheep are selectively bred for various qualities, including the color, length and texture of their coat, the abundance of their milk, or their general hardiness.*

If breeding patterns and inheritance have been of interest since ancient times, why did it take until the mid 1800s to describe the laws that govern them? What was so special about Mendel that motivated him to perform and understand the experiments as he did?

Previous explanations of inhereted characteristics

In Mendel's time, there were many explanations for how characteristics were inherited. Because offspring often appear related but not identical to their parents, one theory proposed that physical traits became blended in each new generation, just as paints can be mixed to give new colors. However, even supporters of the "blending" theory had difficulty explaining how traits, like blue eyes, could reappear, unblended, in later generations.

Another popular theory in Mendel's time proposed that sperm cells held a miniature but fully formed offspring and that the female's egg contributed an "essence," allowing the offspring to grow. This theory explained that pregnant females stopped menstruating because the blood was redirected into the growing fetus, but it could not satisfactorily describe the evolution of new species (Darwin's *Origin of Species* would not be published until 1859, when Mendel was already collecting data from his genetic experiments. For more information see our Charles Darwin I module). The "miniature being" theory was debunked with improved light microscopes of the 1830s when researchers could directly observe the subcellular world of plants and animals, and no evidence for preformed offspring could be found.

A few years later, in 1859, Louis Pasteur's experiments dispelled another popular idea referred to as *spontaneous generation*, which proposed that life arose from a special brew of non-living materials. In this era of failed and failing theories, Mendel began his work.

Mendel's experiment

Gregor Johann Mendel was an Austrian monk who performed experiments in a monastery known for its scientific as well as its religious pursuits. Beginning in 1843, Mendel undertook experiments to understand the particulars of heredity, initially breeding normal and albino mice and then looking at the coat color of the offspring. Mendel's experiments with mice proved unsatisfactory since the mice took too long to breed and bore so few young in each litter. Additionally, they smelled terrible and some people felt animal breeding experiments were carnal and inappropriate work for a monk. Consequently, Mendel began looking at inheritance in plants, using *Pisum stavium*, the formal name for simple garden peas. Many varieties of this plant existed, peas were inexpensive and could be grown in rows of pots in the monastery garden, and each plant gave Mendel many peas to examine.

Breeding plants was different from breeding mice, but Mendel still had matchmaking work to perform. Flowering plants have both male and female reproductive parts. The pollen of a flower, found on the flower's anthers, is similar to sperm cells in other organisms; and the flower's egg cells, called ovules, are kept separate from the pollen by hiding them inside a compartment called the carpel. Breezes or bugs can transfer pollen from the anthers of one flower and leave it on the carpel of another ("cross-pollination"). Just as easily, pollen can travel from the anthers to the carpel of the same flower, resulting in self-pollination. Using a paintbrush, Mendel played the part of a selective insect and pollinated particular plants by brushing the powder from the anthers of one variety onto the carpel of another. To avoid any self-pollination, Mendel also "emasculated" the recipient plants, using tweezers to snip off their anthers. Some might have thought that this, too, was odd work for a monk, but Mendel persisted.

Mendel chose seven physical traits (now referred to as phenotypes) to study: flower color and placement, pod color and shape, pea color and shape, and plant size. These were all easily observable properties of the plants and so could be quickly counted. Mendel's goal was to reveal the genetic makeup (now called genotype) underlying each variety of pea plant and to understand how each trait was inherited. Performing his experiments took at least as much patience as skill. Mendel began by making "pure breeding" plants, ones that reliably gave rise to plants of the same physical traits generation after generation. This alone took him two years but gave him confidence in the genetic makeup of his starting plants, which he called the *parental* generation of his experiment.

Using his paintbrush, Mendel's next step was to cross-pollinate parental plants with different physical traits, yielding offspring that were the hybrid of two different plants. He recorded the appearance of each trait in the hybrid offspring plants, called the first filial generation (or F1 generation), and then followed the inheritance pattern to the next generation by self-pollinating the F1 plants to produce the second filial generation (F2) and carefully recording each variety that arose. Mendel's mathematical approach to the question of inheritance is one of his greatest legacies. In genetics (as in other sciences) it is easy to be misled by the results of a few experiments. Flip two coins and they may both show heads, but flip 1,000 coins and the split of heads to tails will be nearly even. In Mendel's case he examined more than 1,000 plants for their size and more than 8,000 peas for their color.

Comprehension Checkpoint

The observable physical traits of an organism are called

A) phenotypes.

B) genotypes.

Mendel's results

The first physical trait that Mendel studied extensively was pea shape. He had two pure breeding lines of plants: one that always gave rise to round peas and another that always gave wrinkled ones. He cross-pollinated these two parental lines and found that every F1 hybrid plant had round peas. This may not have been entirely surprising since most varieties of pure breeding plants in Mendel's collection had round peas, so he might have guessed that the round character would dominate and the wrinkled character would recede into the background. Mendel showed that the result was the same whether the pollen from plants with round peas was used to pollinate plants with wrinkled peas, or the other way around. The consistent results from such "reciprocal crosses" led Mendel to the conclusion that is now called Mendel's First Law: Factors that determine physical traits segregate into *both* egg and sperm cells (collectively called the "gametes" of the organism). Unlike earlier theories that suggested only sperm carried traits, Mendel showed that both egg and sperm carry physical traits to the offspring.

Mendel's next experiment was particularly telling. He self-pollinated each F1 hybrid plant with its own pollen and recorded the pea shape of the next (F2) generation. Despite all the F1 plants having round peas, some F2 plants had round peas and some had wrinkled peas. In other words, traits that had been hidden in the F1 hybrids had reappeared in their offspring. Mendel counted each variety in the F2 generation and observed that 5,474 had round peas and 1,850 wrinkled ones. The ratio of these two traits, very nearly three round peas for each wrinkled one, turned out to be an important number. Later, when Mendel repeated his experiments looking at pea color rather than shape, he found 6,022 yellow peas and 2,001 green peas in his F2 plants, again a ratio of 3:1. This 3:1 ratio held true in experiments examining flower color, flower position, pod shape, pod color, and plant size. What could explain this constant ratio? One of the strengths of Mendel's work is a hallmark of the scientific process: He put together his observations to form a hypothesis.

Three observations led Mendel to his second important proposal. First, Mendel had observed that both the egg and sperm carry factors to the offspring. Second, he had shown that one trait dominates in the initial cross of mixed hybrids (for example, round peas in the F1 generation). Lastly, he had observed a trait that recedes into the background in the F1 generation reappears one-fourth of the time in the F2 generation. Working over the mathematics, Mendel realized that both parents carry two copies of each factor and that each parent must donate one copy to the offspring through their egg or sperm cell. Since all of the offspring in the first cross (F1) carry one factor that dominates (round peas) and one factor that recedes (wrinkled), they all have round peas. However, their offspring (F2) could inherit either a round or wrinkled factor from each the egg and sperm. Only those F2 plants that inherit a wrinkled factor from both the egg and sperm had wrinkled peas – exactly a one-fourth ratio. Thus Mendel concluded that two factors must be involved in producing a physical trait; however, only one factor is passed on from parent to offspring in the sperm or egg cell. At the time Mendel could not explain how the pairs separated into the gametes, or how they rejoined during pollination, but he was correct in thinking that the factors randomly and independently segregated into the plant's gametes, and his idea is now called Mendel's Second Law.

Comprehension Checkpoint

When Mendel crossed two pure breeding lines of pea plants, one with round peas and one with wrinkled peas, the next generation produced round peas

A) only when the pollen from plants with round peas was used to pollinate plants with wrinkled peas.

B) whether the pollen from plants with round peas was used to pollinate plants with wrinkled peas, or the other way around.

Mendel's notation system

Mendel devised a notation system to follow the inheritance of each trait. As an example, consider Mendel's experiment with plants that were tall (6 feet) or short (6 inches). Mendel had reasoned that each parental plant had a pair of factors that separated during reproduction and that the F1 offspring inherited one factor from each parent. Mendel called the pure breeding ("homozygous") parental plants "TT" if they grew tall or "tt" if short. He could have named the short plants "SS," but instead he used uppercase letters for the trait that dominated in the F1 generation and used the same letter, but lowercase, to describe the recessive trait (the one that disappeared in the F1 generation but reappeared in the F2 generation).

Cross-pollinating the TT and tt plants gave hybrids with a mixed ("heterozygous") genotype ("Tt"). These hybrids all showed the dominant trait and grew tall.

In his next experiment Mendel self-pollinated plants of the Tt genotype and saw both tall and short plants arise. Mendel correctly concluded that the tall plants had either received two dominant factors ("TT" like the original pure breeding plants), or one dominant and one recessive factor ("Tt" like the F1 generation). However, the short plants must have inherited two recessive versions of the factor and were once again homozygous "tt." Mendel's insight into the genotype of his plants was remarkable given that nothing was known about the physical nature of inherited material. Mendel's "factors" are now known to be genes encoded by DNA and the variations are called alleles. "T" and "t" are alleles of one genetic factor, the one that determines plant size.

If both the "TT" and "Tt" genotypes give rise to tall plants and only the "tt" genotype gives short plants, shouldn't Mendel have seen two tall plants to every one short? A Punnet square like the one shown below is a useful way to calculate products from genetic crosses and can be used here to understand the 3:1 ratio that Mendel saw. Continuing the tall and short plant example, the "TT" and "tt" gametes from each pure breeding plant can be written across the top or along the left side of a four-quadrant box. Within the box, the individual factors are "donated" to the F1 progeny, resulting in a "Tt" genotype in all four quadrants. All these plants would (and did!) grow tall.

A Punnet square for crosses of the F1 plants shows a different outcome. Both sides of the Punnet square have "T" and "t" to represent the two possible gametes from each heterozygous plant. The genotypes of the offspring are written inside the square at the intersections: "tT" "tt" "TT" and "Tt." Thus the 3:1 ratio that Mendel observed can be understood by realizing that three intersections have one or more dominant factor (it doesn't matter if it's listed first or second in the Punnet square), and thus all three result in tall plants, and only one square has both recessive factors (tt), resulting in short plants.

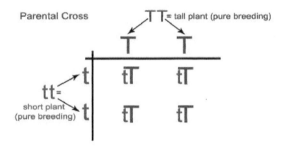

Figure 2: Punnet square showing a parental cross of a two plants, one with alleles TT and the other with alleles tt. All offspring (F1) are tT, possessing the recessive short gene, and expressing the dominant tall gene.

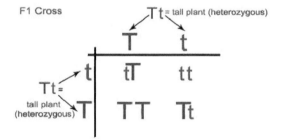

Figure 3: Punnet square showing the F1 cross of two plants with alleles Tt. As Mendel observed, 3/4ths of the offspring possess at least one copy of the dominant tall gene, while 1/4th of the offspring possess two copies of the short gene.

Comprehension Checkpoint

A tall plant of the Tt genotype has

A) two dominant factors for height.

B) one dominant factor and one recessive factor for height.

The monastery had many varieties of pea plants to study, and perhaps it was luck or perhaps it was intuition, but all seven of the traits Mendel chose to study are inherited in a straightforward pattern. The relationship between DNA and chromosomes to heredity was not known in Mendel's time. Modern analysis has since shown that five of the seven traits that Mendel studied are encoded by genes on distinct chromosomes of the pea plant, and the remaining two are at opposite ends of one chromosome and so are separated by lots of other genes. Had Mendel examined two traits encoded by neighboring genes he would have observed what Thomas Hunt Morgan found in the early 20th century from his experiments with fruit flies. Genes that are close to each other (called "linked" genes) have different inheritance patterns than the unlinked genes that Mendel studied.

It was also Mendel's good fortune (or perhaps his genius) to study quantifiable traits determined by only one pair of genes. Pea plants were either tall or short, their peas either green or yellow. There was nothing in between; many genes are now known to show "incomplete dominance," and there are numerous phenotypes that arise from the combined action of many genes. For example, some plants show incomplete dominance in flower color; when pure varieties that have either red (RR) flowers or white (rr) flowers are bred, the hybrid (Rr) offspring have flowers that are pink.

Mendel studied this phenomenon using a bean plant called *P. multiflorus* and noted that the outcome did not confirm the 3:1 ratio he had seen with the flower color of his pea plants. Mendel corresponded with many colleagues, and one of these, a Professor of Botany at the University in Munich named Carl Nageli, sent Mendel some hawkweed seeds to study. But this plant has an unusual mode of reproduction in which some of the maternal tissue is reused in the offspring, and so the crosses of the pure breeding plants did not show the expected 3:1 ratio. Mendel was reportedly discouraged by this and wondered if his "laws of inheritance" were universal.

Fur color on animals is another good example of a complex phenotype. In labrador retrievers, fur color is determined by two gene pairs. One pair colors the fur brown or black and another pair gives rise to a yellow coat. Coat color on Siamese cats is even more complex, being influenced by environmental factors as well as genes so that it grows darker around the nose, tail, and paws of these cats where their bodies are colder. For mice, determination of fur color is more complicated, with five gene pairs involved. Fortunately, Mendel abandoned his experiments with mice early and did not pursue any complex traits like these for his experiments.

Comprehension Checkpoint

A cross of a snapdragon plant with red flowers with another with white flowers results in plants with pink flowers due to

A) incomplete dominance.

B) a pure genotype.

Mendel presented his major findings in a two-part lecture in 1865 followed by a paper entitled "Experiments on Plant Hybridization" in 1866. Unlike the furor created a few years earlier by Darwin's publication, Mendel's proposals were essentially ignored, their truth unrecognized for years, even though the prevalent notions of inheritance were clearly insufficient and the intellectual room to accept his ideas was available.

Mendel did what he could to generate interest in his findings by sending reprints of his article to other people studying inheritance, but to his disappointment, Mendel never enjoyed wide readership or even a common understanding of his work in his lifetime. Today, no one disputes the significance of Mendel's contribution, although some have argued that his insights arose more from luck than from genius. Whatever the balance of intellect and fortune, Mendel's impact on modern thought is unquantifiable, unlike the inheritance of traits he studied.

Key Concepts for this chapter

▶ Mendel determined that an organism inherits two copies of the genetic material that determines an individual's physical traits, one copy coming from each the male and female parent.

▶ Mendel observed that for each trait, sometimes what is inherited from one parent masks what is inherited from the other. He called the hidden trait recessive and the expressed trait dominant.

▶ Since the time of Mendel, other scientists have observed that not all traits are inherited with the simple dominant-recessive pattern; incomplete dominance and co-dominance can result in a variety of phenotypes for some traits.

Take the Quiz ▶ ▶ ▶

Mendel and Inheritance Quiz

1. What does "genotype" refer to?

   A) the chromosomes of an organism

   B) the genetic make-up of an organism

   C) the type of gene in question

   D) the physical expression of genes

2. Mendel's First Law states that the factors that determine physical traits are carried only by sperm cells.

   A) True

   B) False

3. When two organisms are crossed, the offspring are referred to as

   A) the F2 generation.

   B) recessive.

   C) the F1 generation.

   D) a genotye.

4. Mendel believed that physical traits of pea plants are determined by

   A) inheritance of factors from both parents.

   B) inheritance of factors from the male parent only.

   C) inheritance of factors from one parent.

   D) inheritance of factors from the female parent only.

5. A chart used to determine the offspring of a genetic cross is called a

   A) cross chart.

   B) Punnet Square.

   C) Periodic Table.

   D) Genetic Square.

6. Mendel's Second Law states that alleles randomly and independently segregate into an organism's gametes.

   A) True

   B) False

7. Incomplete dominance results in

   A) a trait that is a mix of those seen in the parent.

   B) the offspring having a different trait than either parent

   C) both of the choices

   D) neither of the choices

8. If snapdragons demonstrate incomplete dominance in flower color, what would be the result of a cross between a red-flowered snapdragon with a white-flowered snapdragon?

   A) All the offspring will have white flowers.

   B) All the offspring will have pink flowers.

   C) All the offspring will have red flowers.

   D) Three-fourths of the offspring will have red flowers and one-fourth will have white flowers.

Answers and feedback can be found on Page 283

Taxonomy I: What's in a name?

by Alfred Rosenberger, PhD

Did you know that people started classifying living things as early as 300 BCE? But our modern classification system officially began in the 18th century when Carolus Linneaus listed every plant and animal species known in the world – more than 12,000 in all. He produced one of the great works in the history of science, *Systema Naturae*, which we still use today.

Module Summary

Modern taxonomy officially began in 1758 with *Systema Naturae*, the classic work by Carolus Linnaeus. This module, the first in a two-part series on species taxonomy, focuses on Linnaeus' system for classifying and naming plants and animals. The module discusses the contribution of diverse cultures to the development of our modern biological classification and describes the historical development of a scientific basis for classifying species.

Many people whose life and work depend on the natural environments are highly aware of the organisms around them. People who subsist on the food they grow or hunt, whether they are farmers in the rural United States or native hunter-gathers in the Amazon rainforest, are attuned to the variety of organisms around them, and can easily describe their benefits and problems. Some scientists have found that we have a genetic, instinctual fondness for nature that explains why humans are so preoccupied with plants and animals.

But there are surely practical reasons, for carefully observing behaviors and patterns in organisms, too. For those living off either a lush rain forest or the inhospitable Arctic, local plants and animals can provide food, shelter, clothing and fuel for cooking fires or warmth. Even in less extreme regions, a basic knowledge of environmental biology, including food-related facts like the fruiting patterns of trees and the grazing habits of large mammals, has always been important to survival, so it has become a significant part of the cultural traditions of people virtually everywhere. As you might expect, each culture has its own system for naming the plants and animals with which they live.

The process of naming and classifying organisms according to set of rules is called taxonomy. In some cultures, taxonomic rules are based traditional uses for plants and animals, and the existence of classification system facilities the transfer of that knowledge through generations. In modern scientific culture, taxonomic rules are based on physical appearance as well as genetic and evolutionary relationships between species, but having a classification system serves a very similar purpose by allowing scientists to communicate efficiently and effectively about the nature of a given organism with only a few words.

Early history of taxonomy

Among Europeans, we can trace the beginnings of organized, written taxonomies to ancient Greece. As early as 300 BCE, the philosopher and naturalist Theophrastus, a disciple of Aristotle, classified plants into three categories: herbs, shrubs, or trees. In addition to classifying local specimens, Theophrastus was able to add species from other regions because Alexander the Great sent him specimens collected during his expeditions to conquer much Europe and Asia.

During the 16th and 17th centuries, another round of famous expeditions marked the Age of Exploration. Dozens of explorers, including Ferdinand Magellan, Henry Hudson, and Hernando Cortes, traveled to distant parts of the globe and returned not only with stories of what they had seen, but also with samples of the plants and animals they encountered. European naturalists were kept busy describing these many new species and naming them in Latin, which was the language generally used for scholarly purposes.

By the 19th century, the idea of collecting exotic species became common practice and laid the foundation for research in the natural sciences. Charles Darwin, who developed the modern theory of evolution by natural selection in the middle 1800s, was one of many naturalists commissioned to collect, record and describe the species he saw during his travels.

Cataloging of species

Progress was also being made cataloging the kinds of plants and animals that existed. Naturalists in the 17th century, such as John Ray, began to develop a scientific basis for recognizing species. Ray and others began to inventory species by arranging them into logical classes based on their appearance and characteristics.

As a result of this widespread effort to describe new species, names proliferated, resulting in overlaps and redundancies and a lot confusion. Without sharing commonly accepted standards for composing names - even regarding such a simple rule as how long a name ought to be - whole purpose of a classification scheme as a communication tool is lost. For example, before a widely accepted taxonomic system was in place, the common Wild Briar Rose was identified by botanists as *Rosa sylvestris alba cum rubore folio glabro* roughly meaning pinkish white woodland rose with hairless leaves), and *Rosa sylvestris inodora seu canina* (odorless woodland dog rose). How was one to know if these names referred to one thing or two, that is, to one or two species?

Carolus Linnaeus and modern taxonomy

In the 18th century, the Swedish scientist Carolus Linnaeus more or less invented our modern system of taxonomy and classification. Linnaeus was one of the leading naturalists of the 18th century, a time when the study of natural history was considered one of the most prestigious areas of science.

Figure 1: *The cover of Linnaeus' classic work,* Systema Naturæ, *which is generally considered to be the start of modern taxonomy.*

Unlike his predecessors, Linnaeus adhered rigidly to the principal that each species must be identified by a set of names, which are termed the "genus" and "species," and classified on the basis of their similarities and differences. Although he was primarily a botanist, Linnaeus produced a comprehensive list of all organisms then known worldwide, some 7,700 plant and 4,400 animal species. He wrote one of the great classic works in the history of science, *Systema Naturæ*, and revised it many times.

Old Naming Convention	
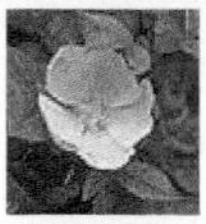	*Rosa sylvestris alba cum rubore folio glabro*
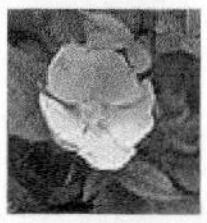	*Rosa sylvestris inodora seu canina*
Linnaean System	
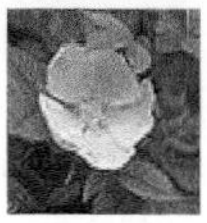	*Rosa canina*

We now consider the 10th revision of *Systema Naturæ*, published in 1758, as the official start of modern taxonomy and the first formal biological classification. It is a benchmark of modern taxonomy, an important reference to help biologists keep the many names straight. This is why when we come across taxonomic names, such as the official-looking labels identifying an animal in the zoo, Linnaeus's authorship is often acknowledged, and no dates of authorship are ever earlier than 1758. For instance, the plaque outside a gorilla exhibit may read as in Figure 2:

Primates,
Linnaeus, 1758
Gorilla,
I. Geoffroy, 1853

Figure 2.

This is more than a simple caption. Its purpose is to let us know, clearly, that the gorillas on display are the same type of animal that the French naturalist Isidore Geoffroy named Gorilla in his publication of 1853. It also tells us that the gorilla belongs to a group of mammals known as Primates, which in turn was named by Linnaeus in the 10th edition of his *Systema Naturæ*. Where did that odd name "gorilla" come from? As far as we know, it was introduced to Europe by the Greek explorer Hanno, who visited northwestern Africa during the 6th century BCE. It was the word that Hanno thought the local African people used to call gorillas (and supposedly meaning wild or hairy women). In other words, it was adopted by Hanno and is still in fashion today after being introduced into the formal Linnaean taxonomic system by Geoffroy in 1853.

Comprehension Checkpoint

How was the classification system devised by Carolus Linnaeus different from previous systems?

A) Plants and animals were given Latin names.

B) Plants and animals were identified by genus and species.

Key Concepts for this chapter

▶ Under Linnaeus's system, every species is known by a unique Latin-sounding genus and species name that distinguishes it from other species.

▶ Linnaeus's work organized organisms into logical classes based on their appearance and characteristics, and thus provides a basis for comparing different species.

 *Take the Quiz* ▶ ▶ ▶

Taxonomy I Quiz

1. Which branch of the Life Sciences is primarily concerned with the naming of species?

   A) phylogeny

   B) synonomy

   C) taxonomy

   D) zoology

2. Who wrote what we might call the "bible of taxonomy" in 1758?

   A) Aristotle

   B) I. Geoffroy

   C) Linnaeus

   D) Ray

3. The primary objective of our modern classification system is to accomplish which of the following conditions?

   A) a Latin-sounding name for each species

   B) a unique name for each species

   C) natural species names that describe the organism

   D) species names we can easily remember

4. Rather accurate, traditional, non-scientific biological knowledge can be found in

   A) allegorical classification.

   B) folk taxonomy.

   C) mythological anecdote.

   D) historical sagas.

5. Which one of the following pairs of historical figures contributed to the early development of taxonomy?

   A) Hanno and Cortez

   B) Linnaeus and Darwin

   C) Linnaeus and Ray

   D) Magellan and Theophrastus

6. Which pair of taxonomic terms or ranks are requirements for constructing a Linnaean name?

   A) Class and Phylum

   B) Family and Subfamily

   C) Genus and Species

   D) Kingdom and Legion

7. On what basis did Linnaeus group species in his classifications?

   A) their geographic origin

   B) their phylogenetic relationships

   C) their similarities and differences

   D) their taxonomy

Answers and feedback can be found on Page 285

Scientific Controversy

by Anne Egger, PhD and Anthony Carpi, PhD

Did you know that science is full of controversy? And that controversy in science can be a good thing? A scientific controversy is more than a disagreement between scientists. In fact, controversies are found in all scientific fields and usually lead to progress in science.

Module Summary

Controversy isn't always a bad thing. It exists in every field of science and in many cases clarifies and advances our scientific understanding. This module explains what scientific controversies are and how they differ from other kinds of controversy. Using the example of climate change, the module identifies factors that lead to controversies in science and explains how they are resolved.

Terms you should know:

controversy = an argument, disagreement, or difference of opinion that involves many people

debate = a reasoned discussion of opposing points in an argument

evidence = support for an idea, opinion, or hypothesis

The first offshore oil well out-of-sight from land was drilled in 1947 by the Kerr-McGee Corporation, off the coast of Louisiana (see Figure 1 in the online version of this module). Within a few years, there were a dozen such wells in the Gulf of Mexico, followed by wells drilled off of the coast of California and other locations. In the early 1950s, the United States government passed legislation that gave the federal government jurisdiction over the submerged continental shelf, and allowed the Department of the Interior to lease these areas for mineral development. By the late 1950s, these offshore oil leases were one of the largest revenue generators in the United States, second only to income taxes (Freudenburg and Gramling, 1994).

On January 28, 1969, just as oil workers completed the fifth well on an offshore platform off the coast of Santa Barbara, a blowout occurred that would eventually spill millions of gallons of oil into the water, soil popular beaches, and bring the previously out-of-sight drilling practice back into view. A process that had previously seemed to have largely positive effects – revenue generation for the government and a domestic source of energy – now had visible detrimental effects: local beaches were blackened by oil, dead and dying sea birds littered the area, and scores of coastal communities reeked with the stench of oil.

On March 21, President Nixon visited the spill and told the assembled crowd of residents and reporters that he would consider a ban on offshore drilling and would convert the area into a permanent ecological preserve. But the ban was lifted on April 1, angering local residents and sparking a controversy over the merits of offshore drilling. Were the benefits worth the risks? Some felt that having a reliable source of domestic oil provided security for the country, and outweighed environmental concerns. Others cited the toxic effects of oil spills on fisheries, tourism, and the environment in general as a reason to shut down offshore drilling. The government placed some coastal areas off-limits to drilling, such as the Arctic National Wildlife Refuge, while in other regions, such as the Gulf of Mexico, drilling moved further and further offshore into deeper water.

A massive blow-out from one of these wells in April 2010 reinvigorated the controversy over whether or not offshore drilling should be allowed and how it should be regulated. People on all sides of the controversy are using different data as evidence to support their position: a decline in shrimp fishing industry, lax regulation of drilling companies, domestic security and the need for energy resources, the interaction between hurricanes and surface oil. Though it is unlikely that the controversy will ever be resolved to the point where everyone agrees, additional legislation and regulations put in place by the government will determine the future of offshore drilling.

Science is also full of controversy. Similar to the controversy over offshore drilling, scientists appeal to evidence to support their claims, and the nature of the debate changes as new evidence comes to light. But there are some key differences between a scientific controversy and other types of controversy. For example, many people think that the controversy over offshore drilling is holding up progress, whether that progress is economic, environmental or political. In contrast, a controversy in science often creates progress, because it spurs new research and therefore is an essential part of the process of science.

What is scientific controversy?

Scientists can disagree about lots of things, from the mundane (like what is the best kind of analytical instrument to use) to the profound (whether or not string theory, a recently developed theory in physics, is an accurate representation of reality). Two scientists disagreeing over an instrument or string theory – or even the interpretation of data – does not count as a controversy, however. A true scientific controversy involves a sustained debate within the broader scientific community (McMullin, 1987). In other words, a significant number of people must be actively engaged in research that addresses the controversy over time. No matter what the content of the disagreement, the scientists involved all share some fundamental knowledge and agree that the subject matter is worth being concerned about and that the various arguments are legitimate.

What makes the arguments legitimate is that they are based on data. It is not enough for a scientist to simply say, "I don't agree with you." Instead, they must conduct the research to garner enough evidence to support their claim. An argument must explain the majority of data available – not just the data collected to support one side. This is not necessarily the case in public controversies such as that over offshore drilling, where a group or individual can decide that some data are more important than other data – the number of birds that died or the economic impact of drilling or the percentage of oil imports. In a scientific controversy, all of the data must be explained and taken into account.

Though controversies are often discussed in informal settings (the same way you might discuss a controversial issue with your friends), the real debate is carried out at research meetings and through the publication of journal articles (see our Scientific Journal Articles module). It is only through this process that the debate becomes part of the scientific literature (see our Utilizing the Scientific Literature module) and helps science progress. There is no authoritative body in science that decides what the right answer in a controversy is, nor does it require complete consensus among all scientists.

The resolution to a controversy comes when one argument is widely accepted and other arguments fade away. Often, the evidence in favor of one side of the controversy becomes so overwhelming that people simply stop arguing about it. Usually, that happens when multiple lines of evidence coming from multiple research methods (and perhaps multiple disciplines) all converge.

Controversies are ongoing in every field of science on a regular basis. For example, as of 2010, geophysicists are engaged in a debate about the existence of mantle plumes, thin columns of hot rock that rise from the Earth's core to the surface and cause volcanic activity (see, for example, Kerr, 2010). The concept of a mantle plume as a non-moving source of magma for island chains like Hawaii (Figure 2 in the online version of this module) was first postulated by J. Tuzo Wilson shortly after the development of the theory of plate tectonics (see our Origins of Plate Tectonic Theory module) and was widely accepted over the next thirty years. In 2003, however, a group of scientists led by John Tarduno, a geophysicist at the University of Rochester, presented strong evidence that the mantle plume thought to be responsible for forming the Hawaiian islands had moved more than 1000 km over time (Tarduno et al., 2003). That paper launched a multitude of additional studies that began to question the very existence of mantle plumes. The ongoing debate has been heated at times (see our Research links in the online version of this module for more information), but has also caused a tremendous leap in our understanding of the volcanic processes associated with mantle plumes, and our scientific knowledge has advanced.

The debate over the existence of mantle plumes is clearly a scientific controversy, and most scientific controversies similarly have little to do with personal, ethical, or political controversies. On the other end of the spectrum, the controversy about the use of stem cells harvested from human embryos in biomedical research is not a scientific controversy – scientists agree about what stem cells are and how they work. Instead, the controversy revolves around whether or not it is ethical to use stem cells. Sometimes, however, the lines between scientific controversy and other kinds of controversy get blurred. Scientists are human, after all, and what starts as a scientific controversy may also include personal disagreements (see our Scientists and the Scientific Community module). In other cases, the media may exaggerate a scientific controversy and turn it into a political debate. One example of this kind of blurring of the lines is the study of the relationship between hurricanes and climate change.

Comprehension Checkpoint

A scientific controversy ends when

A) all scientists come to an agreement on a resolution.
B) evidence in support of one side of the controversy becomes convincing.

Development and resolution of a scientific controversy: Will global warming increase hurricanes?

On his second voyage, the explorer Christopher Columbus encountered a storm while on the island of Hispaniola in 1494: "Eyes never beheld the seas so high, angry, and covered by foam," he wrote in a letter to his benefactor, Queen Isabella. "Never did the sky look more terrible; for one whole day and night it blazed like a furnace. The flashes came with such fury and frightfulness that we all thought the ships would be blasted. All this time, the water never ceased to fall from the sky" (Barnes and Lyons, 2007). Though this was, perhaps, a new experience for Columbus, the storms were well known to the Caribbean locals, who called them *furacano*, a word that became common in English around 1650 as "hurricane." Columbus wrote the first account of a hurricane in the Atlantic (Millás and Pardue, 1968), but there were many more to come.

Figure 3: Galveston residents sifting through the wreckage of the 1900 hurricane.

Throughout the 1800s, hurricanes were observed and described. Early on, several observers noted that these storms were vortices, rotating in a counter-clockwise direction. By the middle part of the century, weather observatories had been established in many locations in North America, and some scientists were recording hurricane tracks. After a major hurricane struck the city of Galveston, Texas, in 1900, killing at least 8,000 people (see Figure 3), analysis of these observations took on a new urgency.

Many of the earliest studies of hurricanes, also called tropical cyclones (or typhoons in the Pacific Ocean), were carried out by scientists who had studied with Vilhelm Bjerknes, a physicist who had determined the equations that govern circulation in the atmosphere (see our Modeling module for more information). In 1917, Bjerknes started the Bergen School of Meteorology in Bergen, Norway, bringing together a group of well-known and accomplished meteorologists (Liljequist, 1980). Their initial research focus was on cyclonic weather systems in the temperate zones, the latitude of most of Europe.

A new research direction: Water temperature and hurricanes

By 1928, the group felt that their methods and understanding of these systems were mature, and could be applied to rarer and more complicated storm systems – tropical cyclones (Bergeron, 1954). Erik Palmén, a Finnish meteorologist who moved to Chicago after his time at Bergen, recognized that hurricanes formed only above sea water that was warmer than 26–27° C (~80° F), a critically important observation that he published in 1948 (Palmén, 1948). His publication included a map of sea surface temperature during the warmest part of the year called "hurricane season" with arrows showing the tracks of major hurricanes (see Figure 4 in the online version of this module). All of the arrows began in a narrow band of the ocean where water temperatures were highest.

Sea surface temperature is one manifestation of climate. As global climate changes, the distribution of warmer and colder waters on the sea surface also changes. Tor Bergeron, another member of the Bergen group, went beyond thinking about how sea surface temperature changes annually and considered what happened over longer periods of time, placing hurricanes in the context of long-term climate changes. In a review paper in 1954, Bergeron speculated that the frequency and intensity of hurricanes, as well as where and when they formed, could have changed dramatically over geologic time with small changes in the Earth's orbit and solar intensity – both of which affect global climate (Bergeron, 1954). He urged scientists who studied climate in the past to keep that in mind. At the time, however, the techniques available to assess past climate to the level of detail of individual hurricanes simply didn't exist, and few scientists took up the challenge.

New data fuels controversy: Climate change and hurricanes

Starting in the 1980s, however, this idea re-emerged as scientists began to see variability in the frequency and intensity of hurricanes that correlated well with short-term climatic cycles that operate on the order of 10–12 years, like the El Niño-Southern Oscillation (ENSO) in the tropical Pacific. El Niño is familiar to many people around the world for its effects on local weather patterns, but now there was evidence showing that this cycle in the tropical Pacific affected hurricane generation in the Atlantic Ocean (Gray, 1984). At the same time, more and more scientists began to recognize that global sea surface temperatures were steadily rising as the climate warmed, and they began to explore the links between how global warming would affect both the climatic cycles and hurricane formation (Emanuel, 2003). Most who studied the phenomena found that sea surface temperature changes of the magnitude they were seeing would, indeed, influence hurricane formation, but not nearly as much as natural variability within the climatic cycles.

That general sentiment began to be questioned, however, as more data came in. In June of 2005, Kevin Trenberth, a climate scientist at the National Center for Atmospheric Research (NCAR), published a short article in *Science* entitled "Uncertainty in Hurricanes and Global Warming" (Trenberth, 2005). In it, he stated:

> During the 2004 hurricane season in the North Atlantic, an unprecedented four hurricanes hit Florida; during the same season in the Pacific, 10 tropical cyclones or typhoons hit Japan (the previous record was six). Some scientists say that this increase is related to global warming; others say that it is not. Can a trend in hurricane activity in the North Atlantic be detected? Can any such trend be attributed to human activity? Are we even asking the right questions?

Trenberth was highlighting a controversy that was just beginning to develop at the time, pointing out that we did not yet have enough data or enough theoretical understanding of the process to make valid, reliable interpretations. His questions inspired several other scientists to analyze the available data searching for trends (see our Data Analysis and Interpretation module for more information on this process) and to begin new research into the issue. Among those was a group of four atmospheric scientists, three from the Georgia Institute of Technology and one from NCAR. They worked through the early part of the summer and had submitted their work for publication in August 2005.

Hurricane Katrina: Scientific controversy goes public

Prior to publication, however, a dramatic and pertinent event occurred: on Monday, August 29, 2005, Hurricane Katrina made landfall near New Orleans, Louisiana (Figure 5). The hurricane brought with it widespread physical destruction and loss of life, and created a social, political, and economic crisis. Within hours of landfall, however, a question arose in the media: Was this particularly destructive hurricane caused by global warming? While this was not a scientific question or one that could be answered through research, it brought the public into the scientific controversy about the relationship between climate change and hurricanes.

Figure 5: GOES satellite image of Hurricane Katrina on August 29, 2005, with sea surface temperatures.

A little over two weeks later, on September 16, the work by the scientists at Georgia Tech and NCAR was published in *Science*. Their analysis showed that, although the number of total hurricanes had not increased significantly since 1970, the proportion of hurricanes that were category-4 and -5, the strongest storms, had (Webster et al., 2005). In other words, they concluded that there had been more intense hurricanes, even though the total number had not changed. They correlated these changes with an increase in global sea-surface temperature (SST), which had been steadily rising as global atmospheric temperatures increased. In a very general way, the work by Webster and colleagues implied that there could be more hurricanes like Katrina in the future.

Social and political implications of scientific controversy

The results of their work had significant social and political implications: if global warming caused more intense hurricanes, there would be additional reason to take action to reduce the magnitude of warming in order to reduce destruction. As a result, the authors of the article received an unusually high number of responses to their work, both responses from scientists that are typical of scientific publications and letters, and personal responses from the general public. In an article published in the Bulletin of the American Meteorological Society the following year, three of the original four authors reported on those responses (Curry et al., 2006). Some of the comments they received were valid scientific arguments, but unfortunately, that was not always the case. Many of the comments were based in political and social concerns, and some involved personal attacks on the scientists.

For example, one of the frequent comments that the authors received is that they weren't qualified to analyze the hurricane data, despite the fact that the researchers were all atmospheric scientists who had been working on similar types of climate data for decades (Curry et al., 2006). This type of personal attack can be damaging and create controversy in the media, but it is not a component of the scientific controversy. Of course, scientists are people, and any public debate involves differences in personality and opinion, but those personal differences are not based on the data.

In contrast, some of the points raised in response to the article had a valid scientific basis. For example, one of these more substantial arguments centered on the reliability of the early part of the hurricane record. Accurate, worldwide tracking of hurricanes is a relatively recent phenomenon that only became easy with satellites starting in the 1970s. Aircraft started recording hurricanes in the mid 1940s, but the data were limited to common flight lines over the oceans. Prior to that, the majority of observations about hurricanes were made from land, and even that record only goes back to 1851. Given that hurricanes spend most of their time over the ocean, this meant that the data could be inaccurate and thus difficult to interpret.

Comprehension Checkpoint

Scientific controversy can spur people to take action in society or pass legislation.

A) True

B) False

Scientific controversy spurs new research

Many scientists recognized that much more work was needed in order to make progress in our understanding. As a result, the number of studies addressing the relationship between global warming and hurricanes proliferated over the next few years (see Figure 6). Some scientists used detailed global climate models and found that natural, local climate variability seemed to have a greater effect on hurricane intensity than current global warming (Vecchi and Soden, 2007). Others reanalyzed older hurricane records to correct for systematic bias, removing some storms that were poorly constrained from the record and adding new ones (Landsea et al., 2008). Still others extended the record further back in time by collecting descriptions of independent records that did not rely on human observations (Mann et al., 2009). Throughout this process, scientists disagreed and debated what was really going on with hurricanes as the Earth's climate warmed. Were they increasing in frequency? Intensity? No change? A NOVA documentary in 2006 pitted MIT scientist Kerry Emanuel against Chris Landsea, a meteorologist at the Miami Hurricane Center, suggesting that the two scientists had a fundamental disagreement about the nature of strong hurricanes (Public Broadcasting System (PBS), 2006).

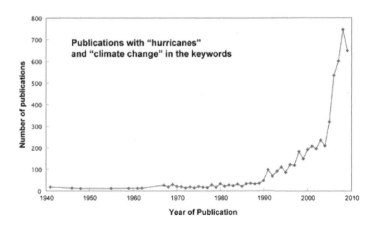

Figure 6: Graph showing the number of scientific publications annually with the words "hurricane" and "climate change" included as keywords. Data is from ISI Web of Science.

Within a few years, however, much of the disagreement had subsided. In 2010, the Expert Team on Climate Impacts on Tropical Cycles, a group of scientists assembled by the World Meteorological Organization (WMO), attempted to bring all of the new research together and summarize what scientists had learned since 2005. The team, which included both Kerry Emanuel and Chris Landsea, published an article in *Nature Geoscience* entitled "Tropical cyclones and climate change" (Knutson et al., 2010). In the abstract, they summarize the state of the scientific controversy:

> Whether the characteristics of tropical cyclones have changed or will change in a warming climate – and if so, how – has been the subject of considerable investigation, often with conflicting results. Large amplitude fluctuations in the frequency and intensity of tropical cyclones greatly complicate both the detection of long-term trends and their attribution to rising levels of atmospheric greenhouse gases. Trend detection is further impeded by substantial limitations in the availability and quality of global historical records of tropical cyclones. Therefore, it remains uncertain whether past changes in tropical cyclone activity have exceeded the variability expected from natural causes. However, future projections based on theory and high-resolution dynamical models consistently indicate that greenhouse warming will cause the globally averaged intensity of tropical cyclones to shift towards stronger storms, with intensity increases of 2–11% by 2100. Existing modeling studies also consistently project decreases in the globally averaged frequency of tropical cyclones, by 6–34%.

In other words, the authors acknowledge the complexity of the issue, noting what aspects make it a difficult subject to study (large natural fluctuations, a limited historical dataset), and that these complexities have caused mixed results from different scientific studies. They also point out, however, where there is agreement: there is consistency in all of the models that predict more strong storms in the future as global climate changes. Their statement also emphasizes that science is a work in progress that relies on the creativity of scientists to overcome problems, and controversy is a natural outcome of that process.

This debate on the relationship between tropical storms and global warming fulfills the requirements for a scientific controversy – it involves a large number of scientists doing active research into the issue, and the debate took place (and continues to take place) in public, through a peer-reviewed process, over a sustained period of time. The nature of the subject under investigation meant that some social and political components were involved, but ultimately the scientific progress that was made was unrelated to a particular storm or situation.

Comprehension Checkpoint

Scientific controversy generally

A) causes hostility within the scientific community.

B) inspires scientists to begin new research.

Does the publication of the article by the WMO team mean that the controversy is resolved? Well, yes and no. As stated in the article, most of the current evidence suggests that the occurrence of hurricanes will be affected by climate change, and the number of publications concerning the topic so far seems to have peaked in 2008 (see Figure 5). Other arguments have not faded away completely, however, and there will undoubtedly be more research in this field as new data are collected, the resolution and power of computer models increases, and as warming continues.

More complete resolution is possible, however, such as in the debate over plate tectonic theory that occurred in the 1960s, where the accumulated evidence became overwhelming in support of plate tectonics. In other cases, resolution awaits the development of a new technology or technique that can acquire the kind of data that can really address the question. For example, the definition of "race" in humans was the subject of significant study and controversy throughout much of human history, but it wasn't until the sequencing of the human genome that scientists were truly able to examine claims for a genetic basis for race and found none (Jorde and Wooding, 2004).

In most cases, controversy is a sign of health in the scientific endeavor, and the more people that are involved in the controversy, conducting research to address the issues, the more rapidly progress is made. Sometimes the scientists involved in a controversy are portrayed as rivals, similar to the environmentalists vs. the oil companies in the controversy over offshore drilling, but this is not an accurate portrayal. The "winner" in scientific controversies is not one side, but the entire scientific community.

Key Concepts for this chapter

▶ A scientific controversy is a sustained, public debate among the broader scientific community in which arguments are based on evidence.

▶ Controversies cause progress in science by encouraging research on the topic in question.

▶ Controversies are resolved when the evidence overwhelmingly favors one argument.

▶ Scientific controversies are distinct from political, ethical, and personal controversies, though sometimes they overlap or can have complex interactions.

References

Barnes, J., & Lyons, S. (2007). *Florida's hurricane history.* Chapel Hill, NC: The University of North Carolina Press.

Bergeron, T. (1954). REVIEWS OF MODERN METEOROLOGY–12. The problem of tropical hurricanes. *Quarterly Journal of the Royal Meteorological Society,* 80, 131-164.

Curry, J. A., Webster, P.J., & Holland, G.J. (2006). Mixing politics and science in testing the hypothesis that greenhouse warming is causing a global increase in hurricane intensity. *Bulletin of the American Meteorological Society*, 87, 1025-1037.

Emanuel, K. (2003). Tropical cyclones. *Annual Review of Earth and Planetary Sciences*, 31, 75-104.

Freudenburg, W. R., & Gramling, R. (1994). *Oil in troubled waters: Perception, politics, and the battle over offshore drilling.* Albany, NY: State University of New York Press.

Gray, W. M. (1984). Atlantic seasonal hurricane frequency. Part I: El Niño and 30 mb quasi-biennial oscillation influences. *Monthly Weather Review,* 112, 1649-1668.

Jorde, L. B., & Wooding, S. P. (2004). Genetic variation, classification and 'race'. *Nature Genetics,* 36, S28-S33.

Kerr, R. A. (2010). Another quarry sighted in the great mantle plume hunt? *Science,* 328,(5986), 1622-a.

Knutson, T. R., McBride, J. L., Chan, J., Emanuel, K., Holland, G., Landsea, C., . . . Sugi, M. (2010). Tropical cyclones and climate change. *Nature Geoscience,* 3, 157-163.

Landsea, C. W., Glenn, D. A., Bredemeyer, W., Chenoweth, M., Ellis, R., Gamache, J., . . . Woolcock, L. (2008). A reanalysis of the 1911-20 Atlantic hurricane database. *Journal of Climate,* 21, 2138-2168.

Liljequist, G. H. (1980). Tor Bergeron: A biography. *Pure and Applied Geophysics*, 119, 409-442.

Mann, M. E., Woodruff, J. D., Donnelly, J. P., & Zhang, Z. (2009). Atlantic hurricanes and climate over the past 1,500 years. *Nature,* 460, 880-883.

McMullin, E. (1987). Scientific controversy and its termination. In Engelhardt Jr., H. T., & Caplan, A. L. (Eds.). *Scientific controversies: Case studies in resolution and closure of disputes in science and technology.* Cambridge, MA: Cambridge University Press.

Millás, J. C., & Pardue, L. (1968). *Hurricanes of the Caribbean and adjacent regions, 1492-1800.* Miami, FL: Academy of the Arts and Sciences of the Americas.

Palmén, E. (1948). On the formation and structure of tropical hurricanes. *Geophysica,* 3, 26-38.

Public Broadcasting Service (PBS). (2006). Stronger hurricanes. *NOVA*, WGBH.

Simkin, T., Tilling, R. I., Vogt, P. R., Kirby, S. H., Kimberley, P., & Stewart, D. B. (2006). This dynamic planet: Geological investigations map I-2800. US Geological Survey.

Tarduno, J. A., Duncan, R. A., Scholl, D. W., Cottrell, R. D., Steinberger, B., Thordarson, T., . . . Carvallo, C. (2003). The Emperor Seamounts: Southward motion of the Hawaiian hotspot plume in Earth's mantle. *Science,* 301(5636). 1064-1069.

Trenberth, K. (2005). CLIMATE: Uncertainty in hurricanes and global warming. *Science,* 308(5729), 1753-1754.

Vecchi, G. A., & Soden, B. J. (2007). Increased tropical Atlantic wind shear in model projections of global warming. *Geophysical Research Letters,* 34, L08702.

Webster, P. J., Holland, G. J., Curry, J. A., & Chang, H. -R. (2005). Changes in tropical cyclone number, duration, and intensity in a warming environment. *Science,* 309(5742), 1844-1846.

Take the Quiz ▶ ▶ ▶

Scientific Controversy Quiz

1. In order for a scientific controversy to be resolved, which of the following is most likely to occur?

   A) All scientists must agree on a resolution.

   B) A vote is taken among interested scientists.

   C) Multiple lines of evidence favor one side.

   D) Controversies are never really resolved.

2. Scientists contribute to scientific controversies primarily by

   A) publishing articles in newspapers.

   B) discussions with individual scientists.

   C) debating on TV.

   D) publishing in the peer-reviewed literature.

3. Why did the World Meteorological Organization appoint an expert panel to write a paper about tropical cyclones?

   A) because so much new research had been done, it needed to be summarized

   B) to resolve the controversy about global warming and hurricanes

   C) because scientists couldn't agree on the answer

   D) to prevent more people from getting involved in the controversy

4. A valid argument in a scientific controversy must be based on

   A) personal disagreements between scientists.

   B) explanations of all of the available data.

   C) political and social implications of the research.

   D) only the most recently collected data.

5. Controversies are rare in science.

   A) True

   B) False

6. The Delta smelt is a minnow (a type of fish) that lives only in the estuary of the Sacramento River delta in California. The delta is also a source of drinking and agricultural water for California residents, and intake valves for pipelines are located near the breeding waters of the smelt. Scientists have determined that the smelt populations are in rapid decline and that they need more freshwater than is currently available to them after drinking water is pumped out. Nearby farmers argue that they need more freshwater to grow their crops, and regulatory agencies have faced criticisms from all sides on their management of the water resources. This a scientific controversy.

   A) True

   B) False

7. Many large mammals went extinct in North America around 11,000 years ago, including the woolly mammoth and the mastodon. Based on archaeological evidence, some scientists have argued that hunting by humans, who were relatively new to the continent, caused the extinctions. Based on climate data, other scientists have argued that sudden warming that led to the melting of the ice sheets was the primary cause of the extinctions. In a number of recent studies, scientists have reported sequencing the woolly mammoth genome and running detailed climate models for the time period around the extinction, and new evidence is being discovered. This is a scientific controversy.

   A) True

   B) False

Answers and feedback can be found on Page 286

Uncertainty, Error, and Confidence

by Anthony Carpi, PhD and Anne Egger, PhD

> Did you know that when scientists use the word "uncertainty," it does not mean that they are unsure about their research results? Likewise, when scientists talk about "error," they do not mean that their research is flawed. Scientists actually measure error and report it along with their findings.

Module Summary

There is uncertainty in all scientific data, and even the best scientists find some degree of error in their measurements. This module uses familiar topics - playing baseball, shooting targets, and calculating the age of an object - to show how scientists identify and measure error and uncertainty, which are reported in terms of confidence.

Terms you should know:

inherent = part of the fundamental nature of something, belonging as an inseparable characteristic

quantify = to express something in terms of a number value, measurement, or amount

value = a number that is assigned based on measurement or a calculation

The Olympic sport of biathlon is a cross-country ski race of 20 km in which the athletes stop on four occasions to shoot 0.57 cm diameter bullets from a .22 caliber rifle at targets. The sport requires not only great endurance, but exceptional accuracy as the athletes shoot on two occasions from the prone position (lying down) and on two occasions while standing. The targets the athletes aim for are all 50 m away, but the size varies to match the precision expected of them; those targeted while shooting in the prone position are 4.5 cm in diameter while those targeted from the more difficult standing position are 11.5 cm in diameter. In both cases, however, the diameter of the target is many times larger than the diameter of the bullet itself – why?

While the legend of Robin Hood splitting one arrow with another is well-known, it is also unrealistic. Biathlon targets are purposely sized many times larger than the bullets the athletes shoot to account for the inherent error and uncertainty involved in long distance riflery. Even the most skilled marksman cannot account for every variable affecting the path of the bullet, like sudden gusts of wind or variations in air pressure. Shooting from the standing position involves even greater uncertainty, as indicated by the larger targets used, because even the simple rise and fall of an athlete's chest as they breathe can affect the aim of their rifle.

Categorizing uncertainty: Accuracy vs. precision

Scientific measurements also incorporate variability, and scientists report this as uncertainty in an effort to share with others the level of error that they found acceptable in their measurements. But uncertainty in science does not imply doubt as it does in everyday use. Scientific uncertainty is a quantitative measurement of variability in the data. In other words, uncertainty in science refers to the idea that all data have a range of expected values as opposed to a precise point value. This uncertainty can be categorized in two ways: accuracy and precision.

- *Accuracy* is a term that describes how well a measurement approximates the theoretically correct value of that measurement, for example, how close the arrow is to the bullseye (Figure 1).

- The term *precision*, by comparison, describes the degree to which individual measurements vary around a central value. Measurements with high precision are highly reproducible because repeated measurement will reliably give a similar result; however, they may or may not be accurate (Figure 1).

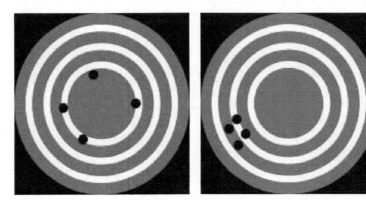

Figure 1: *A representation of accuracy and precision as hits on a target. The target at left depicts good accuracy as the marks are close to the bullseye, but poor precision; in contrast, the target at right depicts good precision as the marks are grouped closely, but poor accuracy.*

Uncertainty in nature

Karl Pearson, the English statistician and geneticist, is commonly credited with first describing the concept of uncertainty as a measure of data variability in the late 1800s (Salsburg, 2001). Before Pearson, scientists realized that their measurements incorporated variability, but they assumed that this variability was simply due to error. For example, measurement of the orbits of planets around the sun taken by different scientists at different times varied, and this variability was thought to be due to errors caused by inadequate instrumentation. The French mathematician Pierre-Simon Laplace discussed a method for quantifying error distributions of astronomical measurements caused by small errors associated with instrument shortcomings as early as 1820. As technology improved through the 1800s, astronomers realized that they could reduce, but not eliminate this error in their measurements.

Pearson put forward a revolutionary idea: Uncertainty, he proposed, was not simply due to the limits of technology in measuring certain events – it was inherent in nature. Even the most careful and rigorous scientific investigation (or any type of investigation for that matter) could not yield an exact measurement. Rather, repeating an investigation would yield a scatter of measurements that are distributed around some central value. This scatter would be caused not only by error, but also by natural variability. In other words, measurements themselves, independent of any human or instrument inaccuracies, exhibit scatter.

Whether it is the flight path of an arrow, the resting heart rate of an adult male, or the age of a historical artifact, measurements do not have exact values, but instead always exhibit a range of values, and that range can be quantified as uncertainty. This uncertainty can be expressed as a plot of the probability of obtaining a certain value, and the probabilities are distributed about some central, or mean, value.

Comprehension Checkpoint

Certain large scale scientific measurements, such as the orbit of planets, have no uncertainty associated with them.

A) True

B) False

Uncertainty and error in practice: Carbon-14 dating

Archaeologists, paleontologists, and other researchers have long been interested in dating objects and artifacts in an effort to understand their history and use. Unfortunately, written records are a relatively recent human invention, and few historical artifacts are accompanied by precise written histories.

In the first half of the 20th century, an American nuclear chemist by the name of Willard F. Libby became interested in using the radioactive isotope ^{14}C to date certain objects. The theory of radiocarbon dating is relatively simple. Most carbon in the Earth's atmosphere is in the form of ^{12}C, but a small amount of the isotope ^{14}C is produced naturally through the bombardment of ^{14}N with cosmic rays (W. F. Libby, 1946). As plants take up carbon from the atmosphere through respiration, they incorporate both ^{14}C as well as the more abundant ^{12}C into their tissues. Animals also take up both carbon isotopes through the foods that they eat. Thus, all living organisms have the same ratio of ^{14}C and ^{12}C isotopes in their body as the atmosphere.

Unlike ^{12}C, ^{14}C is a radioactive isotope that is constantly undergoing decay to its daughter product ^{14}N at a known rate. While an organism is alive, it is taking up new ^{14}C from the environment and thus remains in equilibrium with it. When that organism dies, however, the carbon in its tissues is no longer replaced, and the amount of ^{14}C slowly decreases in time as it decays to ^{14}N. Thus, the amount of radioactive ^{14}C remaining in a piece of wood or an animal bone can be used to determine when that organism died. In essence, the longer the organism has been dead, the lower the ^{14}C levels.

The amount of radioactive material (such as ^{14}C) in a sample can be quantified by counting the number of decays that the material undergoes in a specific amount of time, usually reported in counts per minute (cpm). When Libby began his radiocarbon work in the 1940s, the technology available was still quite new. A simple Geiger counter was only first invented in 1908 by the German scientist Hans Wilhelm Geiger, a student of Ernest Rutherford's, and it was not perfected until 1928 when Walther Müller, a student of Geiger's, improved on the design, allowing it to detect all types of radiation. Libby himself is credited with building the first Geiger counter in the United States in the 1930s.

Libby, however, faced a major hurdle with using the instrument to measure ^{14}C. The problem was that naturally-occurring background radiation from cosmic rays and Earth, along with the variability associated with that background signal, would overwhelm the small ^{14}C signal he expected to see. In 1949, he reported on a method for reducing the background signal and variability: He placed the entire sample and the detector inside of a tube shielded by 2 inches of lead and 4 inches of iron (W. F. Libby, Anderson, & Arnold, 1949). In this way, Libby and his colleagues reduced the background signal from 150 cpm to 10 cpm and minimized the variability associated with the signal to "about 5-10% error," or less than 1 cpm.

Libby and colleagues do not use the word *error* as we do in common language, where it refers to a mistake such as a typographical error or a baseball error. The Latin origin of the word error (*errorem*) means *wandering* or *straying*, and the scientific use of the word is closer to this original meaning. In science, error is the difference between the true value and the measured value, and that difference can have many different causes. Libby calculated the error associated with his measurements by counting the number of decay events in the sample in a known amount of time, repeating the measurement over multiple periods, and then using statistical techniques to quantify the error (see our Statistics in Science module).

In 1949, Libby, working with his post-doctoral student James Arnold, reported the first use of radiocarbon dating for determining the age of wood fragments from archaeological sites around the world (Arnold & Libby, 1949). Because the method was new, Arnold and Libby were careful to replicate their measurements to provide a detailed estimate of different types of error, and they compared the results of their method with samples of a known age as a control (Table 1).

Table 1: *Age determinations on samples of known age from Arnold & Libby (1949).*

Sample	Specific Activity (cpm/g carbon)	Age (years)	
	Found	Found	Expected
Tree Ring	11.10 ± 0.31	1100 ± 150	1372 ± 50
	11.52 ± 0.35		
	11.34 ± 0.25		
	10.15 ± 0.44		
	11.08 ± 0.31		
	Average: 10.99 ± 0.15		

The specific activities for five different replicates of a sample of wood from a Douglas fir excavated from the Red Rock Valley are shown in the second column of Table 1. Each individual measurement has an error shown to the right of it, indicated by the ± sign. Arnold and Libby describe these measurements in their paper, stating, "The errors quoted for the specific activity measurements are standard deviations as computed from the Poisson statistics of counting random events." In other words, the individual error is calculated from the expected uncertainties associated with radioactive decay for each sample.

As seen in Table 1, an average specific activity value (10.99) is provided at the bottom with an overall error. The overall error (0.15) is smaller than the individual error reported with each measurement. This is an important feature of the statistical calculation of error associated with scientific data – as you increase the number of measurements of a value, you decrease the uncertainty and increase the confidence associated with the approximation of the value. The error reported alongside of the specific activity provides a measure of the precision of the value, and is commonly referred to as statistical error. Statistical error is what Pearson described as the inherent uncertainty of a measurement. It is caused by random fluctuations within a system, such as the random fluctuation of radioactive decay, and is sometimes referred to as *random error* as the researcher has little control over it. Statistical error cannot be eliminated, as Pearson described, but it can be measured and reduced by conducting repeated observations of a specific event.

In column 3 of Table 1, Arnold and Libby estimate the age of the Douglas fir sample based on the ^{14}C activity as 1100 years old (placing its first season of growth in the year 849 CE). In column 4 of Table 1, they report the actual age of the Douglas fir as calculated by counting tree rings in the sample as 1372 years old (placing its first season in the year 577 CE). By comparing the ^{14}C age to a theoretically correct value as determined by the tree ring count, Arnold and Libby allow the reader to gauge the accuracy of their method, and this provides a measure of a second type of error encountered in science: systematic error. *Statistical error* cannot be eliminated, but it can be measured and reduced by conducting repeated observations of a specific event. *Systematic error*, in contrast, can be corrected for – like if you know your oven is 50° too hot, you set it for 300° rather than 350°.

Based on their data, Arnold and Libby state that the "agreement between prediction and observation is seen to be satisfactory." However, as he continued to do research to establish the method of ^{14}C-dating, Libby began to recognize that the discrepancy between radiocarbon dating and other methods was even larger for older objects, especially those greater than 4,000 years old (W.F. Libby, 1963). Where theoretically correct dates on very old objects could be established by other means, such as in samples from the temples of Egypt, where a calendar system was well-established, the ages obtained through the radiocarbon dating method (the "found" ages in Table 1) were consistently older than the "expected" dates, often by as much as 500 years.

Libby knew that there was bound to be statistical error in these measurements and had anticipated using ^{14}C-dating to calculate a range of dates for objects. But the problem he encountered was different: ^{14}C-dating systematically calculated ages that differed by as much as 500 years from the actual ages of older objects. Systematic error, like Libby encountered, is due to an unknown but non-random fluctuation, like instrumental bias or a faulty assumption. The radiocarbon dating method had achieved good precision, replicate analyses gave dates within 150 years of one another as seen in Table 1; but initially it showed poor precision – the "found" ^{14}C age of the Douglas fir was almost 300 years different than the "expected" age, and other objects were off by some 500 years.

Unlike statistical error, systematic error can be compensated for, or sometimes even eliminated if its source can be identified. In the case of ^{14}C-dating, it was later discovered that the reason for the systematic error was a faulty assumption: Libby and many other scientists had assumed that the production rate for ^{14}C in the atmosphere was constant over time, but it is not. Instead, it fluctuates with changes in Earth's magnetic field, the uptake of carbon by plants, and other factors. In addition, levels of radioactive ^{14}C increased through the 20th century because nuclear weapons testing released high levels of radiation to the atmosphere.

In the decades since Libby first published his method, researchers have recalibrated the radiocarbon dating method with tree-ring dates from bristlecone pine trees (Damon et al., 1974) and corals (Fairbanks et al., 2005) to correct for the fluctuations in the production of ^{14}C in the atmosphere. As a result, both the precision and accuracy of radiocarbon dates have increased dramatically. For example, in 2000, Xiaohong Wu and colleagues at Peking University in Beijing used radiocarbon dating on bones of the Marquises (lords) of Jin recovered from a cemetery in Shanxi Province in China (see Table 2) (Wu et al., 2000). As seen in Table 2, not only is the precision of the estimates (ranging from 18 to 44 years) much tighter than Libby's reported 150 year error range for the Douglas fir samples, but the radiocarbon dates are highly accurate, with the reported deaths dates of the Jin (the theoretically correct values) falling within the statistical error ranges reported in all three cases.

Table 2: Radiocarbon estimates and documented death dates of three of the Marquises of Jin from Wu et al. (2000).

Name of Jin Marquis	Radiocarbon Date (BCE)	Documented Death Date (BCE)
Jing	860 – 816	841
Li	834 – 804	823
Xian	814 – 796	812

Comprehension Checkpoint

Which type of error is not random and can be compensated for?

A)   statistical error

B)   systematic error

Confidence: Reporting uncertainty and error

As a result of error, scientific measurements are not reported as single values, but rather as ranges or averages with error bars in a graph or ± sign in a table. Karl Pearson first described mathematical methods for determining the probability distributions of scientific measurements, and these methods form the basis of statistical applications in scientific research (see our Statistics in Scientific Research module). Statistical techniques allow us to estimate and report the error surrounding a value after repeated measurement of that value. For example, both Libby and Wu reported their estimates as ranges of one standard deviation around the mean, or average, measurement. The standard deviation provides a measure of the range of variability of individual measurements, and specifically, defines a range that encompasses 34.1% of individual measurements above the mean value and 34.1% of those below the mean. The standard deviation of a range of measurements can be used to compute a confidence interval around the value.

Confidence statements do not, as some people believe, provide a measure of how "correct" a measurement is. Instead, a confidence statement describes the probability that a measurement range will overlap the mean value of a measurement when a study is repeated. This may sound a bit confusing, but consider a study by Yoshikata Morimoto and colleagues, who examined the average pitch speed of eight college baseball players (Morimoto et al., 2003). Each of the pitchers was required to throw six pitches, and the average pitch speed was found to be 34.6 m/s (77.4 mph) with a 95% confidence interval of 34.6 ± 0.2 m/s (34.4 m/s to 34.8 m/s). When he later repeated this study requiring that each of the eight pitchers throw 18 pitches, the average speed was found to be 34.7 m/s, exactly within the confidence interval obtained during the first study.

In this case, there is no "theoretically correct" value, but the confidence interval provides an estimate of the probability that a similar result will be found if the study is repeated. Given that Morimoto determined a 95% confidence interval, if he repeated his study 100 times (without exhausting his baseball pitchers), his confidence interval would overlap the mean pitch speed 95 times, and the other five studies would likely yield pitch speeds that fall outside of his confidence interval.

In science, an important indication of confidence within a measurement is the number of significant figures reported. Morimoto reported his measurement to one decimal place (34.6 m/s) because his instrumentation supported this level of precision. He was able to distinguish differences in pitches that were 34.6 m/s and 34.7 m/s. Had he just rounded his measurements to 35 m/s, he would have lost a significant amount of detail contained within his data. Further, his instrumentation did not support the precision needed to report additional significant figures (for example, 34.62 m/s). Incorrectly reporting significant figures can introduce substantial error into a data set.

Comprehension Checkpoint

Scientific measurements are reported as ranges or with the +/- sign rather than as single values because

A) every measurement has some degree of error.

B) some scientists are not sure that their calculations are correct.

Error propagation

As Pearson recognized, uncertainty is inherent in scientific research, and for that reason it is critically important for scientists to recognize and account for the errors within a dataset. Disregarding the source of an error can result in the propagation and magnification of that error. For example, in 1960 the American mathematician and meteorologist Edward Norton Lorenz was working on a mathematical model for predicting the weather (see our Modeling in Scientific Research module) (Gleick, 1987; Lorenz, 1993). Lorenz was using a Royal McBee computer to iteratively solve 12 equations that expressed relationships such as that between atmospheric pressure and wind speed. Lorenz would input starting values for several variables into his computer, such as temperature, wind speed, and barometric pressure on a given day at a series of locations. The model would then calculate weather changes over a defined period of time. The model recalculated a single day's worth of weather changes in single minute increments and printed out the new parameters.

On one occasion, Lorenz decided to rerun a particular model scenario. Instead of starting from the beginning, which would have taken many hours, he decided to pick up in the middle of the run, consulting the printout of parameters and re-entering these into his computer. He then left his computer for the hour it would take to recalculate the model, expecting to return and find a weather pattern similar to the one predicted previously.

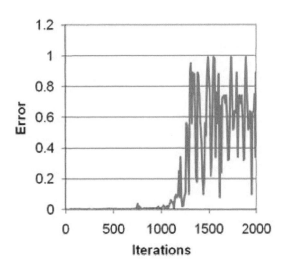

Figure 2: Representation of error propagation in an iterative, dynamic system. After ~1,000 iterations, the error is equivalent to the value of the measurement itself (~0.6), making the calculation fluctuate wildly. Adapted from IMO (2007).

Unexpectedly, Lorenz found that the resulting weather prediction was completely different from the original pattern he observed. What Lorenz did not realize at the time was that while his computer stored the numerical values of the model parameters to six significant figures (for example 0.639172), his printout, and thus the numbers he inputted when restarting the model, were rounded to three significant figures (0.639). The difference between the two numbers is minute, representing a margin of systematic error less than 0.1% – less than one thousandth of the value of each parameter. However, with each iteration of his model (and there were thousands of iterations), this error was compounded, multiplying many times over so that his end result was completely different from the first run of the model. As can be seen in Figure 2, the error appears to remain small, but after a few hundred iterations it grows exponentially until reaching a magnitude equivalent to the value of the measurement itself (~0.6).

Lorenz published his observations in the now classic work Deterministic Nonperiodic Flow (Lorenz, 1963). His observations led him to conclude that accurate weather prediction over a period of more than a few weeks was extremely difficult – perhaps impossible – because even infinitesimally small errors in the measurement of natural conditions were compounded and quickly reached levels equal to the measurements themselves.

The work motivated other researchers to begin looking at other dynamic systems that are similarly sensitive to initial starting conditions, such as the flow of water in a stream or the dynamics of population change. In 1975, the American mathematician and physicist James Yorke and his collaborator, the Chinese-born mathematician Tien-Yien Li, coined the term *chaos* to describe these systems (Li & Yorke, 1975). Again, unlike the common use of the term chaos, which implies randomness or a state of disarray, the science of chaos is not about randomness. Rather, as Lorenz was the first to do, chaos researchers work to understand underlying patterns of behavior in complex systems toward understanding and quantifying this uncertainty.

Comprehension Checkpoint

Scientists should look for the source of error within a dataset

A) *only when* the error is very large.

B) *even when* the error is very small.

Error propagation is not limited to mathematical modeling. It is always a concern in scientific research, especially in studies that proceed stepwise in multiple increments because error in one step can easily be compounded in the next step. As a result, scientists have developed a number of techniques to help quantify error. Here are two examples:

Controls: The use of controls in scientific experiments (see our Experimentation in Scientific Research module) helps quantify statistical error within an experiment and identify systematic error in order to either measure or eliminate it.

Blind trials: In research that involves human judgment, such as studies that try to quantify the perception of pain relief following administration of a pain-relieving drug, scientists often work to minimize error by using "blinds." In blind trials, the treatment (i.e. the drug) will be compared to a control (i.e. another drug or a placebo); neither the patient nor the researcher will know if the patient is receiving the treatment or the control. In this way, systematic error due to preconceptions about the utility of a treatment is avoided.

Error reduction and measurement efforts in scientific research are sometimes referred to as *quality assurance* and *quality control.* Quality assurance generally refers to the plans that a researcher has for minimizing and measuring error in his or her research; quality control refers to the actual procedures implemented in the research. The terms are most commonly used interchangeably and in unison, as in "quality assurance/quality control" (QA/QC). QA/QC includes steps such as calibrating instruments or measurements against known standards, reporting all instrument detection limits, implementing standardized procedures to minimize human error, thoroughly documenting research methods, replicating measurements to determine precision, and a host of other techniques, often specific to the type of research being conducted, and reported in the *Materials and Methods* section of a scientific paper (see our Understanding Scientific Journals and Articles module).

Reduction of statistical error is often as simple as repeating a research measurement or observation many times to reduce the uncertainty in the range of values obtained. Systematic error can be more difficult to pin down, creeping up in research due to instrumental bias, human mistakes, poor research design, or incorrect assumptions about the behavior of variables in a system. From this standpoint, identifying and quantifying the source of systematic error in research can help scientists better understand the behavior of the system itself.

Uncertainty as a state of nature

While Karl Pearson proposed that individual measurements could not yield exact values, he felt that careful and repeated scientific investigation coupled with statistical analysis could allow one to determine the true value of a measurement. A younger contemporary of Pearson's, the English statistician Ronald Aylmer Fisher, extended and, at the same time, contradicted this concept. Fisher felt that because all measurements contained inherent error, one could never identify the exact or "correct" value of a measurement. According to Fisher, the true distribution of a measurement is unattainable; statistical techniques therefore do not estimate the "true" value of a measurement, but rather they are used to minimize error and develop range estimates that approximate the theoretically correct value of the measurement. A natural consequence of his idea is that occasionally the approximation may be incorrect.

In the first half of the 20th century, the concept of uncertainty reached new heights with the discovery of quantum mechanics. In the quantum world, uncertainty is not an inconvenience; it is a state of being. For example, the decay of a radioactive element is inherently an uncertain event. We can predict the probability of the decay profile of a mass of radioactive atoms, but we can never predict the exact time that an individual radioactive atom will undergo decay. Or consider the Heisenberg Uncertainty Principle in quantum physics, which states that measuring the position of a particle makes the momentum of the particle inherently uncertain, and, conversely, measuring the particle's momentum makes its position inherently uncertain.

Once we understand the concept of uncertainty as it applies to science, we can begin to see that the purpose of scientific data analysis is to identify and quantify error and variability toward uncovering the relationships, patterns, and behaviors that occur in nature. Scientific knowledge itself continues to evolve as new data and new studies help us understand and quantify uncertainty in the natural world.

Key Concepts for this chapter

▶ Uncertainty is the quantitative estimation of error present in data; all measurements contain some uncertainty generated through systematic error and/or random error..

▶ Acknowledging the uncertainty of data is an important component of reporting the results of scientific investigation.

▶ Uncertainty is commonly misunderstood to mean that scientists are not certain of their results, but the term specifies the degree to which scientists are confident in their data.

▶ Careful methodology can reduce uncertainty by correcting for systematic error and minimizing random error. However, uncertainty can never be reduced to zero.

References

Arnold, J. R., & Libby, W. F. (1949). Age determinations by radiocarbon content: Checks with samples of known age. *Science*, 110, 678-680.

Damon, P. E., Ferguson, C. W., Long, A., & Wallick, E. I. (1974). Dendrochronologic calibration of the radiocarbon time scale. *American Antiquity*, 39(2), 350-366.

Fairbanks, R. G., Mortlock, R. A., Chiu, T.-C., Cao, L., Kaplan, A., Guilderson, T. P., . . . Nadeau, M. (2005). Radiocarbon calibration curve spanning 0 to 50,000 years BP based on paired 230Th/ 234U/ 238U and 14C dates on pristine corals. *Quaternary Science Reviews*, 24, 1781-1796.

Gleick, J. (1987) *Chaos: Making a new science*. New York: Penguin Books.

IMO. (2007). Long range weather prediction. *The Icelandic Meteorological Office*. Retrieved December 18, 2007, from http://andvari.vedur.is/~halldor/HB/Met210old/pred.html

Li, T. Y., & Yorke, J. A. (1975). Period three implies chaos. *American Mathematical Monthly*, 82, 985.

Libby, W. F. (1946). Atmospheric helium three and radiocarbon from cosmic radiation. *Physical Review*, 69(11-12), 671-672.

Libby, W. F. (1963). Accuracy of radiocarbon dates. *Science*, 140, 278-280.

Libby, W. F., Anderson, E. C., & Arnold, J. R. (1949). Age determination by radiocarbon content: World-wide assay of natural radiocarbon. *Science*, 109(2827), 227-228.

Lorenz, E. (1963). Deterministic nonperiodic flow. *Journal of the Atmospheric Sciences*, 20, 130-141.

Lorenz, E. (1993). *The essence of chaos*. The University of Washington Press.

Morimoto, Y., Ito, K., Kawamura, T., & Muraki, Y. (2003). Immediate effect of assisted and resisted training using different weight balls on ball speed and accuracy in baseball pitching. *International Journal of Sport and Health Science*, 1(2), 238-246.

Peat, F. D. (2002). *From certainty to uncertainty: The story of science and ideas in the twentieth century*. Joseph Henry Press, National Academies Press.

Salsburg, D. (2001). *The lady tasting tea: How statistics revolutionized science in the twentieth century*. New York: W. H. Freeman & Company.

Wagner, C. H. (1983). Uncertainty in science and statistics. *The Two-Year College Mathematics Journal*, 14(4), 360-363.

Wu, X., Yuan, S., Wang, J., Guo, Z., Liu, K., Lu, X., . . . Cai, L. (2000). AMS radiocarbon dating of cemetery of Jin Marquises in China. *Nuclear Instruments and Methods in Physics Research*, B, 172(1-4), 732-735.

Take the Quiz ▶ ▶ ▶

Uncertainty, Error, and Confidence Quiz

1. When scientists report uncertainty in their data, they are

    A) stating that they do not know what their research means.

    B) expressing concern over whether their data is correct.

    C) suggesting that others should not trust their conclusions.

    D) quantifying the degree of error and variability present in the data.

2. The picture below provides an example of

    A) high accuracy, low precision.

    B) low accuracy, high precision.

    C) low accuracy, low precision

    D) high accuracy, high precision.

3. Karl Pearson proposed that uncertainty in scientific measurements

    A) is the cause of poor science.

    B) is avoidable in most circumstances.

    C) is primarily due to instrument error.

    D) is inherent in nature.

4. The difference between statistical error and systematic error is best described by which of the following?

    A) Statistical error is due to random fluctuations, while systematic error is due to an introduced bias.

    B) Statistical error is due to an introduced bias, while systematic error is due to random fluctuations.

    C) Statistical error is due to statistics, while systematic error is due to the system.

    D) Statistical error can be eliminated, while systematic error cannot.

5. Increasing the number of measurements of a value generally increases the confidence one has in that value.

    A) True

    B) False

6. When scientists report error in their data, they are

    A) admitting that their research is wrong.

    B) detailing the mistakes that they have made.

    C) quantifying the variability associated with their measurements.

    D) presenting the probability that their research will turn out to be wrong.

7. When a confidence interval is reported with a measurement, what does it indicate?

    A) The level to which a reader can be confident in the author's conclusions.

    B) The probability that a similar result will be found if a study is repeated.

    C) The reasons that a researcher should be confident in their data.

    D) The probability that the research has found the exact value of an individual measurement.

8. The efforts scientists make toward minimizing and measuring error in their research are generally referred to as:

    A) error propagation/minimization.

    B) replication.

    C) confidence assurance.

    D) quality assurance/quality control.

Answers and feedback can be found on Page 288

Data Analysis and Interpretation

by Anne Egger, PhD and Anthony Carpi, PhD

Did you know that scientists don't always agree on what data mean? Different scientists can look at the same set of data and come up with different explanations for it, and disagreement among scientists doesn't point to bad science.

In this module

Data analysis is at the heart of any scientific investigation. Using weather as an example, this module takes you through the steps of data collection, analysis, interpretation, and evaluation. You will see how scientists (1) collect and record data, (2) find patterns in data, (3) explain those patterns, and (4) share their research with the larger scientific community.

Terms you should know:

analysis = careful study of data to look for patterns

data = pieces of information collected through observation and measurement

dataset = a collection of measurements and observations that can be analyzed

interpretation = an explanation of patterns observed in the data

Before you decide what to wear in the morning, you collect a variety of data: the season of the year, what the forecast says the weather is going to be like, which clothes are clean and which are dirty, and what you will be doing during the day. You then analyze those data. Perhaps you think, "It's summer, so it's usually warm." That analysis helps you determine the best course of action, and you base your apparel decision on your interpretation of the information. You might choose a t-shirt and shorts on a summer day when you know you'll be outside, but bring a sweater with you if you know you'll be in an air-conditioned building.

Though this example may seem simplistic, it reflects the way scientists pursue data collection, analysis, and interpretation. Data (the plural form of the word *datum*) are scientific observations and measurements that, once analyzed and interpreted, can be developed into evidence to address a question. Data lie at the heart of all scientific investigations, and all scientists collect data in one form or another. The weather forecast that helped you decide what to wear, for example, was an interpretation made by a meteorologist who analyzed data collected by satellites. Data may take the form of the number of bacteria colonies growing in soup broth (see our Experimentation in Science module), a series of drawings or photographs of the different layers of rock that form a mountain range (see our Description in Science module), a tally of lung cancer victims in populations of cigarette smokers and non-smokers (see our Comparison in Science module), or the changes in average annual temperature predicted by a model of global climate (see our Modeling in Science module).

Scientific data collection involves more care than you might use in a casual glance at the thermometer to see what you should wear. Because scientists build on their own work and the work of others, it is important that they are systematic and consistent in their data collection methods and make detailed records so that others can see and use the data they collect.

But collecting data is only one step in a scientific investigation, and scientific knowledge is much more than a simple compilation of data points. The world is full of observations that can be made, but not every observation constitutes a useful piece of data. For example, your meteorologist could record the outside air temperature every second of the day, but would that make the forecast any more accurate than recording it once an hour? Probably not. All scientists make choices about which data are most relevant to their research and what to do with those data: how to turn a collection of measurements into a useful dataset through processing and analysis, and how to interpret those analyzed data in the context of what they already know. The thoughtful and systematic collection, analysis, and interpretation of data allow them to be developed into evidence that supports scientific ideas, arguments, and hypotheses.

Data collection, analysis, and interpretation: Weather and climate

The weather has long been a subject of widespread data collection, analysis, and interpretation. Accurate measurements of air temperature became possible in the mid 1700s when Daniel Gabriel Fahrenheit invented the first standardized mercury thermometer in 1714 (see our Temperature module). Air temperature, wind speed, and wind direction are all critical navigational information for sailors on the ocean, but in the late 1700s and early 1800s, as sailing expeditions became common, this information was not easy to come by. The lack of reliable data was of great concern to Matthew Fontaine Maury, the superintendent of the Depot of Charts and Instruments of the US Navy. As a result, Maury organized the first international Maritime Conference, held in Brussels, Belgium, in 1853. At this meeting, international standards for taking weather measurements on ships were established and a system for sharing this information between countries was founded.

Defining uniform data collection standards was an important step in producing a truly global dataset of meteorological information, allowing data collected by many different people in different parts of the world to be gathered together into a single database. Maury's compilation of sailors' standardized data on wind and currents is shown in Figure 1 (see the Resources section in the online version of this module for the original text). The early international cooperation and investment in weather-related data collection has produced a valuable long-term record of air temperature that goes back to the 1850s.

This vast store of information is considered "raw" data: tables of numbers (dates and temperatures), descriptions (cloud cover), location, etc. Raw data can be useful in and of itself – for example, if you wanted to know the air temperature in London on June 5th, 1801. But the data alone cannot tell you anything about how temperature has changed in London over the past two hundred years, or how that information is related to global-scale climate change. In order for patterns and trends to be seen, data, must be analyzed and interpreted first. The analyzed and interpreted data may then be used as evidence in scientific arguments, to support a hypothesis or a theory.

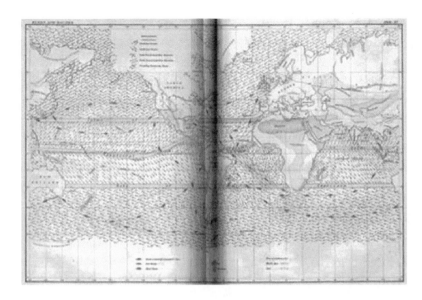

Figure 1: *Plate XV from Maury, Matthew F. 1858. The Winds. Chapter in:* Explanations and Sailing Directions. *Washington: Hon. Issaac Toucey.*

Good data are a potential treasure trove – they can be mined by scientists at any time – and thus an important part of any scientific investigation is accurate and consistent recording of data and the methods used to collect those data. The weather data collected since the 1850s have been just such a treasure trove, based in part upon the standards established by Matthew Maury. These standards provided guidelines for data collection and recording that assured consistency within the dataset. At the time, ship captains were able to utilize the data to determine the most reliable routes to sail across the oceans. Many modern scientists studying climate change have taken advantage of this same dataset to understand how global air temperatures have changed over the recent past. In neither case can one simply look at the table of numbers and observations and answer the question – which route to take, or how global climate has changed. Instead, both questions require analysis and interpretation of the data.

Comprehension Checkpoint

Data are most valuable when they are collected

A) based on uniform standards.

B) by many different people.

Data analysis: A complex and challenging process

Though it may sound straightforward to take 150 years of air temperature data and describe how global climate has changed, the process of analyzing and interpreting those data is actually quite complex. Consider the range of temperatures around the world on any given day in January (see Figure 2): in Johannesburg, South Africa, where it is summer, the air temperature can reach 35° C (95° F), and in Fairbanks, Alaska at that same time of year, it is the middle of winter and air temperatures might be -35° C (-31° F). Now consider that over huge expanses of the ocean, where no consistent measurements are available. One could simply take an average of all of the available measurements for a single day to get a global air temperature average for that day, but that number would not take into account the natural variability within and uneven distribution of those measurements.

Figure 2: *Satellite image composite of average air temperatures (in degrees Celsius) across the globe on January 2, 2008.*

Defining a single global average temperature requires scientists to make several decisions about how to process all of those data into a meaningful set of numbers. In 1986, climatologists Phil Jones, Tom Wigley, and Peter Wright published one of the first attempts to assess changes in global mean surface air temperature from 1861 to 1984 (Jones, Wigley, & Wright, 1986). The majority of their paper – three out of five pages – describes the processing techniques they used to correct for the problems and inconsistencies in the historical data that would not be related to climate. For example, the authors note that

> Early SSTs [sea surface temperatures] were measured using water collected in uninsulated, canvas buckets, while more recent data come either from insulated bucket or cooling water intake measurements, with the latter considered to be 0.3-0.7° C warmer that uninsulated bucket measurements.

Correcting for this bias may seem simple, just adding ~0.5° C to early canvas bucket measurements, but it becomes more complicated than that because, the authors continue, the majority of SST data do not include a description of what kind of bucket or system was used.

Similar problems were encountered with marine air temperature data. Historical air temperature measurements over the ocean were taken aboard ships, but the type and size of ship could affect the measurement because size "determines the height at which observations were taken." Air temperature can change rapidly with height above the ocean. The authors therefore applied a correction for ship size in their data. Once Jones, Wigley, and Wright had made several of these kinds of corrections, they analyzed their data using a spatial averaging technique that placed measurements within grid cells on the Earth's surface in order to account for the fact that there were many more measurements taken on land than over the oceans.

Developing this grid required many decisions based on their experience and judgment, such as how large each grid cell needed to be and how to distribute the cells over the Earth. They then calculated the mean temperature within each grid cell, and combined all of these means to calculate a global average air temperature for each year. Statistical techniques such as averaging are commonly used in the research process and can help identify trends and relationships within and between datasets (see our Statistics in Science module). Once these spatially averaged global mean temperatures were calculated, the authors compared the means over time, from 1861 to 1984.

A common method for analyzing data that occurs in a series, such as temperature measurements over time, is to look at anomalies, or differences from a pre-defined reference value. In this case, the authors compared their temperature values to the mean of the years 1970–1979 (see Figure 3). This reference mean is subtracted from each annual mean to produce the jagged lines in Figure 3, which display positive or negative anomalies (values greater or less than zero). Though this may seem to be a circular or complex way to display this these data, it is useful because the goal is to show *change* in mean temperatures rather than absolute values.

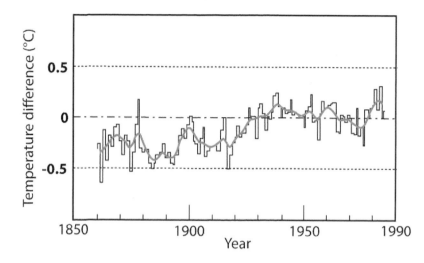

Figure 3: The black line shows global temperature anomalies, or differences between averaged yearly temperature measurements and the reference value for the entire globe. The smooth, gray line is a filtered 10-year average. (Based on Figure 5 in Jones et al., 1986).

Putting data into a visual format can facilitate additional analysis (see our Using Graphs and Visual Data module). Figure 3 shows a lot of variability in the data: there are a number of spikes and dips in global temperature throughout the period examined. It can be challenging to see trends in data that have so much variability; our eyes are drawn to the extreme values in the jagged lines like the large spike in temperature around 1876 or the significant dip around 1918. However, these extremes do not necessarily reflect long-term trends in the data.

In order to more clearly see long-term patterns and trends, Jones and his co-authors used another processing technique and applied a filter to the data by calculating a 10-year running average to smooth the data. The smooth lines in the graph represent the filtered data. The smooth line follows the data closely, but it does not reach the extreme values.

Data processing and analysis are sometimes misinterpreted as manipulating data to achieve the desired results, but in reality, the goal of these methods is to make the data clearer, not to change it fundamentally. As described above, in addition to reporting data, scientists report the data processing and analysis methods they use when they publish their work (see our Understanding Scientific Journals and Articles module), allowing their peers the opportunity to assess both the raw data and the techniques used to analyze them.

The analyzed data can then be interpreted and explained. In general, when scientists interpret data, they attempt to explain the patterns and trends uncovered through analysis, bringing all of their background knowledge, experience, and skills to bear on the question and relating their data to existing scientific ideas. Given the personal nature of the knowledge they draw upon, this step can be subjective, but that subjectivity is scrutinized through the peer review process (see our Peer Review in Science module). Based on the smoothed curves, Jones, Wigley, and Wright interpreted their data to show a long-term warming trend. They note that the three warmest years in the entire dataset are 1980, 1981, and 1983. They do not go further in their interpretation to suggest possible causes for the temperature increase, however, but merely state that the results are "extremely interesting when viewed in the light of recent ideas of the causes of climate change."

Comprehension Checkpoint

There is only one correct way to analyze and interpret scientific data.

A) True

B) False

Different interpretations in the scientific community

The data presented in this study were widely accepted throughout the scientific community, in large part due to their careful description of the data and their process of analysis. Through the 1980s, however, a few scientists remained skeptical about their interpretation of a warming trend.

In 1990, Richard Lindzen, a meteorologist at the Massachusetts Institute of Technology, published a paper expressing his concerns with the warming interpretation (Lindzen, 1990). Lindzen highlighted several issues that he believed weakened the arguments for global temperature increases. First, he argued that the data collection was inadequate, suggesting that the current network of data collection stations was not sufficient to correct for the uncertainty inherent in data with so much natural variability (consider how different the weather is in Antarctica and the Sahara Desert on any given day). Second, he argued that the data analysis was faulty, and that the substantial gaps in coverage, particularly over the ocean, raised questions regarding the ability of such a dataset to adequately represent the global system. Finally, Lindzen suggested that the interpretation of the global mean temperature data is inappropriate, and that there is no trend in the data. He noted a decrease in the mean temperature from 1940 to 1970 at a time when atmospheric CO_2 levels, a proposed cause for the temperature increases, were increasing rapidly. In other words, Lindzen brought a different background and set of experiences and ideas to bear on the same dataset, and came to very different conclusions.

This type of disagreement is common in science, and generally leads to more data collection and research. In fact, the differences in interpretation over the presence or absence of a trend motivated climate scientists to extend the temperature record in both directions – going back further into the past and continuing forward with the establishment of dedicated weather stations around the world. In 1998, Michael Mann, Raymond Bradley, and Malcolm Hughes published a paper that greatly expanded the record originally cited by Jones, Wigley, and Wright (Mann, Bradley, & Hughes, 1998). Of course, they were not able to use air temperature readings from thermometers to extend the record back to 1000 CE; instead, the authors used data from other sources that could provide information about air temperature to reconstruct past climate, like tree ring width, ice core data, and coral growth records (Figure 4, dark gray line).

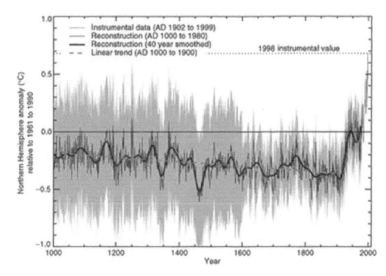

Figure 4: *Differences between annual mean temperature and mean temperature during the reference period. Medium gray line represents data from tree ring, ice core and coral growth records, light dotted line represents data measured with modern instruments. Graph adapted from Mann et al. published in IPCC Third Assessment Report.*

Mann, Bradley, and Hughes used many of the same analysis techniques as Jones and co-authors, such as applying a ten-year running average, and in addition, they included measurement uncertainty on their graph: the gray region shown on the graph in Figure 4. Reporting error and uncertainty for data does not imply that the measurements are wrong or faulty – in fact, just the opposite is true. The magnitude of the error describes how confident the scientists are in the accuracy of the data, so bigger reported errors indicate less confidence (see our Uncertainty, Error, and Confidence module). They note that the magnitude of the uncertainty increases going further back in time, but becomes more tightly constrained around 1900.

In their interpretation, the authors describe several trends they see in the data: several warmer and colder periods throughout the record (for example, compare the data around year 1360 to 1460 in Figure 4), and a pronounced warming trend in the twentieth century. In fact, they note that "almost all years before the twentieth century [are] well below the twentieth-century ... mean", and these show a linear trend of decreasing temperature (Figure 4, dashed line). Interestingly, where Jones et al. reported that the three warmest years were all within the last decade of their record, the same is true for the much more extensive dataset: Mann et al. report that the warmest years in their dataset, which runs through 1998, were 1990, 1995, and 1997.

Debate over data interpretation spurs further research

The debate over the interpretation of data related to climate change as well as the interest in the consequences of these changes have led to an enormous increase in the number of scientific research studies addressing climate change, and multiple lines of scientific evidence now support the conclusions initially made by Jones, Wigley, and Wright in the mid 1980s. All of these results are summarized in the Fourth Assessment Report (AR4) of the Intergovernmental Panel on Climate Change (IPCC), released to the public in 2007 (IPCC, 2007). Based on the agreement between these multiple datasets, the team of contributing scientists wrote:

> Warming of the climate system is unequivocal, as is now evident from observations of increases in global average air and ocean temperatures, widespread melting of snow and ice, and rising global average sea level.

The short phrase "now evident" reflects the accumulation of data over time, including the most recent data up to 2007.

A higher level of data interpretation involves determining the reason for the temperature increases. The AR4 goes on to say:

> Most of the observed increase in global average temperatures since the mid-20th century is very likely due to the observed increase in anthropogenic greenhouse gas concentrations.

This statement relies on many data sources in addition to the temperature data, including data as diverse as the timing of the first appearance of tree buds in spring, greenhouse gas concentrations in the atmosphere, and measurements of isotopes of oxygen and hydrogen from ice cores. Analyzing and interpreting such a diverse array of datasets requires the combined expertise of the many scientists that contributed to the IPCC report. This type of broad synthesis of data and interpretation is critical to the process of science, highlighting how individual scientists build on the work of others and potentially inspiring collaboration for further research between scientists in different disciplines.

Data interpretation is not a free-for-all, nor are all interpretations equally valid. Interpretation involves constructing a logical scientific argument that explains the data. Scientific interpretations are neither absolute truth nor personal opinion: They are inferences, suggestions, or hypotheses about what the data mean, based on a foundation of scientific knowledge and individual expertise. When scientists begin to interpret their data, they draw on their personal and collective knowledge, often talking over results with a colleague across the hall or on another continent. They use experience, logic, and parsimony to construct one or more plausible explanations for the data. As within any human endeavor, scientists can make mistakes or even intentionally deceive their peers (see our Scientific Ethics module), but the vast majority of scientists present interpretations that they feel are most reasonable and supported by the data.

Comprehension Checkpoint

If scientists disagree on how a set of data is interpreted, this generally

A) means that the data are not valid and the research was a waste of time.

B) leads to additional data collection and research.

Making data available

The process of data collection, analysis, and interpretation happens on multiple scales. It occurs over the course of a day, a year, or many years, and may involve one or many scientists whose priorities change over time. One of the fundamentally important components of the practice of science is therefore the publication of data in the scientific literature (see our Utilizing the Scientific Literature module). Properly collected and archived data continue to be useful as new research questions emerge. In fact, some research involves re-analysis of data with new techniques, different ways of looking at the data, or combining the results of several studies.

For example, in 1997, the Collaborative Group on Hormonal Factors in Breast Cancer published a widely-publicized study in the prestigious medical journal *The Lancet* entitled,

"Breast cancer and hormone replacement therapy: collaborative reanalysis of data from 51 epidemiological studies of 52,705 women with breast cancer and 108,411 women without breast cancer" (Collaborative Group on Hormonal Factors in Breast Cancer, 1997). The possible link between breast cancer and hormone replacement therapy (HRT) had been studied for years, with mixed results: some scientists suggested a small increase of cancer risk associated with HRT as early as 1981 (Brinton et al., 1981), but later research suggested no increased risk (Kaufman et al., 1984). By bringing together results from numerous studies and reanalyzing the data together, the researchers concluded that women who were treated with hormone replacement therapy were more likely to develop breast cancer. In describing why the reanalysis was used, the authors write:

> The increase in the relative risk of breast cancer associated with each year of [HRT] use in current and recent users is small, so inevitably some studies would, by chance alone, show significant associations and others would not. Combination of the results across many studies has the obvious advantage of reducing such random fluctuations.

In many cases, data collected for other purposes can be used to address new questions. The initial reason for collecting weather data, for example, was to better predict winds and storms to help assure safe travel for trading ships. It is only more recently that interest shifted to long-term changes in the weather, but the same data easily contribute to answering both of those questions.

Technology for sharing data advances science

One of the most exciting advances in science today is the development of public databases of scientific information that can be accessed and used by anyone. For example, climatic and oceanographic data, which are generally very expensive to obtain because they require large-scale operations like drilling ice cores or establishing a network of buoys across the Pacific Ocean, are shared online through several web sites run by agencies responsible for maintaining and distributing those data, such as the Carbon Dioxide Information Analysis Center run by the US Department of Energy (see the Resources section in the online version of this module). Anyone can download those data to conduct their own analyses and make interpretations. Likewise, the Human Genome Project has a searchable database of the human genome, where researchers can both upload and download their data.

The number of these widely available datasets has grown to the point where the National Institute of Standards and Technology actually maintains a database of databases. Some organizations require their participants to make their data publicly available, such as the Incorporated Research Institutions for Seismology (IRIS): the instrumentation branch of IRIS provides support for researchers by offering seismic instrumentation, equipment maintenance and training, and logistical field support for experiments. Anyone can apply to use the instruments as long as they provide IRIS with the data they collect during their seismic experiments. IRIS then makes these data available to the public.

Making data available to other scientists is not a new idea, but having those data available on the Internet in a searchable format has revolutionized the way that scientists can interact with the data, allowing for research efforts that would have been impossible before. This collective pooling of data also allows for new kinds of analysis and interpretation on global scales and over long periods of time. In addition, making data easily accessible helps promote interdisciplinary research by opening the doors to exploration by diverse scientists in many fields.

Key Concepts for this chapter

▶ Data collection is the systematic recording of information; data analysis involves working to uncover patterns and trends in datasets; data interpretation involves explaining those patterns and trends.

▶ Scientists interpret data based on their background knowledge and experience, ; thus, different scientists can interpret the same data in different ways.

▶ By publishing their data and the techniques they used to analyze and interpret those data, scientists give the community the opportunity to both review the data and use it them in future research.

References

Brinton, L. A., Hoover, R. N., Szklo, M., & Fraumeni, J. F. J. (1981). Menopausal estrogen use and risk of breast cancer. *Cancer*, 47(10), 2517-2522.

Collaborative Group on Hormonal Factors in Breast Cancer. (1997). Breast cancer and hormone replacement therapy: Collaborative reanalysis of data from 51 epidemiological studies of 52,705 women with breast cancer and 108,411 women without breast cancer. *The Lancet*, 350(9084), 1047-1059.

IPCC. (2007). *Climate change 2007: The physical science basis. Contribution of Working Group I to the Fourth Assessment Report of the Intergovernmental Panel on Climate Change*. New York: Cambridge University Press.

Jones, P. D., Wigley, T. M. L., & Wright, P. B. (1986). Global temperature variations between 1861 and 1984. *Nature*, 322(6078), 430-434.

Kaufman, D. W., Miller, D. R., Rosenberg, L., Helmrich, S. P., Stolley, P., Schottenfeld, D., & Shapiro, S. (1984). Noncontraceptive estrogen use and the risk of breast cancer. *Journal of the American Medical Association*, 252(1), 63-67.

Lindzen, R. S. (1990). Some coolness concerning global warming. *Bulletin of the American Meteorological Society*, 71(3), 288-299.

Mann, M. E., Bradley, R. S., & Hughes, M. K. (1998). Global-scale temperature patterns and climate forcing over the past six centuries. *Nature*, 392(6678), 779-787.

 *Take the Quiz* ▶ ▶ ▶

Data Analysis and Interpretation Quiz

1. Which of the following would NOT be considered raw data?

   A) A dictionary definition of a word.

   B) A measurement of water temperature on a river gauge.

   C) A satellite image of a hurricane in the Atlantic Ocean.

   D) Latitude and longitude coordinates of the location of a certain tree species.

2. Data analysis can involve many steps, including

   A) statistical analysis.

   B) filtering.

   C) removing bad data.

   D) All of these answers.

3. When scientists develop explanations for their observations and data, they

   A) shouldn't use their intuition.

   B) avoid making assumptions.

   C) use their background knowledge.

   D) try not to be creative.

4. Why have different scientists interpreted air temperature data differently?

   A) The data aren't very high quality.

   B) None of the scientists understand the data.

   C) Different scientists analyze the data differently.

   D) Because many of the interpretations are wrong.

5. A group of scientists is preparing their work for publication. Although they collected 100 data points, they only used 87 of them in the final analysis. Which of the following approaches should they take in publishing their data?

   A) They should publish all the data and describe why they did not use some data.

   B) They should publish all the data and let the reader determine why they did not use some data.

   C) They should publish only the data included in their analysis and explain that they eliminated some.

   D) They should publish only the data included in their analysis and not mention additional data.

6. If data have been carefully and systematically collected, the analysis will provide only one conclusion and eliminate any disagreement.

   A) True

   B) False

7. A scientist might re-analyze data if

   A) another scientist wanted to combine the data with their own.

   B) new data analysis techniques became available.

   C) they decided to create a similar study.

   D) they wanted to use the data in a journal article.

8. Study the graph below. The data shown represents atmospheric CO_2 measurements collected over a period of 36 years. Based on this graph, what trend can you identify about CO_2 concentrations in the atmosphere?

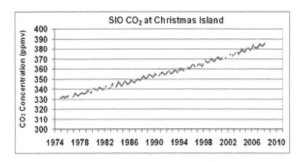

A) Concentrations of CO_2 in the atmosphere are decreasing.

B) Concentrations of CO_2 in the atmosphere are increasing.

C) Concentrations of CO_2 in the atmosphere fluctuate widely.

D) Concentrations of CO_2 in the atmosphere remain constant.

Answers and feedback can be found on Page 289

Utilizing the Scientific Literature

by Anne Egger, PhD and Anthony Carpi, PhD

Did you know that when scientists refer to the "literature," they are not talking about the works of Shakespeare? The scientific literature goes back to the 6th century BCE, when ancient Babylonians recorded lunar eclipses on clay tablets. Science builds on previous findings, so understanding how scientists utilize the scientific literature is key to understanding how science works.

Module Summary

Scientific literature is central to the development of science as a whole. This module explains what scientists mean when they refer to the scientific literature and offers specific examples of how scientists use it to (1) discover what other work has been done on a topic, (2) cite sources of their data, and (3) show how their interpretations relate to existing knowledge.

Terms you should know:

archive = a collection of documents or resource material

literature = printed material; a body of written work; a collection of writings in a subject area

publish = to produce a work in printed form, such as in a journal, book, or newspaper

---

Think about something you know and understand very well. Maybe you know everything about your favorite musical group, and when your friend asks you about them, you can list all of their songs and the band members' names and maybe even something about their history. Maybe you even predict when their next big hit will come out, based on what you know. Your friend asks how you know so much, and you admit that you read a book about them, and have all their albums, and you keep up on their tour dates on their web page. You've been to their concerts and seen them perform. You are referencing your sources, explaining how you know the facts, and why you are so comfortable making a prediction about them – and your friend trusts your knowledge and thus gives your opinion some weight.

Scientists use references in much the same way, drawing on available information to conduct their research. But unlike you when expressing your opinion about your favorite band, scientists are, in fact, obligated to provide the details about where they got that information. The scientific literature is designed to be a reliable archive of scientific research, providing a growing, stable base for new research investigations. When scientists present their new ideas and results to the community, they are expected to support their ideas with knowledge of the scientific literature and the work that has come before them. If they don't show their understanding of the literature, it's like you telling your friend that you love everything a particular band has done even though you've only heard one of their songs. In short, the scientific literature is of central importance to the growth and development of science as a whole.

A brief history of scientific literature

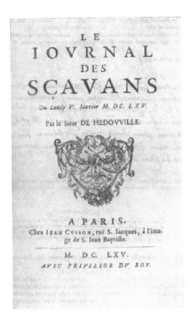

Figure 1: *Title page of the first issue of* le Journal des Scavans.

In its earliest stages, the scientific literature took the form of letters, books, and other writings produced and published by individuals for the purpose of sharing their research. For example, the Babylonians recorded significant astronomical events like lunar eclipses on clay tablets as early as the 6th century BCE (see our Description in Scientific Research module). The notable scientist Alhazen from Basra, Iraq, hand-wrote a seven-volume treatise on his experiments in the field of optics while he was under house arrest in Cairo, Egypt between 1011 and 1021 CE (see our Experimentation in Scientific research module). Much of Galileo Galilei's ground-breaking work was published as a series of letters, such as his *Letters on sunspots* or the *Letter to Grand Duchess Christina*. Isaac Newton's landmark *Philosophiæ Naturalis Principia Mathematica* was published as a series of books in 1686, largely paid for from the personal fortune of the English astronomer Edmund Halley.

Today, although scientists still publish books and letters, the vast majority of the scientific literature is published in the form of journal articles, a practice that started in the mid- 600s. This means that the articles are reviewed by at least two to three scientists with expertise in the same area of science who comment on the article and decide whether it should be published. In March 1665, the Royal Society of London (see our Scientific Institutions and Societies module) began publishing *Philosophical Transactions of the Royal Society of London*. The serial not only included a description of events that occurred at the weekly meetings of the Society, but it also included results from scientific investigations conducted outside of the Society meetings by its members. This publication was made available to other scientists as well as the general public, and thus it helped establish an archive of scientific research.

Other journals in which scientists could publish their findings appeared around the same time. The French *Journal des sçavans* (translated as *Journal of the Savants* – a "savant" is a member of a scholarly society) actually began publishing a few months before *Philosophical Transactions*, but it did not carry scientific research reports until after (Figure 1). The Italian journal *Saggi di naturali esperienzi* (*Essays of natural experiments*) was first published in 1667 by the Accademia del Cimento in Florence. By the mid 18th century, most major European cities had their own scientific society, each with its own scientific publication.

As the number of scientific journals expanded, they helped promote the progress of science itself. Whereas Newton had to seek a wealthy donor to fund the publication of his research, it was no longer the wealthiest or best-known individuals who had the ability to publish their findings. As a result, many more individuals were encouraged to take up the study of science and publish their own research. This in turn led to an explosion in the number of scientific studies that were conducted and the resulting knowledge that was generated from this research.

However, the expansion of the scientific literature also created challenges. As the knowledge base of science grew, it became more difficult to keep track of the discoveries that were made. By the 18th century, many journals also included abstracts or short summaries of scientific research papers published in other journals so that their readers could stay current with the latest scientific advances.

In 1945, Vannevar Bush, an American scientist and statesman, highlighted the importance of the archive of research contained within the scientific literature when, in an essay first published in *The Atlantic Monthly*, he wrote, "A record if it is to be useful to science, must be continuously extended, it must be stored, and above all it must be consulted." Inspired by Bush's essay, Eugene Garfield, an American scientist, founded the Institute for Scientific Information (ISI). In 1960, ISI introduced *Science Citation Index*, the first citation index for scientific scholarly journals. *Science Citation Index* makes use of the inherent linking characteristics of scientific papers: A single scientific paper contains citations to any number of earlier studies on which that work builds, and eventually it too is cited by future research studies. Thus, each published manuscript is one node in a network of citations. In making these networks explicit, *Science Citation Index* emphasizes a key aspect of the scientific literature – the way that it is continuously extended and builds on itself. Evidence that scientists consult that continuously growing record is seen in the reference list that accompanies every scientific journal article. Understanding how scientists utilize the scientific literature is a key component to understanding how science works.

The scientific literature in practice

In a lecture discussing the connections between scientific writing and scientific discovery, Frederic Holmes, an American biologist and historian of science, has said:

> When scientists refer to the "literature" of their fields, they have in mind something very different from what we mean when we talk of literature in general. The literature of a scientific specialty area is the accumulated corpus of research articles contained in the journals of the field, and it is regarded as the primary repository of the knowledge that defines the state of that field. (Holmes, 1987)

As Vannevar Bush noted, literature is only useful if it is consulted, and scientists must make it clear in their own work when they have, in fact, consulted that "accumulated corpus of research articles." You are probably familiar with the notion of citing sources, the way that, for example, a journalist indicates the experts that he or she consulted to write a news article. When scientists cite sources in their scientific journal articles, they are doing more than just showing which experts they consulted, however. Scientists consult the literature to learn all they can about a specific area of study, and then cite those articles to both acknowledge the authors as the originators of the idea they are discussing and also to help readers understand their line of reasoning in coming to their own conclusions.

Using the literature is an ongoing, iterative process for all scientists. For example, when beginning to conduct a geologic field investigation in the Warner Range in northeastern California, Anne Egger first did a search in GeoRef, a geosciences-themed database of journal articles, to see if anyone had published geologic maps or other investigations in this region. She did not want to duplicate any work that had already been done, and also wanted to see what information was already available. She first came across a paper published in 1986 by two geologists from the U.S. Geological Survey, where they presented their work on determining the ages of volcanic rocks in the region (Duffield & McKee, 1986). These data would be very useful in understanding the volcanic history of the region. In addition, she used a technique that many scientists use when searching the literature: She consulted the reference list in this paper, as it provided a wealth of additional papers for her to search. One such paper was a publication entitled "Basin Range Structure and Stratigraphy of the Warner Range, Northeastern California," by Richard Joel Russell, published by the University of California Press in 1928. This appeared to be the first published scientific investigation in this region (Russell, 1928). The USGS geologists had added more detail to Russell's work, but only in the southern part of the range. Therefore, these and other resources helped Egger and her colleagues decide to focus on the central and northern parts of the range, where less was known about the geology. In addition, they helped define where there were still unanswered questions.

Figure 2: Sedimentary rocks in the Warner Range.

One such unanswered question was the origin of the sedimentary rock layers in the Warner Range (see Figure 2). Several geologists had noted the presence of granite cobbles in these sedimentary rock layers. Cobbles in general indicate that the sediments were deposited by a large river, but the presence of granite cobbles indicates something else: Although granite is common in other parts of California, there is none nearby, so they had to be carried a long distance by that ancient river. By looking at the age and chemical make-up of the granite cobbles, Egger and her colleagues could compare them to granite in other areas and try to determine where the cobbles came from. They collected data in the field and in the laboratory, eventually preparing a scientific journal article about the work they did, entitled "Provenance and paleogeographic implications of Eocene-Oligocene sedimentary rocks in the northwestern Basin and Range" (Egger, Colgan, & York, 2009).

The authors recognized that a number of different names had been applied to the sedimentary rocks they were investigating, and they wanted to make it clear to others how the terminology they were using fit into what others had done. In the excerpt that follows, they explain the historical progression of work in the region starting with the first investigation in 1928, and referring to articles along the way in order to show how their new work utilizes the previously established names:

> The Warner Range exposes a thick sequence of ... sedimentary and volcanic rocks... The base of this sequence is primarily sedimentary and volcaniclastic; it was originally called the Lower Cedarville Formation by Russell (1928). Based on detailed field mapping in a portion of the range between Cedarville and Lake City, Martz (1970) subdivided the Lower Cedarville Formation into five units and mapped at least one unconformity within it. In their mapping of the South Warner Wilderness area between Granger Canyon and Eagleville, Duffield et al. (1976) did not subdivide the sedimentary sequence, though they alluded to the presence of at least three recognizable units based on composition, color, and vegetation. Myers (1998) and (2006) retained the nomenclature of Martz (1970) in paleofloral analyses of fossil assemblages in this sequence (Myers, 1998; 2006). Our new mapping in 2004 and 2005 confirmed the formation boundaries suggested by Martz (1970) and extend-

ed these subdivisions to the south between Cedar Pass and the South Warner Wilderness, and thus here we use those formation names.

- from Egger et al., 2009

This explicit acknowledgement of other scientists' work shows that the authors examined the research archive in order to build on it, making use of the accumulated knowledge and understanding about the region in order to ask new questions about the sedimentary rocks. Later in the paper, the authors wanted to establish the age of the rocks they are describing. One kind of data that can help them make this determination is the fossils present in the rock, but these are not data they themselves collected. In this case, they cite papers where other scientists did look closely at the fossils:

> The Steamboat Formation includes two fossiliferous layers... At its base north of Cedarville, a well-documented floral assemblage marks the transition from the latest Eocene to Oligocene (Myers, 2006). The fossils occur in a 1 m-thick ... siltstone that extends laterally (mainly to the south) approximately 7 km (Myers, 2006). ... [and] include ferns and conifers that occur throughout the sequence...

- from Egger et al., 2009

Myers' data about the fossils helped establish the age of the sedimentary rocks (Eocene to Oligocene, about 35 million years old). Building on these existing data, Egger and her co-authors could then show what the rivers were like in the region during that time. One of the kinds of data that they collected in the field is paleocurrent indicators, or measurements that show which direction the currents that deposited the sediments were flowing. In this case, they measured the orientation of granite cobbles in a channel, called *imbrication* (see Figure 3).

Figure 3: Joe Colgan measuring imbrication in cobbles in the field, and a close-up view of imbrications (right). The red lines indicate the orientations that the authors measured.

Imbrication directions were largely consistent within a single ... channel, but varied as much as 180 degrees between different channels. Data from Cottonwood Canyon exemplify this relationship: 17 measurements in a channel near the base of the exposure show a strong paleocurrent direction towards the NW, while 16 measurements in a bed approximately 30 m stratigraphically higher in the sequence show a bit more variability with an average paleocurrent to the ESE (Fig. 2). While braided rivers tend to display more consistency in their paleocurrent directions, a spread in paleocurrent directions of 180° is expected in a coarse alluvial fan or alluvial plain (e.g. Miall, 1977).

- from Egger et al., 2009

In the passage quoted above, the authors describe their own data (the measurements of the paleocurrent indicators), then suggest a possible reason or interpretation for these data – that this large variability in the orientation of the cobbles is typical of a river that is very broad and steep – an *alluvial plain*. They cite Miall to indicate that he was the first person to describe the finding that a "spread in paleocurrent directions," or the fact that the cobbles were oriented in many directions, indicated the presence of a broad alluvial plain. Because he came to a similar conclusion in a different context, they are using the literature to find analogous situations and similar findings, to indicate that their interpretation is reasonable and show how it integrates into the existing research.

Throughout this paper and in scientific articles in general, the authors refer to the literature to do at least three key things: (1) to indicate what other work has been done in the region or on the topic, (2) to cite sources of data that they use, and (3) to support their interpretation of the data (or show how their interpretation differs from previous interpretations). Citing these sources is an integral part of communicating research (see our Understanding Scientific Journals and Articles module for more information). Peer reviewers are usually familiar with the literature that authors are using, so one of their duties is to closely examine these references to see if the authors accurately describe their sources or if they missed any important sources (see our Peer Review module for more information about the peer review process).

Comprehension Checkpoint

Scientists

A) make use of other scientists' work in order to build on existing research.

B) should not consult other scientists' work. All new research should be free of influence from others.

The literature as a data source

In some cases, the literature itself can serve as source for data collection. This has been the case in paleontology, for example, where many investigations over the past several hundred years have involved publishing descriptions of fossil localities, including which species and genera are present in different rock layers. In 1982, John Sepkoski Jr. published a compilation of data of when individual species of marine fossils first appear in the rock record, and when they are no longer seen in rocks. These data came from thousands of published reports (Sepkoski, 1982). In several earlier papers, Sepkoski had analyzed these compiled data and, based on that analysis, developed new ideas about taxonomic diversity through time (for example Sepkoski, 1979). In 1984, Sepkoski and his colleague David Raup published a controversial paper on the apparent regular occurrence of mass extinction events through time (Raup & Sepkoski, 1984), based entirely on the collection of data from the published literature. This type of analysis – often called *meta-analysis* – could not be done without the reliable archive of research provided by the scientific literature. Meta-analysis is especially useful in fields like medicine and climate science, where the results of studies with disparate methods can be combined to yield more robust results.

Of course, our knowledge and understanding of the natural world continue to evolve, inevitably revealing some mistakes in interpretation in the existing literature, as well as causing some material and ideas to become out of date. Sepkoski recognized this likelihood, and in 1993, he published a paper entitled "Ten Years in the Library: New Data Confirm Paleontological Patterns" (Sepkoski, 1993). In that article, he notes:

> As soon as the manuscript for the 1982 Compendium went to press, I began discovering new and old paleontological literature that changed times of origination and extinction … After publication…, the original data received special scrutiny from taxonomic experts, and embarrassing errors and promulgations of antiquated data were revealed.

Sepkoski collected the changes and reanalyzed the data. Interestingly, he found little difference in the conclusions about evolutionary patterns that he had published earlier (Sepkoski, 1993). For paleontology, this result has important implications. As Sepkoski states:

> the major patterns of … evolution are rather insensitive to new fossil discoveries and changes in taxonomic interpretation, indicating that analyses of transitory data can be robust, so long as a large component of the biosphere is being considered.

A similar conclusion can be drawn for the scientific literature as a whole, as well. Though some mistakes get published, and our interpretations change, as a whole, the literature is robust and a reliable source of scientific data.

Comprehension Checkpoint

Mistakes have been published in the scientific literature,

A) so the scientific literature as a whole cannot be trusted.

B) but the scientific literature as a whole is a reliable source.

Accessing the scientific literature

Staying current with the literature in one's field is a challenge – far more research is being published every day than is possible to read. Many journals now send out email notices to subscribers when a new issue comes out, including the table of contents and links to each of the articles. This allows scientists to quickly browse a new issue and see if there is an article of relevance to their work. Very often, however, scientists have seen or heard preliminary versions of published articles through presentations at meetings or other interactions with colleagues at different institutions (see our module on Scientific Institutions and Societies).

Having access to the scientific literature is critical to "doing science." Today, digital and online databases make it easier for people to search the literature and sometimes to access scientific journals articles. Access to the vast majority of journals, however, even digital journals, is limited by subscription, which may run into the thousands of dollars. As a result, scientists at institutions without the resources to pay for these subscriptions are at a disadvantage (Evans & Reimer, 2009). More recently, many journals are providing open access to their content after a set time period, often a year, in the case of *Science* magazine, and some provide open access from the very beginning, such as the Public Library of Science. This change reflects awareness that a diversity of viewpoints improves our scientific understanding, and that everyone should have access to the scientific literature.

The reason why access to the literature is so important is because it is a reliable archive of scientific research. The fact that it is reliable does not mean that every published paper is correct, but it means that progress in our understanding can be tracked through time. When mistakes or even fraud are discovered, a paper can be retracted, which removes it from the literature and ensures that the record continues to be reliable (see our module on Scientific Ethics). In this way, earlier ideas can be built upon or refuted, and multiple lines of evidence can accumulate that help scientists establish the "big ideas" of science – robust theories like plate tectonics, atomic theory, and evolution.

Key Concepts for this chapter

▶ The scientific literature provides an archive of research, which scientists make use of throughout the process of investigation.

▶ Scientists reference the literature to indicate what other work has been done on a research topic, to cite sources of data that they use, and to show how their interpretations integrate with the published knowledge base of science.

▶ New research questions can be investigated by reanalyzing or compiling data from the literature.

▶ While individual scientists can make errors, the knowledge-base of science as reflected in the scientific literature is self-correcting as new studies and new interpretations come to light.

References

Duffield, W. A., & McKee, E. H. (1986). Geochronology, structure, and basin-range tectonism of the Warner Range, northeastern California. *Geological Society of America Bulletin*, 97(2), 142-146.

Egger, A. E., Colgan, J. P., & York, C. (2009). Provenance and paleogeographic implications of Eocene-Oligocene sedimentary rocks in the northwestern Basin and Range. *International Geology Review*, 51(9-11), 900–919.

Evans, J. A., & Reimer, J. (2009). Open access and global participation in science. *Science*, 323(5917), 1025-.

Gross, A. G., Harmon, J. E., & Reidy, M. (2009). *Communicating science: The scientific article from the 17th century to the present.* Parlor Press.

Holmes, F. L. (1987). Scientific writing and scientific discovery. *Isis*, 220-235.

Raup, D. M., & Sepkoski, J. J. (1984). Periodicity of extinctions in the geologic past. *Proceedings of the National Academy of Sciences of the United States of America*, 81(3), 801-805.

Russell, R. J. (1928). Basin Range structure and stratigraphy of the Warner Range, northeastern California. *University of California Publications in Geological Sciences*, 17(11), 387-496.

Sepkoski, J. J. (1979). A kinetic model of Phanerozoic taxonomic diversity; II, Early Phanerozoic families and multiple equilibria. *Paleobiology*, 5(3), 222-251.

Sepkoski, J. J. (1982). A compendium of fossil marine families. *Contributions in Biology and Geology*, 51.

Sepkoski, J. J. (1993). Ten years in the library; new data confirm paleontological patterns. *Paleobiology*, 19(1), 43-51.

Take the Quiz ▶ ▶ ▶

Utilizing the Scientific Literature Quiz

1. Which of the following publications would be considered part of the scientific literature?

    A) A peer reviewed article in a scientific journal

    B) A peer reviewed textbook written by a scientist

    C) A newspaper article about a new scientific breakthrough

    D) A science fiction book written by a scientist

2. Which of the following statements best describes the role of the scientific literature in conducting research?

    A) The literature is usually only consulted at the beginning of the research process in order to formulate a question.

    B) The literature is rarely consulted by scientists as they conduct research.

    C) Old contributions to the scientific literature are no longer useful in modern research.

    D) Consulting and adding to the scientific literature is an integral part of the research process.

3. A research paper by several scientists was published in *Nature* (a prestigious science journal). One year later, other scientists in the same discipline discovered mistakes in the procedures used and alerted the authors. The authors agreed that they had made mistakes, which they had not recognized earlier. They could no longer be confident in their results, so they asked *Nature* to retract their paper, or remove it from publication. Which of the following statements best describes this situation?

    A) The literature is an archive of knowledge; thus, any known mistakes should be removed.

    B) The authors simply made a mistake; there is no need to retract the paper.

    C) The scientists who found the mistakes were just being picky.

    D) The mistakes should have been caught earlier through the peer review process.

4. In writing up the results of a recent experiment for publication, a scientist comes across a study in which the authors describe a similar experiment with different results. What would be the most appropriate way for the scientist to address this in her journal article?

    A) Avoid citing the study since the results differed.

    B) Cite the study to say that the experiment was done and avoid discussing the different results.

    C) Cite the study and offer an explanation why the results might have differed.

    D) Cite the different results as evidence that her experiment was better.

5. How do most scientists search for and find relevant information in the scientific literature?

    A) by browsing in a bookstore

    B) by subscribing to several journals in their discipline

    C) through databases that archive titles and abstracts

    D) through web search engines like Yahoo!

6. Once data are published in the scientific literature, there would be no reason to reanalyze those data later.

    A) True

    B) False

7. Citing others in your research papers is good practice because

    A) other researchers know more about your topic than you.

    B) it shows that you have been thorough in your research.

    C) it fills in the gaps of your own knowledge.

    D) it shows that you don't think you have all of the answers.

Answers and feedback can be found on Page 291

Quiz Answers and Feedback

The Practice of Science

Question 1:

A) **Incorrect.** In the 5th century BCE, the Greek mathematician Pythagoras proposed that the Earth was round. There are also recorded examples of research by ancient Greek, Persian, Indian, Chinese, and European scientists.

B) **Correct.** In the 5th century BCE, the Greek mathematician Pythagoras proposed that the Earth was round. There are also recorded examples of research by ancient Greek, Persian, Indian, Chinese, and European scientists.

Question 2:

A) **Incorrect.** Although there are many research methods in science, they all share common components: (1) All scientific research is based on gathering and analyzing data. (2) Even though scientists cannot be completely objective, they must be open to any potential result. (3) Results must be shared in the scientific community so that other scientists can review methods and findings. Which choice covers all these components of scientific research?

B) **Incorrect.** Although there are many research methods in science, they all share common components: (1) All scientific research is based on gathering and analyzing data. (2) Even though scientists cannot be completely objective, they must be open to any potential result. (3) Results must be shared in the scientific community so that other scientists can review methods and findings. Which choice covers all these components of scientific research?

C) **Incorrect.** Although there are many research methods in science, they all share common components: (1) All scientific research is based on gathering and analyzing data. (2) Even though scientists cannot be completely objective, they must be open to any potential result. (3) Results must be shared in the scientific community so that other scientists can review methods and findings. Which choice covers all these components of scientific research?

D) **Correct.** Manipulation of variables is part of one research method, *experimentation*, but is not common to all methods of scientific research

Question 3:

A) **Correct.** Bacon proposed a cycle of observation, hypothesis, and experimentation. His work served as a basis for the development of research methodology in science.

B) **Incorrect.** Bacon proposed a research method that involved a repeating cycle of observation, hypothesis, and experimentation, and the need for independent verification. His work served as a basis for the development of research methodology in science. Which choice fits this description?

C) **Incorrect.** Bacon's is known for his method of scientific reasoning. He proposed a cycle of observation, hypothesis, and experimentation. His method served as a basis for the development of research methodology in science. Which choice best describes Bacon's contribution?

D) **Incorrect.** Bacon proposed a cycle of observation, hypothesis, and experimentation. His work served as a basis for the development of research methodology in science, which later included statistical techniques for data analysis and research design. Which choice best describes Bacon's contribution?

Question 4:

A) **You are partly correct.** While it is true that scientific research rarely proceeds in a neat, linear fashion, there are other problems with the traditional description of the scientific method. Which choice more fully accounts for problem?

B) **You are partly correct.** While it is true that experimentation is not the only research method available to scientists, there are other problems with the traditional description of the scientific method. Which choice more fully accounts for the problem?

C) **You are partly correct.** While it is true that not all research studies begin with a question, there are other problems with the traditional description of the scientific method. Which choice more fully accounts for the problem?

D) **Correct.** The problem with the traditional presentation of the scientific method is that: (a) Sscientific research rarely proceeds in a neat, linear fashion; (b) experimentation is not the only research method available; and (c) not all research studies begin with a question. There are several methods. These methods often overlap or are used in combination.

Question 5:

A) **Incorrect.** The Montreal Protocol was enacted in 1988 to limit the use of CFCs in order to preserve the ozone layer. This act was based on a long history of research that was diverse and yet interrelated. Ozone research involved modeling, experiments, comparative research, and descriptive studies. Which choice reflects this?

B) **Incorrect.** The Montreal Protocol was enacted in 1988 to limit the use of CFCs in order to preserve the ozone layer. This act was based on a long history of research that was diverse and yet interrelated. Ozone research involved modeling, experiments, comparative research, and descriptive studies. Which choice reflects this?

C) Correct. The Montreal Protocol was enacted in order to preserve the ozone layer. This act was based on a history of research that was diverse and yet related. Ozone research involved many different methods. These include modeling, experiments, comparative research, and descriptive studies.

D) Incorrect. The Montreal Protocol was enacted in 1988 to limit the use of CFCs in order to preserve the ozone layer. This decision was based on a long history of research that involved many methods: modeling, experiments, comparative research, and descriptive studies. Which choice reflects this?

The Nature of Scientific Knowledge

Comprehension Checkpoints:
p15: A; p17: A; p19: B; p21: A

Question 1:

A) Correct. The scientific process is a way of building knowledge and making predictions about the world in such a way that they are testable. Different scientific fields may use different methods to investigate the natural world, but testing lies at the heart of all scientific inquiry.

B) Incorrect. The scientific process is a way of building knowledge by making predictions about the world that can be verified. Different scientific fields may use different methods to investigate the natural world, but testing lies at the heart of all scientific inquiry. Which choice includes this essential component of the process of science?

C) Incorrect. The scientific process is a way of building knowledge by making predictions about the world that can be verified. Different scientific fields may use different methods to investigate the natural world, but testing lies at the heart of all scientific inquiry. Which choice includes this essential component of the process of science?

D) Incorrect. The scientific process is a way of building knowledge by making predictions about the world that can be verified. Different scientific fields may use different methods to investigate the natural world, but testing lies at the heart of all scientific inquiry. Which choice includes this essential component of the process of science?

Question 2:

A) Incorrect. Greek philosophers referred to the Earth as a sphere as early as the 6th century BCE. An accumulation of evidence over the following centuries confirmed that the Earth was round long before or astronauts sent pictures of Earth from space in 1968, and even long before explorers sailed around the world in 1522.

B) Correct. Greek philosophers referred to the Earth as a sphere as early as the 6th century BCE. An accumulation of evidence over the following centuries confirmed that the Earth was round long before or astronauts sent pictures of Earth from space in 1968, and even long before explorers sailed around the world in 1522.

Question 3:

A) Incorrect. The second law of thermodynamics states that energy always flows from a high energy state to a low energy state (hot to cold) through entropy. If the universe was infinite, all of the energy within the universe would have been lost to entropy by now. In other words, the stars themselves would have burned out long ago. Since there are still active stars, what can we conclude about the age of the universe?

B) Correct. The second law of thermodynamics states that energy always flows from a high energy state to a low energy state (hot to cold) through entropy. If the universe was infinite, all of the energy within the universe would have been lost to entropy by now. In other words, the stars themselves would have burned out long ago. Since there are still active stars, we can conclude that the universe has existed for a finite amount of time.

C) Incorrect. The second law of thermodynamics states that energy always flows from a high energy state to a low energy state (hot to cold) through entropy. If the universe was infinite, all of the energy within the universe would have been lost to entropy by now. In other words, the stars themselves would have burned out long ago. Since there are still active stars, what can we conclude about the age of the universe?

D) Incorrect. The second law of thermodynamics states that energy always flows from a high energy state to a low energy state (hot to cold) through entropy. If the universe was infinite, all of the energy within the universe would have been lost to entropy by now. In other words, the stars themselves would have burned out long ago. Since there are still active stars, what can we conclude about the age of the universe?

Question 4:

A) Correct. The color of the stars would shift toward the red end of the spectrum if they were moving away from the observer (called redshift) and toward the blue end of the spectrum if they were moving toward the observer (called blueshift). You can see that the emission lines in Section 2 (for SN1 and SN2) of the image have shifted toward the red end of the spectrum and that SN2 has shifted farther than SN1.

B) Incorrect. The color of the stars would shift toward the red end of the spectrum if they were moving away from the observer (called redshift) and toward the blue end of the spectrum if they were moving toward the observer (called blueshift). Look again at the image to compare the SN1 and SN2 spectra in Section 2 against the Section 1 spectrum and against each other.

C) Incorrect. The color of the stars would shift toward the red end of the spectrum if they were moving away from the observer (called redshift) and toward the blue end of the spectrum if they were moving toward the observer (called blueshift). Look again at the image to compare the SN1 and SN2 spectra in Section 2 against the Section 1 spectrum and against each other.

D) Incorrect. The color of the stars would shift toward the red end of the spectrum if they were moving away from the observer (called redshift) and toward the blue end of the spectrum if they were moving toward the observer (called blueshift). Look again at the image to compare the SN1 and SN2 spectra in Section 2 against the Section 1 spectrum and against each other.

Question 5:

A) Correct. Edwin Hubble and Milton Humason plotted the distances they had calculated for 46 different galaxies against Slipher's recession velocity and found a linear relationship. Their graph showed that more distant galaxies were receding faster than closer ones, confirming the idea that the universe was expanding.

B) Incorrect. Edwin Hubble and Milton Humason plotted the distances for 46 different galaxies against Slipher's recession velocity and found a linear relationship. Their graph showed that more distant galaxies were receding faster than closer ones. Which choice describes the relationship between velocity and distance shown in the graph?

C) Incorrect. Edwin Hubble and Milton Humason plotted the distances for 46 different galaxies against Slipher's recession velocity and found a linear relationship. Their graph showed that more distant galaxies were receding faster than closer ones, confirming the idea that the universe was expanding. Which choice describes the relationship between velocity and distance shown in the graph?

D) Incorrect. Edwin Hubble and Milton Humason plotted the distances for 46 different galaxies against Slipher's recession velocity and found a linear relationship. Their graph showed that more distant galaxies were receding faster than closer ones. Which choice describes the relationship between velocity and distance shown in the graph?

Question 6:

A) Incorrect. Einstein's theory of general relativity predicts that the universe must be expanding or contracting, not static. However, the dominant cultural belief at

the time was that the universe was static. Because of Einstein's cultural biases, he refused to accept the idea of an expanding universe at first.

B) Correct. Einstein's theory of general relativity predicts that the universe must be expanding or contracting, not static. However, the dominant cultural belief at the time was that the universe was static. Because of Einstein's cultural biases, he refused to accept the idea of an expanding universe at first.

Question 7:

A) Incorrect. The age of the universe was predicted as a result of a long chain of research by multiple scientists using different methods over many decades. The age estimates have been confirmed and verified by many different scientific studies. New studies, new technology, or new research methods might cause us to refine our estimate of the age of the universe in the future. Which choice reflects how scientific knowledge is built?

B) Incorrect. The age of the universe was estimated by multiple researchers using different methods over many decades. New studies, new technology, or new research methods might cause us to refine our estimate of the age of the universe in the future. Which choice reflects how scientific knowledge is built?

C) Correct. Scientists build on the work of others to create scientific knowledge. The age of the universe was estimated as a result of a long chain of research by multiple scientists using different methods over many decades. New studies, new technology, or new research methods might cause us to refine our estimate of the age of the universe in the future.

D) Incorrect. Scientists build on the work of others to create scientific knowledge. The age of the universe was estimated as a result of a long chain of research by multiple scientists using different methods over many decades. Which choice reflects how scientific knowledge is built?

Energy

Comprehension Checkpoints:
p28: A; p30 (top): B; p30 (bottom): B

Question 1:

A) Incorrect. These are not exactly the four elements that Ancient Greeks believed made up all matter. Look again at the choices.

B) Incorrect. This more modern view of states of matter did not take hold until later. Ancient Greek philosophers thought that all matter was composed of four elements. Look again at the choices.

C) **Correct.** Ancient Greek philosophers thought that all matter could be described in terms of combinations of four elements earth, air, water and fire. They associated earth, air, and water with the physical conditions of objects and fire with heat, motion, and life force.

D) **Incorrect.** This concept of matter did not gain ground until later. The Ancient Greeks thought that all matter was made of four elements. Look again at the choices.

Question 2:

A) **Correct.** Because of Aristotle's influence, the four-element view of matter held strong for almost 2,000 years.

B) **Incorrect.** Heraclitus extended the view of matter that was made popular by other philosophers. Who was the most famous champion of the four-element theory proposed by Ancient Greek philosophers?

C) **Incorrect.** It was mainly due to another Ancient Greek philosopher that the four-element view of matter prevailed for so long. Look again at the choices.

D) **Incorrect.** It was due to the influence of another Ancient Greek philosopher that the four-element view of matter prevailed for so long. Look again at the choices.

Question 3:

A) **Incorrect.** Ancient Greeks associated fire with energy and credited it with the life-force of living beings. Which choice reflects a modern definition of energy?

B) **Correct.** Energy is the ability for an object to perform work on another object. Work can be thought of as a process in which one form of energy is transformed into another.

C) **Incorrect.** Energy is required to turn on a light. However, the definition of energy is broader than this. Look again at the choices.

D) **Incorrect.** While it is true that energy is required to cook food, the definition of energy is not limited to cooking. Look again at the choices.

Question 4:

A) **Incorrect.** Energy takes many forms, including mechanical. Mechanical energy is related to the movement or position of an object. Which of the choices does not name one of the main forms of energy?

B) **Incorrect.** Electrical energy is one of main forms of energy. Electrical energy is based on the flow of electrons in a system. Which of the choices does not name one of the main forms of energy?

C) **Incorrect.** Nuclear energy is a well known form of energy. This form of energy involves breaking or forming interactions between protons and neutrons in

the nucleus of an atom. Which of the choices does not name one of the main forms of energy?

D) **Correct!** Main forms of energy include mechanical, thermal, chemical, nuclear, electromagnetic, and electrical.

Question 5:

A) **You are partially correct.** While it is true that potential energy can be converted to kinetic energy, other statements about potential energy are also accurate. Which choice gives a more complete description of potential energy?

B) **You are partially correct.** While it is true that the potential energy of an object rises as you lift it, other statements describe additional aspects of potential energy. Which choice gives a more complete description of potential energy?

C) **You are partially correct.** While it is true that potential energy can be found in many forms of energy, other statements about potential energy are also accurate. Which choice gives a more complete description of potential energy?

D) **Correct!** It is true that (1) potential, or "stored," energy can be converted to kinetic energy, (2) the potential energy of an object rises as you lift the object higher from the ground, and (3) potential energy can be found in many forms of energy.

Question 6:

A) **Incorrect.** It is possible to transform any form of energy into any other. Which statement about energy is not true?

B) **Correct!** Michael Faraday discovered that he could convert mechanical energy into electrical energy and vice versa. In fact, it is possible to transform all forms of energy into any other.

C) **Incorrect.** It is possible to convert the potential energy in a battery to kinetic energy that can drive a machine. Which statement about energy is not true?

D) **Incorrect.** Energy is the ability for an object to perform work -- or exert force -- on another object. Which statement about energy is not true?

Question 7:

A) **Incorrect.** Joule did not name the energy unit after himself. However, because he was among the first scientists to unequivocally document energy conversion, we now call the unit used to measure energy the Joule. Which choice describes the results of Joule's experiments?

B) **Incorrect.** Michael Faraday is credited with building the first generator, but Joule was the first scientist to show definitively that powering a paddle wheel could raise the temperature of water. Which choice describes the results of Joule's experiments?

C) Correct! Joule conducted careful experiments that showed without a doubt that powering a paddle wheel could raise the temperature of water. Thus, he was the first scientist to provide solid data that mechanical energy can be converted to thermal energy.

D) Incorrect. Joule contributed to our understanding of energy through his well designed experiments. Which choice describes the results of Joule's experiments?

Early Ideas about Matter

Comprehension Checkpoints:
p35: B; p36: A; p37: B

Question 1:

A) Incorrect. Priestley observed that when heated, a red stone called mercury calx breaks down into liquid mercury and a strange gas. The gas made flames burn brighter. Also, a mouse placed in a sealed container with this gas lived longer than a mouse placed in a sealed container of ordinary air. Which choice lists a familiar gas that helps fire burn and living creatures breathe?

B) Incorrect. Priestley observed that when heated, a red stone called mercury calx breaks down into liquid mercury and a strange gas. The gas made flames burn brighter. Also, a mouse placed in a sealed container with this gas lived longer than a mouse placed in a sealed container of ordinary air. Which choice lists a familiar gas that helps fire burn and living creatures breathe?

C) Incorrect. Priestley observed that when heated, a red stone called mercury calx breaks down into liquid mercury and a strange gas. The gas made flames burn brighter. Also, a mouse placed in a sealed container with this gas lived longer than a mouse placed in a sealed container of ordinary air. Which choice lists a familiar gas that helps fire burn and living creatures breathe?

D) Correct! Priestley observed that when heated, a red stone called mercury calx breaks down into liquid mercury and a strange gas. The gas made flames burn brighter. Also, a mouse placed in a sealed container with this gas lived longer than a mouse placed in a sealed container of ordinary air. Priestley called the gas "dephlogisticated air," but the name was later changed to "oxygen."

Question 2:

A) Correct! Democritus reasoned that matter is made from building blocks of infinitesimally small pieces which he called atomos, meaning "indivisible." He theorized that these were specific to the material that they made up and that different materials would be made up of different kinds of atomos.

B) Incorrect. Empedocles proposed that all matter was made up of four elements—fire, air, water, and earth—that could be combined in different ratios, resulting in different materials. Look again for the scientist who in ancient times reasoned that matter is made from tiny building blocks, which he called atomos (meaning "indivisible").

C) Incorrect. In the late 18th century, Lavoisier established the Law of Conservation of Mass. Look again for the scientist who in ancient times reasoned that matter is made from tiny building blocks, which he called atomos (meaning "indivisible").

D) Incorrect. Priestley is credited for discovering oxygen. Look again for the scientist who in ancient times reasoned that matter is made from tiny building blocks, which he called atomos (meaning "indivisible").

Question 3:

A) Incorrect. The ancient Greeks believed that all matter was composed of four elements: fire, air, water, and earth. Look again for which element is not part of the list.

B) Incorrect. The ancient Greeks believed that all matter was composed of four elements: fire, air, water, and earth. Look again for which element is not part of the list.

C) Correct! The ancient Greeks believed that all matter was composed of four elements: fire, air, water, and earth. The ratio of these elements determined the properties of the matter, so, according to them, rabbits were living and soft because they had more water and fire.

D) Incorrect. The ancient Greeks believed that all matter was composed of four elements: fire, air, water, and earth. Look again for which element is not part of the list.

Question 4:

A) Correct! Dalton's theory had four main concepts: (1) All matter is made of atoms. (2) Atoms of a given element are identical; atoms of different elements have different properties. (3) Chemical reactions involve the combination, not destruction, of atoms. (4) When elements react to form compounds, they react in defined, whole-number ratios.

B) Incorrect. Dalton's theory stated: (1) All matter is made of atoms. (2) Atoms of a given element are identical; atoms of different elements have different properties. (3) Chemical reactions involve the combination, not destruction, of atoms. (4) When elements react to form compounds, they react in defined, whole-number ratios. Which choice does not involve one of these concepts?

C) Incorrect. Dalton's theory stated: (1) All matter is made of atoms. (2) Atoms of a given element are identical; atoms of different elements have different properties. (3) Chemical reactions involve the combination, not destruction, of atoms. (4) When elements react to form compounds, they react in defined, whole-number ratios. Which choice does not involve one of these concepts?

D) Incorrect. Dalton's theory stated: (1) All matter is made of atoms. (2) Atoms of a given element are identical; atoms of different elements have different properties. (3) Chemical reactions involve the combination, not destruction, of atoms. (4) When elements react to form compounds, they react in defined, whole-number ratios. Which choice does not involve one of these concepts?

Question 5:

A) Incorrect. Compounds are formed when one atom chemically combines with other atoms. Substances that cannot be broken down into simpler substances by chemical means form the building blocks of the universe. What are substances called in their purest, most elemental form?

B) Correct! Elements are fundamental substances that cannot be broken down further by chemical means. They are pure substances that form the basis of all of the materials around us, the building blocks of the universe.

C) Incorrect. Substances that cannot be broken down into simpler substances by chemical means form the building blocks of the universe. What are substances called in their purest, most elemental form?

D) Incorrect. Whether solids, liquids, or gases, substances that cannot be broken down into simpler substances by chemical means form the building blocks of the universe. What are substances called in their purest, most elemental form?

Question 6;

A) Correct! The approximately 116 elements we know of form the basis of all of the materials around us. These building blocks can be combined chemically to form different compounds. Most of the substances we come into contact with are compounds rather than pure elements.

B) Incorrect. The approximately 116 elements we know of form the basis of all of the materials around us. These building blocks can be combined chemically to form different compounds. Which choice indicates that

most of the substances we come into contact with are compounds rather than pure elements?

C) Incorrect. The approximately 116 elements we know of form the basis of all of the materials around us. These building blocks can be combined chemically to form different compounds. Which choice indicates that most of the substances we come into contact with are compounds rather than pure elements?

D) Incorrect. The approximately 116 elements we know of form the basis of all of the materials around us. These building blocks can be combined chemically to form different compounds. Which choice indicates that most of the substances we come into contact with are compounds rather than pure elements?

Question 7:

A) Incorrect. We now know of approximately 116 different elements.

B) Correct! We now know of approximately 116 different elements.

C) Incorrect. We now know of approximately 116 different elements.

D) Incorrect. We now know of approximately 116 different elements.

Question 8:

A) Incorrect. Each of the elements has a one- or two-letter symbol. In this abbreviation for an element, the first letter is always capitalized and the second letter (if there is one) is always lowercase. Look again at the choices to decide which symbol could represent an element.

B) Correct! Each of the elements has a one- or two-letter symbol. In this abbreviation for an element, the first letter is always capitalized and the second letter (if there is one) is always lowercase.

C) Incorrect. Each of the elements has a one- or two-letter symbol. In this abbreviation for an element, the first letter is always capitalized and the second letter (if there is one) is always lowercase. Look again at the choices to decide which symbol could represent an element.

D) Incorrect. Each of the elements has a one- or two-letter symbol. In this abbreviation for an element, the first letter is always capitalized and the second letter (if there is one) is always lowercase. Look again at the choices to decide which symbol could represent an element.

Question 9:

A) Incorrect. Compounds are the chemical combination of two or more atoms of the elements. They are written as the symbols of the elements in them without any spaces. When writing elements, the first letter is capitalized and the second letter, if there is one, is lowercase. If more than one atom of an element is part of the compound, a subscript number shows how many atoms of that element are in one molecule of the compound. Look again at the choices to decide which symbol could represent a compound.

B) Correct! Compounds are the chemical combination of two or more atoms of the elements. They are written as the symbols of the elements in them without any spaces. If more than one atom of an element is part of the compound, a subscript number shows how many atoms of that element are in one molecule of the compound.

C) Incorrect. Compounds are the chemical combination of two or more atoms of the elements. They are written as the symbols of the elements in them without any spaces. When writing elements, the first letter is capitalized and the second letter, if there is one, is lowercase. If more than one atom of an element is part of a compound, a subscript number shows how many atoms of that element are in one molecule of the compound. Look again at the choices to decide which symbol could represent a compound.

D) Incorrect. Compounds are the chemical combination of two or more atoms of the elements. When writing compounds, the symbols of the elements in the compound are written without spaces between them. If more than one atom of an element is part of the compound, a subscript number shows how many atoms of that element are in one molecule of the compound. Look again at the choices to decide which symbol could represent a compound.

Question 10:

A) Correct! The chemical combination of two or more atoms of the elements results in a compound.

B) Incorrect. Not all mixtures result in chemical combinations of elements. What is the name for a new substance that is formed by the chemical combination of two or more atoms of the elements?

C) Incorrect. Not all solutions result in chemical combinations of elements. What is the name for a new substance that is formed by the chemical combination of two or more atoms of the elements?

D) Incorrect. Elements are pure substances that form the basis of all of the materials around us. What is the name for a substance that is formed by the chemical combination of two or more atoms of the elements?

Question 11:

A) Incorrect. Although it is true that atoms are microscopically small, the Law of Definite Proportions has to do with the ratio in which atoms combine chemically.

Which choice sates that atoms always react in defined proportions?

B) Correct! Chemical reactions are not random; rather, they proceed according to precise formulas. The Law of Definite Proportions sates that atoms always react in defined proportions. For example, water is always made up of two parts hydrogen and one part oxygen.

C) Incorrect. Although it is true that atoms of the same element are identical, the Law of Definite Proportions has to do with the ratio in which atoms combine chemically. Which choice sates that atoms always react in defined proportions?

D) Incorrect. Although it is true that matter is composed of atoms, the Law of Definite Proportions has to do with the ratio in which atoms combine chemically. Which choice sates that atoms always react in defined proportions?

Question 12:

A) Incorrect. Chemical reactions proceed according to precise and well-defined formulas. For example, water is always made up of two parts hydrogen and one part oxygen. Look again to see which choice has to do with the defined ratio in which atoms combine chemically.

B) Incorrect. Chemical reactions proceed according to precise and well-defined formulas. For example, water is always made up of two parts hydrogen and one part oxygen. Look again to see which choice has to do with the defined ratio in which atoms combine chemically.

C) Correct! Chemical reactions proceed according to precise formulas. For example, water is always made up of two parts hydrogen and one part oxygen. The Law of Definite Proportions sates that atoms always react in defined proportions.

D) Incorrect. Chemical reactions proceed according to precise and well-defined formulas. For example, water is always made up of two parts hydrogen and one part oxygen. Look again to see which choice has to do with the defined ratio in which atoms combine chemically.

Atomic Theory I

Comprehension Checkpoints:
p42: B; p43: B;

Question 1:

A) Incorrect. In 1932, Chadwick discovered a new subatomic particle, the neutron. But more than 30 years earlier, the first model that suggested that atoms were made of smaller pieces was the "plum pudding" model. Whose idea was this?

B) Incorrect. Although Dalton laid the foundation of modern atomic theory, another individual suggested that the atom was not an "indivisible" particle as John Dalton had suggested. Who proposed that the atom was more like a collection of smaller pieces?

C) Correct! Thomson's work suggested that the atom was not an "indivisible" particle, but collection of smaller pieces.

D) Incorrect. In 1911, Rutherford proposed a revolutionary view of the atom that resembled a solar system. It was Rutherford's mentor who actually first proposed that atoms consisted of sub-atomic pieces. Who was his mentor?

Question 2:

A) Incorrect. In the 19th century, scientists knew that a stream of glowing material could be seen if an electric current was passed through a vacuum tube. J. J. Thomson theorized that the stream was made up of small pieces of atoms that carried a negative charge. What is the name for negatively charged subatomic particles?

B) Correct! In the 19th century, scientists knew that a stream of glowing material could be seen if an electric current was passed through a vacuum tube. J. J. Thomson theorized that the stream was made up of small pieces of atoms that carried a negative charge. These particles were later named electrons.

C) Incorrect. In the 19th century, scientists knew that a stream of glowing material could be seen if an electric current was passed through a vacuum tube. J. J. Thomson theorized that the stream was made up of small pieces of atoms that carried a negative charge. What is the name for negatively charged subatomic particles?

D) Incorrect. In the 19th century, scientists knew that a stream of glowing material could be seen if an electric current was passed through a vacuum tube. J. J. Thomson theorized that the stream was made up of small pieces of atoms that carried a negative charge. What is the name for negatively charged subatomic particles?

Question 3:

A) You are partly correct. Rutherford proposed that the atom resembled a tiny solar system with a dense, positively charged nucleus at the center. Tiny electrons revolved around the nucleus. These were spread out at great distances over a mostly empty space. Which choice lists all these characteristics of the atom?

B) Correct! Rutherford proposed that the atom resembled a tiny solar system. Each atom had a positively charged nucleus at the center and electrons revolving around the nucleus. The nucleus was very dense, but the electrons were tiny and spread out at great distances over a mostly empty space.

C) You are partly correct. Rutherford proposed that the atom resembled a tiny solar system with tiny electrons

that were spread out at great distances over a mostly empty space. In addition, each atom had a positively charged, dense nucleus at the center. Which choice lists all these characteristics of the atom?

D) You are partly correct. Rutherford proposed that the atom resembled a tiny solar system with a positively charged, dense nucleus at the center. Tiny electrons revolved around the nucleus. These were spread out at great distances over a mostly empty space. Which choice lists all these characteristics of the atom?

Question 4:

A) Incorrect. Protons carry an equal but opposite charge to electrons, but protons are much larger and heavier than electrons.

B) Incorrect. Protons carry an equal but opposite charge to electrons, but protons are much larger and heavier than electrons.

C) Incorrect. Protons carry an equal but opposite charge to electrons, but protons are much larger and heavier than electrons.

D) Correct! Protons carry an equal but opposite charge to electrons, but protons are much larger and heavier than electrons.

Question 5:

A) Incorrect. Neutrons are about the same size as protons. However, neutrons do not have any electrical charge. Look again at the choices.

B) Incorrect. Electrons are tiny and negatively charged. Neutrons are about the same size as protons but do not carry any electrical charge. Look again at the choices.

C) Correct! Neutrons are about the same size as protons but do not have any electrical charge.

D) Incorrect. Electrons are tiny and negatively charged. Neutrons are about the same size as protons but do not carry any electrical charge. Look again at the choices.

Question 6:

A) Incorrect. The term atomic number (z) is used to describe the number of protons in an atom. Helium has an atomic number of two (z = 2). Given this information, how many protons does a helium atom have?

B) Correct! The term atomic number (z) is used to describe the number of protons in an atom. Helium has an atomic number of two (z = 2) because it has two protons.

C) Incorrect. The term atomic number (z) is used to describe the number of protons in an atom. Helium has an atomic number of two (z = 2). Given this information, how many protons does a helium atom have?

D) Incorrect. The term atomic number (z) is used to describe the number of protons in an atom. Helium has an atomic number of two (z = 2). Given this information, how many protons does a helium atom have?

Question 7:

A) Incorrect. Both protons and neutrons are found in the nucleus of the atom. What is determined solely by the number of protons in the nucleus of an atom?

B) Incorrect. The atomic weight, or atomic mass, of an atom equals the number of protons plus the number of neutrons. What is determined solely by the number of protons in the nucleus of an atom?

C) Incorrect. The atomic mass, or weight, of an atom equals the number of protons plus the number of neutrons. What is determined solely by the number of protons in the nucleus of an atom?

D) Correct! The term atomic number is used to describe the number of protons in an atom.

Question 8:

A) Incorrect. Of the three subatomic particles protons, neutrons, and electrons, protons and neutrons are about the same size, but electrons are more than 1,800 times smaller than the two. Thus the electrons' weight does not help determine the weight of an atom. Given this information, how can atomic weight be calculated?

B) Incorrect. While protons and neutrons are about the same size, the electron is more than 1,800 times smaller than the two. Thus, the electrons' weight does not help determine the weight of an atom. Given this information, how can atomic weight be calculated?

C) Incorrect. While protons and neutrons are about the same size, the electron is more than 1,800 times smaller than the two. Thus, the electrons' weight does not help determine the weight of an atom. Given this information, how can atomic weight be calculated?

D) Correct! The weight of an atom, or atomic mass, is determined by the total number of protons and neutrons in the atom. While protons and neutrons are about the same size, the electron is more than 1,800 times smaller than the two. Thus, the electrons' weight does not help determine the weight of an atom.

Question 9:

A) Incorrect. The atomic number for helium is 2. This number indicates how many protons the atom has. The atomic mass, or weight, of an atom is the number of protons plus the number of neutrons. Helium has an equal number of protons and neutrons. What is the atomic weight of helium?

B) Incorrect. The atomic number for helium is 2. This number indicates how many protons the atom has. The atomic mass, or weight, of an atom is the number of protons plus the number of neutrons. Helium has

an equal number of protons and neutrons. What is the atomic weight of helium?

C) Incorrect. The atomic number for helium is 2. This number indicates how many protons the atom has. The atomic mass, or weight, of an atom is the number of protons plus the number of neutrons. Helium has an equal number of protons and neutrons. What is the atomic weight of helium?

D) Correct! The atomic mass, or weight, of an atom is the number of protons plus the number of neutrons. Helium has two protons and two neutrons, resulting in an atomic mass of 4.

Question 10:

A) Incorrect. Atoms resemble a tiny solar system. Protons and neutrons always reside in the nucleus at the center of the atom, while electrons orbit around the nucleus. Look again at the choices.

B) Incorrect. Atoms resemble a tiny solar system. Protons and neutrons always reside in the nucleus at the center of the atom, while electrons orbit around the nucleus. Look again at the choices.

C) Incorrect. Atoms resemble a tiny solar system. Protons and neutrons always reside in the nucleus at the center of the atom, while electrons orbit around the nucleus. Look again at the choices.

D) Correct! Atoms resemble a tiny solar system. Protons and neutrons always reside in the nucleus at the center of the atom, while electrons orbit around the nucleus.

Question 11:

A) Incorrect. Electrons are subatomic particles that carry a negative charge. They are more than 1,800 times smaller than protons and neutrons. Look again at the choices.

B) Incorrect. Electrons are subatomic particles that carry a negative charge, and they are more than 1,800 times smaller than protons and neutrons. Look again at the choices.

C) Correct! Electrons are subatomic particles that carry a negative charge. They are more than 1,800 times smaller than protons and neutrons.

D) Incorrect. Electrons are subatomic particles that carry a negative charge. However, they are more than 1,800 times smaller than protons and neutrons. Look again at the choices.

Atomic Theory II

Comprehension Checkpoints:
p48: B; p50: A

Question 1:

A) Incorrect. Atoms that carry electrical charges are called ions, regardless of whether they are positive or negative. Electrons are small particles within an atom that carry a negative charge. Which choice provides a definition of ions?

B) Incorrect. Neutrons are particles within an atom that do not carry any electrical charge. Atoms that carry electrical charges are called ions, regardless of whether they are positive or negative. Which choice provides a definition of ions?

C) Incorrect. Protons are particles within an atom that carry a positive electrical charge. Atoms that carry electrical charges are called ions, regardless of whether they are positive or negative. Which choice provides a definition of ions?

D) Correct! Ions are atoms that carry electrical charges.

Question 2:

A) Correct! Two atoms of the same element that contain different numbers of neutrons are called isotopes.

B) Incorrect. Isotopes are two atoms of the same element with different numbers of neutrons. Which choice gives the correct definition of isotopes?

C) Incorrect. Isotopes are two atoms of the same element with different numbers of neutrons. The atomic number stays the same in isotopes because that is determined by the number of protons. When atoms have a different number of protons, they are different elements. Which choice gives the correct definition of isotopes?

D) Incorrect. Isotopes are two atoms of the same element with different numbers of neutrons. When atoms have a different number of protons, they are different elements. Which choice gives the correct definition of isotopes?

Question 3:

A) Correct! Isotopes are two atoms of the same element with different numbers of neutrons. The atomic number stays the same in isotopes because that is determined by the number of protons.

B) Incorrect. Isotopes are two atoms of the same element with different numbers of neutrons. The atomic number stays the same in isotopes because that is determined by the number of protons.

Question 4:

A) Incorrect. Isotopes are two atoms of the same element with different numbers of neutrons. Thus they will have a different mass. Which statement is contradicted by this information?

B) Correct! Isotopes are two atoms of the same element with different numbers of neutrons. Thus they are no longer identical since isotopes of the same atom have a different mass.

C) Incorrect. Isotopes are two atoms of the same element with different numbers of neutrons. Thus they will have a different mass. Which statement is contradicted by this information?

D) Incorrect. Isotopes are two atoms of the same element with different numbers of neutrons. Thus they will have a different mass. Which statement is contradicted by this information?

Question 5:

A) Incorrect. Dalton is known for his investigation of atomic weights and the founding of atomic theory. Who proposed a modification to the theory of atomic structure based on line spectra?

B) Correct! Niels Bohr proposed a modification to the theory of atomic structure based on line spectra.

C) Incorrect. Rutherford's view of the atom suggested that electrons could move freely about the nucleus. However, the appearance of line spectra made scientists think that electron movement was limited to specific quantized shells – who proposed this modification?

D) Incorrect. Chadwick is known for his discovery of the neutron. Who proposed a modification to the theory of atomic structure based on line spectra?

Question 6:

A) Correct! When pure elements are excited by heat or electricity, they give off distinct colors. When light from an excited element is passed through a prism, only specific lines (or wavelengths) of light can be seen. These lines of light are called line spectra. Each element has its own distinct line spectra.

B) Incorrect. When pure elements are excited by heat or electricity, they give off distinct colors. When light from an excited element is passed through a prism, only specific lines of light can be seen rather than the entire color spectrum. What are these lines of light called?

C) Incorrect. When pure elements are excited by heat or electricity, they give off distinct colors. When light from an excited element is passed through a prism, only specific lines of light can be seen rather than the entire color spectrum. What are these lines of light called?

D) Incorrect. When pure elements are excited by heat or electricity, they give off distinct colors. When light from an excited element is passed through a prism, only specific lines of light can be seen rather than the entire color spectrum. What are these lines of light called?

Question 7:

A) Correct! To Bohr, line spectra showed that atoms could emit energy only in very precise quantities. He described the energy emitted as quantized.

B) Incorrect. To Bohr, line spectra showed that atoms could emit energy only in very precise quantities. When an atom is excited, electrons can jump to higher levels. When the electrons fall back to lower energy levels, precise quanta of energy are released as specific lines of light. Which choice describes the energy in atoms according to the theory of line spectra?

C) Incorrect. To Bohr, line spectra showed that atoms could emit energy only in very precise quantities. When an atom is excited, electrons can jump to higher levels. When the electrons fall back to lower energy levels, precise quanta of energy are released as specific lines of light. Which choice describes the energy in atoms according to the theory of line spectra?

D) Incorrect. To Bohr, line spectra showed that atoms could not emit energy continuously, but only in very precise quantities. When an atom is excited, electrons can jump to higher levels. When the electrons fall back to lower energy levels, precise quanta of energy are released as specific lines of light. Which choice describes the energy in atoms according to the theory of line spectra?

Question 8:

A) Incorrect. In Bohr's model, an electron's energy can be imagined as concentric circles around the nucleus. The lowest energy level is closest to the nucleus. When an atom is excited, electrons can jump to higher levels. What happens to the distance of electrons from the nucleus when they are excited?

B) Incorrect. In Bohr's model, an electron's energy can be imagined as concentric circles around the nucleus. The lowest energy level is closest to the nucleus. When an atom is excited, electrons can jump to higher levels. What happens to the distance of electrons from the nucleus when they are excited?

C) Correct! In Bohr's model, an electron's energy can be imagined as concentric circles around the nucleus. The lowest energy level is closest to the nucleus. When an atom is excited, electrons can jump to higher levels farther from the nucleus.

D) Incorrect. In Bohr's model, an electron's energy can be imagined as concentric circles around the nucleus. The lowest energy level is closest to the nucleus. When an atom is excited, electrons can jump to higher levels. What happens to the distance of electrons from the nucleus when they are excited?

Question 9:

A) Incorrect. In Bohr's model, an electron's energy can be imagined as concentric circles around the nucleus. In the normal "ground" state, they occupy the energy shell closest to the nucleus. Which electron shell is closest the nucleus?

B) Incorrect. In Bohr's model, an electron's energy can be imagined as concentric circles around the nucleus. In the normal "ground" state, they occupy the energy shell closest to the nucleus. Which electron shell is closest the nucleus?

C) Correct! In Bohr's model, an electron's energy can be imagined as concentric circles around the nucleus. Normally, electrons exist in the ground state. In this state, they occupy the lowest energy level possible. This means they are in the electron shell closest to the nucleus.

D) Incorrect. In Bohr's model, an electron's energy can be imagined as concentric circles around the nucleus. In the normal "ground" state, they occupy the energy shell closest to the nucleus. Which electron shell is closest the nucleus?

Question 10:

A) Correct! The first electron shell can hold a maximum of two electrons. If an element has more than two electrons, the extra electrons will reside in additional electron shells.

B) Incorrect. The first electron shell can hold only two electrons. If an element has more than two electrons, the extra electrons will be located in additional electron shells. Which choice correctly states the maximum number of electrons that may reside in the first energy level?

C) Incorrect. The first electron shell can hold only two electrons. If an element has more than two electrons, the extra electrons will be located in additional electron shells. Which choice correctly states the maximum number of electrons that may reside in the first energy level?

D) Incorrect. The first electron shell can hold only two electrons. If an element has more than two electrons, the extra electrons will be located in additional electron shells. Which choice correctly states the maximum number of electrons that may reside in the first energy level?

Question 11:

A) Incorrect. When an electron is excited, it will absorb energy and "jump" to a higher energy level. Then it will "fall" back to a lower energy level, giving off a quantum of light energy. The electron could only "jump" and "fall" to precise energy levels, thus emitting a limited spectrum of light. Which choice explains why each element has its own distinct line spectra?

B) Incorrect. When an electron is excited, it will absorb energy and "jump" to a higher energy level. Then it will "fall" back to a lower energy level, giving off a quantum of light energy. The electron could only "jump" and "fall" to precise energy levels, emitting a limited spectrum of light. Which choice explains why each element has its own distinct line spectra?

C) Correct! When an electron is excited, it will absorb energy and "jump" to a higher energy level. Then it will "fall" back to a lower energy level, giving off a quantum of light energy. The electron could only "jump" and "fall" to precise energy levels, emitting a limited spectrum of light. Each element has its own distinct line spectra.

D) Incorrect. When an electron is excited, it will absorb energy and "jump" to a higher energy level. Then it will "fall" back to a lower energy level, giving off a quantum of light energy. The electron could only "jump" and "fall" to precise energy levels, emitting a limited spectrum of light. Which choice explains why each element has its own distinct line spectra?

Nuclear Chemistry

Comprehension Checkpoints:
p54: A; p55: B

Question 1:

A) Incorrect. In 1896, Becquerel discovered that uranium emitted radiation. He shared a Nobel Prize with two others, Pierre and Marie Curie-- for discovering radioactivity. One of his co-recipients went on to become the first person to receive two Nobel Prizes.

B) Incorrect. The first person to win two Nobel Prizes was also the first woman to receive a Nobel Prize. The first--shared with her husband, Pierre Curie, and Henri Becquerel--was for discovering radioactivity. The second was for discovering the radioactive elements radium and polonium. Look again at the choices to see who fits this description.

C) Correct! Marie Curie was the first person to win two Nobel Prizes. The first--shared with her husband, Pierre Curie, and Henri Becquerel--was for discovering radioactivity. The second was for discovering the radioactive elements radium and polonium. She was also the first woman to win a Nobel Prize.

D) Incorrect. The first person to win two Nobel Prizes was also the first woman to receive a Nobel Prize. The first was for discovering radioactivity. The second was for discovering the radioactive elements radium and polonium. Look again at the choices to see who fits this description.

Question 2:

A) Incorrect. While it is true that beta radiation involves the transmutation of a neutron into a proton and an electron, the proton is not emitted from the nucleus. Look again at which particle is emitted.

B) Correct! Beta radiation involves the transmutation of a neutron into a proton and an electron. Then the electron is emitted from the atom's nucleus .

C) Incorrect. Beta radiation involves the transmutation of a neutron into an electron plus a different particle. The electron is then emitted from the nucleus. The other particle increases the atomic number by one. However, the atomic number will increase by one. Which type of particle affects atomic number?

D) Incorrect. Beta radiation involves the transmutation of a neutron into an electron plus a different particle. The electron is then emitted from the nucleus. The other particle increases the atomic number by one. Which type of particle affects atomic number?

Question 3:

A) Correct! Alpha radiation (α) is the emission of an alpha particle from an atom's nucleus. An α particle contains two protons and two neutrons, so the atomic mass will decrease by four units (because two protons and two neutrons are lost). The atomic number (z) will decrease by two units (since two protons are lost).

B) Incorrect. Beta radiation (β) is the transmutation of a neutron into a proton and an electron. When an atom emits a β particle, the atomic number will increase by one because the neutron transmutedinto an additional proton. Which type of radiation results in losing two protons, thus decreasing the atomic number by two units?

C) Incorrect. No particles are emitted during gamma radiation, so the atomic number does not change. Which type of radiation results in losing two protons, thus decreasing the atomic number by two units?

D) Incorrect. Which type of radiation results in losing two protons, thus decreasing the atomic number by two units?

Question 4:

A) Incorrect. Alpha radiation is the emission of an alpha particle from an atom's nucleus. However, no particles are emitted in the type of radiation that produces X-rays. Which type of radiation involves the emission of electromagnetic energy (similar to light energy) from an atom's nucleus?

B) Incorrect. Beta radiation results in an electron being emitted from the atom's nucleus. However, no particles are emitted in the type of radiation that produces X-rays. Which type of radiation involves the emission of electromagnetic energy (similar to light energy) from an atom's nucleus?

C) Correct! X-rays are a common example of gamma radiation.

D) Incorrect. No particles are emitted in the type of radiation that produces X-rays, and this type of radiation does not cause the transmutation of atoms. Which type of radiation involves the emission of electromagnetic energy (similar to light energy) from an atom's nucleus?

Question 5:

A) Incorrect. Alpha radiation (α)is the emission of an alpha particle from an atom's nucleus. An α particle contains two protons and two neutrons, so the atomic number will decrease by two units since two protons are lost. Which type of radiation involves the transmutation of a neutron into a proton and an electron, thus increasing the atomic number by one?

B) Correct! Beta radiation (β) involves the transmutation of a neutron into a proton and an electron followed by the emission of the electron from the atom's nucleus. This increases the atomic number by one because the neutron transmuted into an additional proton.

C) Incorrect. No particles are emitted during gamma radiation, so the atomic number does not change. Which type of radiation involves the transmutation of a neutron into a proton and an electron, thus increasing the atomic number by one?

D) Incorrect. Look again. One of these choices lists a type of radiation that involves the transmutation of a neutron into a proton and an electron (followed by the emission of the electron from the atom's nucleus). This increases the atomic number by one.

Question 6:

A) Incorrect. The half-life is the amount of time necessary for one-half of the radioactive material to decay. After one half-life, half the original isotope remains. After two half-lives, the remaining isotope is halved again, resulting in one fourth ($\frac{1}{2} * \frac{1}{2}$) or $\frac{1}{2}2$ of the original isotope. After three half-lives, the remaining isotope is halved yet again. To figure out the remaining fraction of the original isotope, multiply $\frac{1}{2} * \frac{1}{2} * \frac{1}{2}$.

B) Incorrect. The half-life is the amount of time necessary for one-half of the radioactive material to decay. After one half-life, half the original isotope remains. After two half-lives, the remaining isotope is halved again, resulting in one fourth ($\frac{1}{2} * \frac{1}{2}$) or $\frac{1}{2}2$ of the original isotope. After three half-lives, the remaining isotope is halved yet again. To figure out the remaining fraction of the original isotope, multiply $\frac{1}{2} * \frac{1}{2} * \frac{1}{2}$.

C) Incorrect. The half-life is the amount of time necessary for one-half of the radioactive material to decay. After one half-life, half the original isotope remains. After two half-lives, the remaining isotope is halved again, resulting in one fourth ($\frac{1}{2} * \frac{1}{2}$) or $\frac{1}{2}2$ of the

original isotope. After three half-lives, the remaining isotope is halved yet again. To figure out the remaining fraction of the original isotope, multiply $\frac{1}{2} * \frac{1}{2} * \frac{1}{2}$.

D) Correct! The half-life is the amount of time necessary for one-half of the radioactive material to decay. After one half-life, half the original isotope remains. After two half-lives, the remaining isotope is halved again, resulting in one fourth ($\frac{1}{2} * \frac{1}{2}$) or $\frac{1}{2}2$ of the original isotope. After three half-lives, the remaining isotope is halved yet again, resulting in one eighth -- ($\frac{1}{2} * \frac{1}{2} * \frac{1}{2}$) or $\frac{1}{2}3$ -- of the original isotope.

Question 7:

A) Incorrect. The sun (and all stars) are enormous thermonuclear reactors. Stars are primarily gigantic balls of hydrogen gas under great pressure due to gravitational forces. This pressure causes hydrogen molecules to fuse into helium and heavier elements inside of stars, releasing energy as light and heat. Which choice fits this explanation?

B) Correct! The sun (and all stars) are enormous thermonuclear reactors. Stars are primarily gigantic balls of hydrogen gas under great pressure from the force of gravity. This pressure causes hydrogen molecules to fuse into helium and heavier elements inside of stars, releasing energy as light and heat.

C) Incorrect. The sun (and all stars) are enormous thermonuclear reactors. Stars are primarily gigantic balls of hydrogen gas under great pressure from the force of gravity. This pressure causes hydrogen molecules to fuse into helium and heavier elements inside of stars, releasing energy as light and heat. Which choice fits this explanation?

D) Incorrect. The sun (and all stars) are enormous thermonuclear reactors. Stars are primarily gigantic balls of hydrogen gas under great pressure from the force of gravity. This pressure causes hydrogen molecules to fuse into helium and heavier elements inside of stars, releasing energy as light and heat. Which choice fits this explanation?

Question 8:

A) Incorrect. In nuclear fusion, two or more elements "fuse" together to form one larger element. But in nuclear fission, an atom's nucleus is split into smaller parts, most commonly by "firing" a neutron at the nucleus of an atom. Which choice involves using a source to split an element into two (or more) lighter elements?

B) Incorrect. In nuclear fusion, two or more elements "fuse" together to form one larger element. But in nuclear fission, an atom's nucleus splits into smaller parts . Which choice involves splitting an element into two (or more) lighter elements?

C) Correct! In nuclear fission, an atom's nucleus splits into smaller parts, releasing a large amount of energy in the process.

D) Incorrect. In nuclear fusion, two or more elements "fuse" together to form one larger element. But in nuclear fission, an atom's nucleus is split into smaller parts, most commonly by "firing" a neutron at the nucleus of an atom. Which choice involves using a source to split an element into two (or more) lighter elements?

Question 9:

A) Incorrect. Fusion reactions involve combining rather than splitting nuclei. In which choice are two or more elements "fused" together to form one larger element?

B) Correct! In nuclear fusion, two or more elements "fuse" together to form one larger element, releasing energy in the process.

C) Incorrect. Fusion reactions involve combining rather than splitting nuclei. In which choice are two or more elements "fused" together to form one larger element?

D) Incorrect. Fusion reactions involve combining rather than splitting nuclei. In which choice are two or more elements "fused" together to form one larger element?

Gravity

Comprehension Checkpoints:
p61: B; p62: B

Question 1:

A) Incorrect. A famous 17th-18th century English scientist and mathematician proposed a mathematical model of gravity, which Albert Einstein built upon centuries later. Try again to identify the scientist who is credited with discovering the Law of Universal Gravitation.

B) Incorrect. A different English scientist is given credit for discovering the Law of Universal Gravitation. However, Hooke claimed to have discovered the mathematical relationship at the foundation of this law. Try again to identify the scientist who eventually published his theory of gravitation and became famous as a result.

C) Correct! Isaac Newton proposed a mathematical model to describe the gravitational attraction between objects. Newton's broad and far-reaching theory is called the Law of Universal Gravitation. It applies not only to objects near the surface of the Earth like an apple but also to large distant bodies such as planets.

D) Incorrect. A different English scientist is given credit for proposing a mathematical model to describe the gravitational attraction between objects. However, Henry Cavendish confirmed this scientist's theory and built upon it. Try again to identify the scientist who is credited with discovering the Law of Universal Gravitation.

Question 2:

A) Incorrect. The essential feature of Newton's Law of Universal Gravitation is that the force of gravity between two objects is inversely proportional to the square of the distance between them.

B) Correct! The force of gravity between two objects increases as the masses of those objects increase.

C) Incorrect. Temperature is not a variable that affects the force of gravity. Which answer describes the variable that increases as gravity increases?

D) Incorrect. The force of gravity on Earth is proportional to the mass of Earth, but Newton's law describes universal gravitation, which goes beyond a single planet. Which answer could include Earth?

Question 3:

A) Incorrect. The force of gravity on Earth is directly proportional to the masses of the objects; in other words, as the product of the masses of the objects increases, so does the force of gravity between them. Which answer describes the variable that increases as the force of gravity decreases?

B) Incorrect. The distance between the objects does affect the force of gravity between them, but not linearly. Which answer describes the variable that increases exponentially as the force of gravity decreases?

C) Correct! The essential feature of Newton's Law of Universal Gravitation is that the force of gravity between two objects is inversely proportional to the square of the distance between them. In other words, the force of gravity decreases exponential as the distance between two objects increases.

D) Incorrect. The force of gravity on Earth is directly proportional to the mass of Earth, but Newton's law describes universal gravitation, which goes beyond a single planet. Which answer describes the variable that increases as the force of gravity decreases, beyond just a single planet?

Question 4:

A) Incorrect. Through an experiment, Cavendish determined the value of G in Newton's Law of Universal Gravitation. Using this, he could calculate the mass of Earth. Which choice is based on knowing the numerical value of G?

B) Correct! Through his "torsion balance" experiment, Cavendish determined the value of the gravitational constant (G) in Newton's Law of Universal Gravitation. Since he had determined the value of G, he could do some simple calculations to determine the mass of Earth.

C) Incorrect. Through an experiment, Cavendish determined the value of G in Newton's Law of Universal Gravitation. Using this, he could calculate the mass of Earth. Which choice is based on knowing the numerical value of G?

D) Incorrect. Through an experiment, Cavendish determined the value of G in Newton's Law of Universal Gravitation. Using this, he could calculate the mass of the Earth. Which choice is based on knowing the numerical value of G?

Question 5:

A) Incorrect. Henry Cavendish created a device that twisted i n response to gravitational attraction. Look again at the choices for the apparatus that helped Cavendish confirm Newton's theory and determine the value of the gravitational constant.

B) Incorrect. Henry Cavendish created a device that twisted i n response to gravitational attraction. Look again at the choices for the apparatus that helped Cavendish confirm Newton's theory and determine the value of the gravitational constant.

C) Incorrect. Henry Cavendish created a device that twisted i n response to gravitational attraction. Look again at the choices for the apparatus that helped Cavendish confirm Newton's theory and determine the value of the gravitational constant.

D) Correct! Henry Cavendish created a "torsion balance," which twisted in response to gravitational attraction. Cavendish's experiments with this device confirmed Newton's theory and determined the value of the gravitational constant to an accuracy of about 1 percent.

Question 6:

A) Incorrect. In 1845, John Couch Adams and Urbain Le Verrier used Newton's law to predict the existence of a yet unseen planet. In 1846, German astronomer Johann·Galle confirmed their predictions and officially discovered Neptune.

B) Correct! In 1845, John Couch Adams and Urbain Le Verrier used Newton's law to predict the existence of a yet unseen planet. In 1846, German astronomer Johann Galle confirmed their predictions and officially discovered Neptune.

C) Incorrect. In 1845, John Couch Adams and Urbain Le Verrier used Newton's law to predict the existence of a yet unseen planet. In 1846, German astronomer Johann Galle confirmed their predictions and officially discovered Neptune.

D) Incorrect. In 1845, John Couch Adams and Urbain Le Verrier used Newton's law to predict the existence of a yet unseen planet based on discrepancies between predictions for and observations of the position of Uranus. In 1846, German astronomer Johann Galle confirmed their predictions and officially discovered Neptune.

Question 7:

A) Incorrect. In 1915, Albert Einstein demonstrated that the Law of Universal Gravitation fails to work when gravitation becomes extremely strong. Nonetheless, Newton's gravitational constant plays an important role in Einstein's alternative to Newton's law. Look again for the name of Einstein's theory.

B) Incorrect. In 1915, Albert Einstein demonstrated that the Law of Universal Gravitation fails to work when gravitation becomes extremely strong. Nonetheless, Newton's gravitational constant plays an important role in Einstein's alternative to Newton's law. Look again for the name of Einstein's theory.

C) Correct! In 1915, Albert Einstein demonstrated that the Law of Universal Gravitation fails to work when gravitation becomes extremely strong. Nonetheless, Newton's gravitational constant plays an important role in Einstein's alternative to Newton's law, the Theory of General Relativity.

D) Incorrect. In 1915, Albert Einstein demonstrated that the Law of Universal Gravitation fails to work when gravitation becomes extremely strong. Nonetheless, Newton's gravitational constant plays an important role in Einstein's alternative to Newton's law. Look again for the name of Einstein's theory.

Question 8:

A) You are partly correct. Using the Law of Universal Gravitation, scientists can predict the gravitational force between a comet and Earth if they know the masses and the distance between them. But that's not the only prediction that is possible. Which choice allows for many predictions?

B) You are partly correct. Using the Law of Universal Gravitation, scientists can predict the location of planets based on slight perturbations in the orbits of other planets. But that's not all they can predict. Which choice allows for several possible predictions?

C) You are partly correct. The Law of Universal Gravitation allows scientists to predict the mass of a large body in space based on its orbit around another object. But that's not the only prediction that is possible. Which choice allows for several possible predictions?

D) Correct!

Using the Law of Universal Gravitation, scientists can predict the mass of a large body in space, the location of planets, and the gravitational force between objects.

Light I

Comprehension Checkpoints:
p68: A; p70: B; p73: A

Question 1:

A) **Incorrect.** Refraction is the phenomenon by which an object partially submerged in water appears to be broken. This is because as light crosses the boundary between two different materials, it changes direction and usually speed. Which choice describes refraction?

B) **Incorrect.** Refraction is the phenomenon by which an object partially submerged in water appears to be broken. This is because as light crosses the boundary between two different materials, it changes direction and usually speed. Which choice describes refraction?

C) **Correct!** Refraction is the phenomenon by which an object partially submerged in water appears to be broken. This is because as light crosses the boundary between two different materials—such as a solid and a liquid—it changes direction and usually speed.

D) **Correct!** Refraction is the phenomenon by which an object partially submerged in water appears to be broken. This is because as light crosses the boundary between two different materials—such as a solid and a liquid—it changes direction and usually speed.

Question 2:

A) **Incorrect.** Diffraction is a phenomenon where waves bend or spread when they encounter and obstruction. Which choice involves the bending of light around an obstacle?

B) **Incorrect.** Diffraction is a phenomenon where waves bend or spread when they encounter and obstruction. Which choice involves the bending of light around an obstacle?

C) **Correct!** Diffraction is a phenomenon where waves bend or spread when they encounter and obstruction.

D) **Incorrect.** Diffraction is a phenomenon where waves bend or spread when they encounter and obstruction. Which choice involves the bending of light around an obstacle?

Question 3:

A) **Incorrect.** In Thomas Young's "Double Slit" experiment, light bent around a card because the card was only as thick as the wavelength of the light being split. Which choice explains how waves can be diffracted?

B) **Incorrect.** In Thomas Young's "Double Slit" experiment, light bent around a card because the card was only as thick as the wavelength of the light being split. Which choice explains how waves can be diffracted?

C) **Incorrect.** Both light and sound waves can go around obstacles, depending on the relative size of the wave and the obstacle. In Thomas Young's "Double Slit" experiment, light bent around a card because the card was only as thick as the wavelength of the light being split. Which choice explains how waves can be diffracted?

D) **Correct!** Waves will go around obstacles, but only if the size of the obstacle is comparable to the size, or wavelength, of the wave. In Thomas Young's "Double Slit" experiment, light bent around a card because the card was only as thick as the wavelength of the light being split.

Question 4:

A) **Incorrect.** When two approaching waves reach each other, they combine to form a new, bigger wave (constructive interference) or cancel each other out (destructive interference), depending on their relative amplitudes. Which choice explains constructive and destructive interference?

B) **Incorrect.** When two approaching waves reach each other, they combine to form a new, bigger wave (constructive interference) or cancel each other out (destructive interference), depending on their relative amplitudes. Which choice explains constructive and destructive interference?

C) **Incorrect.** When two approaching waves reach each other, they combine to form a new, bigger wave (constructive interference) or cancel each other out (destructive interference), depending on their relative amplitudes. Which choice explains constructive and destructive interference?

D) **Correct!** When two approaching waves reach each other, they combine to form a new, bigger wave (constructive interference) or cancel each other out (destructive interference), depending on their relative amplitudes.

Question 5:

A) **Incorrect.** Young found that bright spots appeared where two beams of light interfered constructively and created light that was brighter than either beam by itself. Dark spots occurred where the beams of light interfered destructively and canceled each other out. Look again for the explanation of bright and dark spots in Young's experiment.

B) **Incorrect.** Young found that bright spots appeared where two beams of light interfered constructively and created light that was brighter than either beam by itself. Dark spots occurred where the beams of light interfered destructively and canceled each other out. Look again for the explanation of bright and dark spots in Young's experiment.

C) **Incorrect.** Young found that bright spots appeared where two beams of light interfered constructively and created light that was brighter than either beam by itself. Dark spots occurred where the beams of light interfered destructively and canceled each other out. Look again for the explanation of bright and dark spots in Young's experiment.

D) **Correct!** Young found that bright spots appeared where two beams of light interfered constructively and created light that was brighter than either beam by itself. Dark spots occurred where the beams of light interfered destructively.

Question 6:

A) Incorrect. Where constructive interference occurred, the path difference was zero or an integer multiple of a wavelength, and the intensity of the light hitting the screen was at a maximum. Which choice describes path lengths that result in constructive interference?

B) Correct! Where constructive interference occurred, the path difference was zero or an integer multiple of a wavelength, and the intensity of the light hitting the screen was at a maximum.

C) Incorrect. Where constructive interference occurred, the path difference was zero or an integer multiple of a wavelength, and the intensity of the light hitting the screen was at a maximum. Which choice describes path lengths that result in constructive interference?

D) Incorrect. Where constructive interference occurred, the path difference was zero or an integer multiple of a wavelength, and the intensity of the light hitting the screen was at a maximum. Which choice describes path lengths that result in constructive interference?

Question 7:

A) Incorrect. When the path difference was zero or an integer multiple of a wavelength, constructive interference occurred and the light was brighter. However, where the difference in path lengths was a multiple of exactly one half-wavelength, there was no light at all. Which choice describes this destructive interference?

B) Incorrect. When the path difference was zero or an integer multiple of a wavelength, constructive interference occurred and the light was brighter. However, where the difference in path lengths was a multiple of exactly one half-wavelength, there was no light at all. Which choice describes this destructive interference?

C) Incorrect. When the path difference was zero or an integer multiple of a wavelength, constructive interference occurred and the light was brighter. However, where the difference in path lengths was a multiple of exactly one half-wavelength , there was no light at all. Which choice describes this destructive interference?

D) Correct! Destructive interference occurred when the difference in path lengths was a multiple of exactly one half-wavelength. When this happened, there was no light at all .

Light and Electromagnetism

Comprehension Checkpoints:
p76: A; p78: A; p79: B

Question 1:

A) Incorrect. When two parallel wires carry current in opposite directions, they repel each other. What happens when the current runs in the same direction?

B) Incorrect. In the 1800s, physicist Andre-Marie Ampere demonstrated that two current-carrying wires would interact with each other due to the magnetic field that they generated. When two wires carry current in opposite directions, they repel each other. What happens when the current runs in the same direction?

C) Correct! Two parallel wires that carry current interact with each other due to the magnetic field that they generate. When the two wires carry current in the same direction, they attract each other.

D) Incorrect. Two parallel wires that carry current interact with each other due to the magnetic field that they generate no matter which way the current flows. When the two wires carry current in opposite directions, they repel each other. What happens when the current runs in the same direction?

Question 2:

A) Correct! Two parallel wires that carry current interact with each other due to the magnetic field that they generate. When the two wires carry current in opposite directions, they repel each other.

B) Incorrect. In the 1800s, physicist Andre-Marie Ampere demonstrated that two current-carrying wires would interact with each other due to the magnetic field that they generated. When two wires carry current in same direction, they attract each other. What happens when the current in the two wires runs in opposite directions?

C) Incorrect. When two wires carry current in same direction, they attract each other. What happens when the current in the two wires runs in opposite directions?

D) Incorrect. Two parallel wires that carry current interact with each other due to the magnetic field that they generate no matter which way the current flows. When two wires carry current in same direction, they attract each other. What happens when the current in the two wires runs in opposite directions?

Question 3:

A) Incorrect. Michael Faraday, an English physicist, observed how a magnet affected the current in a wire when they were moved near each other. Faraday hypothesized that the magnet "induced" the current in the wire. Which choice describes the principle of induction?

B) Incorrect. Radio waves are a group of wavelengths on the electromagnetic spectrum. Before these waves were identified, Michael Faraday observed that moving a magnet and a coil of wire near each other produced electric current. Faraday hypothesized that the magnet "induced" the current in the wire. Which choice describes the principle of induction?

C) Incorrect. Andre-Marie Ampere found that two parallel current-carrying wires can either attract or repel each other, depending on which way the current is flowing. After Ampere's discovery, Michael Faraday observed that moving a magnet and a coil of wire near each other produced electric current. Faraday hypothesized that the magnet "induced" the current in the wire. Which choice describes the principle of induction?

D) Correct! Physicist Michael Faraday observed that moving a magnet and a coil of wire near each other produced electric current. Faraday hypothesized that the magnet "induced" the current in the wire. This principle is used in electrical generators, which turn mechanical energy into electrical energy.

Question 4:

A) Incorrect. The waves in the electromagnetic spectrum, including light waves, do not travel at such a high speed. Look again at the choices.

B) Correct! All of the waves in the electromagnetic spectrum, including light waves, travel at a speed of approximately 300,000,000 meters per second.

C) Incorrect. Waves in the electromagnetic spectrum, including light waves, travel at a speed that is 10 times faster in meters per second. Look again at the choices.

D) Incorrect. Waves in the electromagnetic spectrum, including light waves, travel at a speed that is 100 times faster in meters per second. Look again at the choices.

Question 5:

A) Incorrect. Radio waves have the longest wavelength of any waves in the electromagnetic spectrum at over 1 meter. The shortest wavelength electromagnetic waves are 1 trillion times shorter than radio waves. What are these shortest waves called?

B) Correct! Gamma rays have the shortest wavelength on the electromagnetic spectrum. At less than 10 picometers, their wavelength is 1 trillion times shorter than radio waves.

C) Incorrect. Radio waves have the longest wavelength of any waves in the electromagnetic spectrum at over 1 meter. The waves with the shortest wavelength, at less than 10 picometers, are 1 trillion times shorter than radio waves. In between these extremes are other bands of electromagnetic waves, including ultraviolet light. Which choice names the shortest waves in the electromagnetic spectrum?

D) Incorrect. Radio waves have the longest wavelength of any waves in the electromagnetic spectrum at over 1 meter. The shortest wavelength electromagnetic waves are 1 trillion times shorter than radio waves. What are these shortest waves called?

Question 6:

A) Incorrect. Wavelengths in the electromagnetic spectrum can range from less than 10 picometers to over 1 meter. In between these extremes are other bands of electromagnetic waves, including ultraviolet light. The waves with the shortest wavelength, gamma rays, are 1 trillion times shorter than the longest waves. Which choice names the longest waves in the electromagnetic spectrum?

B) Correct! The longest wavelength waves are longer than 1 meter, and this band of the electromagnetic spectrum is known as radio waves. Radio waves are 1 trillion times longer than gamma rays, which are the shortest waves on the spectrum!

C) Incorrect. Gamma rays have the shortest wavelength on the electromagnetic spectrum. At less than 10 picometers, their wavelength is 1 trillion times shorter than the waves with the longest wavelength. Which choice names the longest waves in the electromagnetic spectrum?

D) Incorrect. Gamma rays have the shortest wavelength on the electromagnetic spectrum. At less than 10 picometers, their wavelength is 1 trillion times shorter than the waves with the longest wavelength. Which choice names the longest waves in the electromagnetic spectrum?

Question 7:

A) Incorrect. Electromagnetic radiation in the range of wavelengths that humans can detect is called light. Infrared waves are outside of the range of the spectrum that humans can detect. Which choice describes the type of radiation that humans detect with their eyes?

B) Correct! Electromagnetic radiation in the range of wavelengths that we can detect with our eyes is what we call light. The majority of the radiation produced by the Sun and hitting the surface of the planet Earth falls into this range.

C) Incorrect. X-rays make up another group of wavelengths on the electromagnetic spectrum, but these waves are outside of the range that humans can detect. Humans detect wavelengths from 400 to 700 nanometers, known as light. Which choice describes the type of electromagnetic radiation that humans detect with their eyes?

D) Incorrect. Humans detect wavelengths from 400 to 700 nanometers, known as light. Bees and other insects have sensory organs that detect ultraviolet waves. Which choice describes the type of electromagnetic radiation that humans detect with their eyes?

Question 8:

A) Incorrect. Throughout the nineteenth century, many of science's greatest minds dedicated themselves to the study of electricity and magnetism. Hans Christian

Oersted performed early experiments to investigate the connection between electricity and magnetism, but it was a Scottish physicist who synthesized these ideas into a theory of electromagnetism. Which choice identifies the scientist who devised the theory of electromagnetism?

B) Incorrect. In 1831, Michael Faraday discovered that a changing magnetic field produces an electric field. Over 40 years after Faraday, another scientist unified the concepts of electric and magnetic fields into one mathematical model. Which choice names this scientist who devised the theory of electromagnetism?

C) Incorrect. Thomas Young investigated the nature of light many years before the theory of electromagnetism. Throughout the nineteenth century, many of science's greatest minds dedicated themselves to the study of electricity and magnetism. Which choice names a Scottish physicist who synthesized these ideas into a theory of electromagnetism?

D) Correct! Throughout the nineteenth century, many of science's greatest minds dedicated themselves to the study of two exciting new ideas: electricity and magnetism. Maxwell's work synthesized these two ideas, which had previously been considered separate phenomena. His new theory was called "electromagnetism."

Question 9:

A) Incorrect. The wavelength of ultraviolet waves is just shorter than that of the majority of the radiation produced by the Sun. The majority of the energy that radiates from the Sun and hits Earth falls in the 400 to 700 nanometer range. Electromagnetic radiation in this range is what we call "light," but it is no different in form from any of the other electromagnetic waves. Which choice describes the majority of radiation from the sun?

B) Correct! The majority of the energy that radiates from the Sun and hits Earth falls in the 400 to 700 nanometer range. Electromagnetic radiation in this range is what we perceive as visible light, but it is no different in form from microwaves, ultraviolet waves, infrared waves, or any other type of electromagnetic wave.

C) Incorrect. The wavelength of infrared waves is just longer than that of the majority of the radiation produced by the Sun. The majority of the energy that radiates from the Sun and hits Earth falls in the 400 to 700 nanometer range. Electromagnetic radiation in this range is what we call "light," but it is no different in form from any of the other electromagnetic waves. Which choice describes the majority of radiation from the sun?

D) Incorrect. Microwaves have a longer wavelength than that of the majority of the radiation produced by the Sun. The majority of the energy that radiates from the Sun and hits Earth falls in the 400 to 700 nanometer range. Electromagnetic radiation in this range is what

we call "light," but it is no different in form from any of the other electromagnetic waves. Which choice describes the majority of radiation from the sun?

Question 10:

A) Incorrect. It was Maxwell's mathematical calculations that led him to the realization that light was an electromagnetic wave. Which choice describes the type of calculation that provided evidence for light being part of the electromagnetic spectrum?

B) Correct! Maxwell's calculated value for the speed of light was extremely close to the measured value for the speed of light. This was too much for Maxwell to accept as coincidence, and led him to the realization that light was an electromagnetic wave and thus part of the electromagnetic spectrum.

C) Incorrect. Maxwell's evidence for light as an electromagnetic wave did not have to do with the speed of sound. Which choice describes the type of calculation that provided evidence for light being part of the electromagnetic spectrum?

D) Incorrect. It was Maxwell's mathematical calculations that led him to the realization that light was an electromagnetic wave. Which choice describes the type of calculation that provided evidence for light being part of the electromagnetic spectrum?

Earth Structure

Comprehension Checkpoints:
p82: A; p84: A; p85: A

Question 1:

A) Incorrect. The inner and outer core are distinguished from each other by their mechanical properties, while the Moho is a boundary between compositional layers. Look again at the choices.

B) Incorrect. The lithosphere and the asthenosphere are layers defined by their mechanical properties, while the Moho is a boundary between compositional layers. Look again at the choices.

C) Correct! The Moho is named for Andrija Mohorovicic, a Croatian seismologist who in 1909 defined the boundary between the crust, which forms the surface of the Earth, and the layer below, called the mantle.

D) Incorrect. The boundary between the mantle and the core is defined by a difference in composition, like occurs across the Moho, but the Moho occurs between different layers. Look again at the choices.

Question 2:

A) Correct! Every earthquake sends out an array of seismic waves in all directions. Observing the behavior of these seismic waves as they travel through the Earth gives us insight into the layers of the Earth and their composition.

B) Incorrect. While it is true that earthquakes happen below Earth's surface, this is not why they are most useful to scientists studying Earth's interior. Observing the behavior of seismic waves as they travel through the Earth gives us insight into the layers of the Earth and their composition. Look again at the answers.

C) Incorrect. While it is true that earthquakes release stress that has built up over time, they are useful for studying the Earth's interior because of the waves they produce. Observing the behavior of seismic waves as they travel through the Earth gives us insight into the layers of the Earth and their composition. Look again at the answers.

D) Incorrect. Earthquakes can be extremely destructive for humans, but they provide a wealth of information about the Earth's interior. Observing the behavior of seismic waves as they travel through the Earth gives us insight into the layers of the Earth and their composition. Which choice states how earthquakes provide information to scientists?

Question 3:

A) Incorrect. P-waves can travel through liquid although they are refracted and slowed. S-waves, however, are unable to travel through liquid.

B) Correct! P-waves can travel through liquid although they are refracted and slowed. S-waves, however, are unable to travel through liquid.

Question 4:

A) Incorrect. Basalt is the rock that makes up oceanic crust. Seismic waves suggest that the Earth's core contains very high density material, so it must be a metal. A magnetic field around the Earth also indicates a metallic core. Which choice identifies a metal?

B) Correct! Seismic waves suggest that the Earth's core contains very high density material, so it must be a metal. A magnetic field around the Earth also indicates a metallic core. Most scientists believe that the core contains mostly iron.

C) Incorrect. Granite is the rock that makes up continental crust. Seismic waves suggest that the Earth's core contains very high density material, so it must be a metal. A magnetic field around the Earth also indicates a metallic core. Which choice identifies a metal?

D) Incorrect. Peridotite is the rock that makes up the mantle. Seismic waves suggest that the Earth's core contains very high density material, so it must be a metal. A magnetic field around the Earth also indicates a metallic core. Which choice identifies a metal?

Question 5:

A) Incorrect. Oceanic crust, composed of basalt, is approximately 5 km thick and has a density of approximately 3.0 g/cm3. Continental crust, composed primarily of granite, ranges in thickness from 15 to 70 km and has a density of approximately 2.7 g/cm3. Keep this information in mind as you read the choices again.

B) Incorrect. Oceanic crust, composed of basalt, is approximately 5 km thick and has a density of approximately 3.0 g/cm3. Continental crust, composed primarily of granite, ranges in thickness from 15 to 70 km and has a density of approximately 2.7 g/cm3. Keep this information in mind as you read the choices again.

C) Incorrect. Oceanic crust, composed of basalt, is approximately 5 km thick and has a density of approximately 3.0 g/cm3. Continental crust, composed primarily of granite, ranges in thickness from 15 to 70 km and has a density of approximately 2.7 g/cm3. Keep this information in mind as you read the choices again.

D) Correct! Oceanic crust, which is composed of basalt, is thin (~ 5 km) and relatively dense (~3.0 g/cm3). Continental crust, in contrast, is thicker (15 to 70 km) and is made primarily of less dense rock such as granite (~2.7 g/cm3).

Question 6:

A) You are partly correct. It is true that seismic waves refract—or bend—when they cross a boundary into a different material. How else might seismic waves behave when they encounter a different material?

B) You are partly correct. It is true that when seismic waves hit a different material, they may bounce back toward the surface. How else might seismic waves behave when they encounter a boundary with a different material?

C) You are partly correct. It is true that certain seismic waves can change speed and direction when they cross a boundary into a different material. How else might seismic waves behave when they encounter a different material?

D) Correct! When seismic waves hit a boundary with a different material, they might reflect, refract, or change velocity.

Question 7:

A) Incorrect. The S-wave shadow zone is a region where no S waves reach Earth's surface from distant earthquakes. This type of wave is unable to travel through liquid, so the shadow zone indicates that there is a liquid layer deep within the Earth. Which choice identifies this layer of the Earth and the feature of its composition that stops the S-waves?

B) Incorrect. The S-wave shadow zone is a region where no S waves reach Earth's surface from distant earthquakes. This type of wave is unable to travel through liquid, so the shadow zone indicates that there is a liquid layer deep within the Earth. Which choice identifies this layer of the Earth and the feature of its composition that stops the S-waves?

C) Incorrect. The S-wave shadow zone is a region where no S waves reach Earth's surface from distant earthquakes. This type of wave is unable to travel through liquid, so the shadow zone indicates that there is a liquid layer deep within the Earth. Which choice identifies this layer of the Earth and the feature of its composition that stops the S-waves?

D) Correct! The S-wave shadow zone is a region where no S waves reach Earth's surface from distant earthquakes. Since S-waves are unable to travel through liquid, the shadow zone indicates that there is a liquid layer at the core-mantle boundary that stops all of these waves.

Question 8:

A) Correct! Tectonic plates consist of the crust acting together with the uppermost part of the mantle. This rigid layer is called the lithosphere.

B) Incorrect. Tectonic plates consist of the crust acting together with the uppermost part of the mantle. This rigid layer is called the lithosphere.

Question 9:

A) Incorrect. Seismic waves do attenuate with distance, but this is not the behavior that tells us about Earth's interior. Which choice describes how seismic waves respond to what they encounter inside Earth?

B) Correct! If the Earth were the same composition all the way through, seismic waves would radiate outward from their source and become slower and weaker with distance, a process called attenuation. However, seismic waves refract and reflect when they encounter different materials within the Earth's interior, causing them to be delayed or stopped.

C) Incorrect. The fact that there are S- and P- waves helps us understand that the Earth has internal layers, but it is not the reason we know that. S-waves and P-waves do behave differently when traveling through the Earth's interior. This indicates that they encounter different materials. Which choice has to do with the behavior of seismic waves?

D) Incorrect. It is true that, where the mantle is exposed, the rocks look different than those in the crust, but these exposures are very rare and still only tell us about the very upper portion of Earth's interior. Which choice has to do with how we can see much deeper into Earth?

Earth's Atmosphere

Comprehension Checkpoints:
p91: B; p92: B; p93: A

Question 1:

A) Incorrect. Atmospheric gases are often divided up into the major, constant components and the highly variable components. Major components of the atmosphere include nitrogen, oxygen, and a small amount of argon. Which choice is not listed among the major components?

B) Correct! Atmospheric gases are divided into (1) the major, constant components and (2) the highly variable components. Major components of the atmosphere include nitrogen, oxygen, and a small amount of argon. Variable components include carbon dioxide, water vapor, methane, sulfur dioxide, and ozone.

C) Incorrect. Atmospheric gases are divided into (1) the major components and (2) the highly variable components. Major components of the atmosphere include nitrogen, oxygen, and a small amount of argon. Oxygen makes up 20.95% of the atmosphere. Which choice is not listed among the major components?

D) Incorrect. Atmospheric gases are divided into (1) the major components and (2) the highly variable components. Major components of the atmosphere include nitrogen, oxygen, and a small amount of argon. Nitrogen makes up 78.08% of the atmosphere. Which choice is not listed among the major components?

Question 2:

A) Incorrect. Pressure decreases with altitude in the atmosphere, so air is under less pressure at higher altitudes. Temperature increases in the stratosphere because there is a layer of concentrated ozone, which absorbs UV rays and warms the air. Which choice states this feature of the stratosphere?

B) Incorrect. As the density of the atmosphere decreases, its temperature also decreases. Temperature increases in the stratosphere because there is a layer of concentrated ozone, which absorbs UV rays and warms the air. Which choice states this feature of the stratosphere?

C) Incorrect. The tiny change in the distance to the sun cannot account for the change in temperature that we see in the atmosphere. Temperature increases in the stratosphere because there is a layer of concentrated ozone, which absorbs UV rays and warms the air. Which choice states this feature of the stratosphere?

D) Correct! Temperature increases in the stratosphere because there is a layer of concentrated ozone, which absorbs UV rays and warms the air.

Question 3:

A) Incorrect. In the troposphere, the higher the elevation, the lower the temperature. For example, the temperature at the top of Mt. Everest (8,856 m high) averages -36° C, whereas the temperature in New Delhi (233 m above sea level) averages about 28° C. Look again at the choices.

B) Incorrect. Within the troposphere the temperature decreases approximately 6.5 C° for each kilometer gain in altitude. For example, the temperature at the top of Mt. Everest (8,856 m high) averages -36° C, whereas the temperature in New Delhi (233 m above sea level) averages about 28° C. Look again at the choices.

C) Correct! Within the troposphere, the lowest layer of Earth's atmosphere, temperature decreases with altitude at approximately 6.5° C per kilometer. At 8,856 m high, Mt. Everest reaches less than halfway through the troposphere. The temperature at Everest's summit averages -36° C.

D) Incorrect. In the troposphere, the higher the elevation, the lower the temperature. For example, the temperature at the top of Mt. Everest (8,856 m high) averages -36° C, whereas the temperature in New Delhi (233 m above sea level) averages about 28° C. Look again at the choices.

Question 4:

A) Incorrect. Though Earth is not the only planet with an atmosphere, Earth's atmosphere is unique. The presence of free oxygen and water vapor protect life on Earth by providing oxygen for breathing, shielding us from harmful UV rays, and burning up small meteors.

B) Correct! Though Earth is not the only planet with an atmosphere, Earth's atmosphere is unique. The presence of free oxygen and water vapor protect life on Earth by providing oxygen for breathing, shielding us from harmful UV rays, and burning up small meteors.

Question 5:

A) Correct! The outermost layer of the atmosphere is called the thermosphere. The thermosphere goes to about 500 km above the surface of the Earth, still a few hundred kilometers below most orbiting satellites.

B) Incorrect. Scientists have named four layers of Earth's atmosphere. The mesosphere is above the troposphere and the stratosphere. What is the outermost layer of Earth's atmosphere called?

C) Incorrect. Beyond the stratosphere, there are two more layers of atmosphere. What is the outermost layer of Earth's atmosphere called?

D) Incorrect. The troposphere is the innermost layer of the atmosphere. After the troposphere, there are three more atmospheric layer. What is the outermost layer of Earth's atmosphere called?

Question 6:

A) Incorrect. At sea level, pressure ranges from about 960 to 1,050 mb, with an average of 1,013 mb.

B) Correct! At sea level, pressure ranges from about 960 to 1,050 mb, with an average of 1,013 mb.

Question 7:

A) Incorrect. Water vapor, CO2, and other gases are highly variable in the atmosphere, not major components. In addition, they absorb heat emitted by the Earth and thus warm the atmosphere, creating a "greenhouse effect." Without these gases, the surface of the Earth would be too cold for life to exist as we know it. What is the name for these gases?

B) Incorrect. Water vapor and CO2 are highly variable, but that is not why they act to warm the atmosphere. Water vapor, CO2 and other gases absorb heat emitted by the Earth and thus warm the atmosphere, creating a "greenhouse effect." Without these gases, the surface of the Earth would be too cold for life to exist as we know it. What is the name for these gases?

C) Incorrect. Water vapor, CO2, and other gases are highly variable, minor components of the atmosphere, but they also absorb heat emitted by the Earth and thus warm the atmosphere, creating a "greenhouse effect." Without these gases, the surface of the Earth would be too cold for life to exist as we know it. What is the name for these gases?

D) Correct! Water vapor, CO2, and other gases absorb heat emitted by the Earth and thus warm the atmosphere. Without this "greenhouse" effect, the surface of the Earth would be too cold for life to exist as we know it.

Question 8:

A) Incorrect. As altitude increases, gas molecules in the air become fewer and farther between. This is why mountain climbers experience shortness of breath: there are approximately one-third as many gas molecules per breath on top of Mt. Everest as at sea level. Which choice explains how pressure is affected by altitude?

B) Incorrect. As altitude increases, gas molecules in the air become fewer and farther between. This is why mountain climbers experience shortness of breath: there are approximately one-third as many gas molecules per breath on top of Mt. Everest as at sea level. Which choice explains how pressure is affected by altitude?

C) Correct! As altitude increases, gas molecules in the air become fewer and farther between. This is why mountain climbers experience shortness of breath: there are approximately one-third as many gas molecules per breath on top of Mt. Everest as at sea level. In fact, 80 percent of the atmosphere's mass is found within the 18 km closest to the surface.

D) Incorrect. As altitude increases, gas molecules in the air become fewer and farther between. This is why mountain climbers experience shortness of breath: there are approximately one-third as many gas molecules per breath on top of Mt. Everest as at sea level. Although there is an ozone-rich layer at the base of the stratosphere, this does not affect the pressure. Which choice explains how pressure is affected by altitude?

Question 9:

A) You are partly correct. Second only to nitrogen, oxygen makes up at more than one-fifth of the Earth's atmosphere. Without oxygen to breathe, Earth could not sustain life. What other features of the atmosphere help sustain and protect life on Earth?

B) You are partly correct. Without greenhouse gases, the surface of the Earth would be about 30 degrees Celsius cooler – too cold for life to exist as we know it. What other features of the atmosphere help sustain and protect life on Earth?

C) You are partly correct. By absorbing UV rays, the ozone layer both warms the air around it and protects us on the surface from harmful radiation. What other features of the atmosphere help sustain and protect life on Earth?

D) Correct! The presence of oxygen, greenhouse gases, and the ozone layer sustain and protect life on Earth by providing the air we breathe, regulating temperature, and shielding us from harmful UV rays.

The Origins of Plate Tectonic Theory

Comprehension Checkpoints:
p100: A; p101: B; p103: A

Question 1:

A) Incorrect. Into the 1900s, many scientists believed that as Earth cooled after its formation, the planet's surface contracted and wrinkled like the skin of an apple dried in the sun, forcing mountain ranges up. Which choice explains how the contraction theory accounted for the Earth's features?

B) Incorrect. Into the 1900s, many scientists believed that as Earth cooled after its formation, the planet's surface contracted and wrinkled like the skin of an apple dried in the sun, forcing mountain ranges up. Which choice explains how the contraction theory accounted for the Earth's features?

C) Correct! Into the 1900s, many scientists believed that as Earth cooled after its formation, the planet's surface contracted and wrinkled like the skin of an apple dried in the sun. The contraction theory implied that mountain ranges were forced up by the wrinkling process.

D) Incorrect. Into the 1900s, many scientists believed that as Earth cooled after its formation, the planet's surface contracted and wrinkled like the skin of an apple dried in the sun, forcing mountain ranges up. Which choice explains how the contraction theory accounted for the Earth's features?

Question 2:

A) Incorrect. When Alfred Wegener proposed continental drift, the technology available did not permit a detailed understanding of seafloor topography. Alfred Wegener used evidence from the distribution of coal belts and ancient ice sheets, both indicators of past climates, to indicate that the continents had once been joined together and had since moved apart. Which choice identifies coal belts and ice sheets?

B) Incorrect. When Alfred Wegener proposed continental drift, scientists did not understand magnetic stripes. Alfred Wegener used evidence from the distribution of coal belts and ancient ice sheets, both indicators of past climates, to indicate that the continents had once been joined together and had since moved apart. Which choice identifies coal belts and ice sheets?

C) Incorrect. Alfred Wegener used evidence from the distribution of coal belts and ancient ice sheets, both indicators of past climates, to indicate that the continents had once been joined together and had since moved apart. Which choice identifies coal belts and ice sheets?

D) Correct! Alfred Wegener used evidence from the distribution of coal belts and ancient ice sheets, both indicators of past climates, to indicate that the continents had once been joined together and had since moved apart.

Question 3:

A) Incorrect. Wegener's book was translated into different languages, but his idea was ridiculed because he did not propose a mechanism that had caused the continents to move. Technical and scientific developments in World Wars I and II allowed scientists to collect new data to put together the theory of plate tectonics. Which choice explains why Wegener's plan was not widely accepted at first?

B) Incorrect. A main problem with Wegener's theory was that he did not propose a force that had caused the continents to move. Technical and scientific developments during World Wars I and II allowed scientists to collect new data to put together the theory of plate tectonics. Which choice explains why Wegener's plan was not widely accepted at first?

C) Correct. A main problem with Wegener's theory was that he did not propose a force that had caused the continents to move. Technical and scientific developments in World Wars I and II allowed scientists to (1) map the ocean floor and (2) measure the magnetism of seafloor rocks. These new data helped geologists put together plate tectonic theory.

D) **Incorrect.** A main problem with Wegener's theory was that he did not propose a force that had caused the continents to move. Technical and scientific developments during World Wars I and II allowed scientists to collect new data to put together the theory of plate tectonics. Which choice explains why Wegener's plan was not widely accepted at first?

Question 4:

A) **Incorrect.** When Wegener proposed continental drift in 1915, there were no maps of the ocean floor. Who proposed the theory of seafloor spreading in 1962 based on knowledge of the terrain of the ocean floor?

B) **Correct!** Based on sonar maps of the ocean floor, Harry Hess proposed the theory of seafloor spreading. He suggested that magma at mid-ocean ridges pushed the ocean floor away from the ridges like a conveyor belt.

C) **Incorrect.** In 1962, an American scientist proposed the theory of seafloor spreading, suggesting that magma pushed the ocean floor away from mid-ocean ridges. His theory provided a driving force for continental drift. Which choice identifies the scientist who proposed the theory of seafloor spreading based on knowledge of the terrain of the ocean floor?

D) **Incorrect.** In 1963, British geologists Fred Vine and Drummond Matthews added support to the theory of seafloor spreading proposed one year earlier. Which American scientist proposed the theory of seafloor spreading in 1962 based on maps of the ocean floor?

Question 5:

A) **Incorrect.** Prior to the mapping of the ocean floor, it was thought to be flat and featureless. Since most plate boundaries do not occur on the continents, it was not until the patterns of mid-ocean ridges and trenches were revealed that scientists could begin to explain why these features were there. Look at the choices again.

B) **Incorrect.** Prior to the mapping of the ocean floor, it was thought to be flat and featureless. Since most plate boundaries do not occur on the continents, it was not until the patterns of mid-ocean ridges and trenches were revealed that scientists could begin to explain why these features were there. Look at the choices again.

C) **Correct!** Prior to the mapping of the ocean floor, it was thought to be flat and featureless. Since most plate boundaries do not occur on the continents, it was not until the patterns of mid-ocean ridges and trenches were revealed that scientists could begin to explain why these features were there.

D) **Incorrect.** Prior to the mapping of the ocean floor, it was thought to be flat and featureless. Since most plate boundaries do not occur on the continents, it was not until the patterns of mid-ocean ridges and trenches were revealed that scientists could begin to explain why these features were there. It is not just the depth of the ocean that was important, but the patterns seen in these features. Look at the choices again.

Question 6:

A) **Incorrect.** Earth's magnetic field changes in intensity and frequently reverses itself. Today our compass needles point to the north. But at various times in the past, the polarity was reversed and compass needles would have instead pointed south.

B) **Correct!** Earth's magnetic field fluctuates in intensity and frequently reverses itself. Today our compass needles point to the north. But at various times in the past, the polarity was reversed and compass needles would have instead pointed south.

Question 7:

A) **Incorrect.** Flat plains are a common feature on the ocean floor, but did not suggest evidence for subduction zones. Read the choices again. Which feature of the seafloor did Hess attribute to subduction zones?

B) **Incorrect.** Magnetic stripes were important to recognizing spreading ridges, but not subduction zones. Read the choices again. Which feature of the seafloor did Hess attribute to subduction zones?

C) **Correct!** Harry Hess proposed that deep trenches in the seafloor indicated that the spreading ocean floor was forced down below the continents into subduction zones.

D) **Incorrect.** Hess recognized mid-ocean ridges as spreading ridges, where the plates move away from each other, but not features related to subduction zones. Read the choices again. Which feature of the seafloor did Hess attribute to subduction zones?

Question 8:

A) **Incorrect.** According to plate tectonic theory, a supercontinent called Pangaea broke apart and the continents slowly drifted to their present positions. This process took millions of years. Look again at the choices.

B) **Incorrect.** According to plate tectonic theory, a supercontinent called Pangaea broke apart and the continents slowly drifted to their present positions. This process took millions of years. Look again at the choices.

C) **Correct!** According to plate tectonic theory of continental drift, all of the continents had originally been joined together in a supercontinent called Pangaea.

About 200 million years ago, the theory continued, Pangaea broke apart and the continents slowly drifted to their present positions.

D) Incorrect. According to plate tectonic theory of continental drift, a supercontinent called Pangaea broke apart and the continents slowly drifted to their present positions. This process took millions of years. Look again at the choices.

Question 9:

A) Incorrect. The fact that seafloor rocks contain magnetite is important, but it is not itself evidence for plate tectonics. Vine and Matthews joined magnetic data with topographic data and were able to show symmetric patterns centered on the mid-ocean ridges. They attributed this to magma cooling and magnetite crystals "locking in" according to the orientation of the Earth's magnetic field at that time, then being moved away from the mid-ocean ridge. What is the result of cooled magma at the mid-ocean ridges?

B) Correct! Vine and Matthews found symmetric patterns of magnetic "stripes" that were centered on mid-ocean ridges. These proved that new crust was continuously being generated at the mid-ocean ridges, where magma cooled and magnetite crystals "locked in" according to the orientation of the Earth's magnetic field at that time, and then the new material was moved away from the mid-ocean ridges in both directions like a conveyor belt.

C) Incorrect. Vine and Matthews joined magnetic data with topographic data and were able to show symmetric patterns centered on the mid-ocean ridges. They attributed this to magma cooling and magnetite crystals "locking in" according to the orientation of the Earth's magnetic field at that time, then being moved away from the mid-ocean ridge. What is the result of cooled magma at the mid-ocean ridges?

D) Incorrect.

he fact that Earth's magnetic field reverses is important, but it is not evidence for plate tectonic theory. Vine and Matthews joined magnetic data with topographic data and were able to show symmetric patterns centered on the mid-ocean ridges. They attributed this to magma cooling and magnetite crystals "locking in" according to the orientation of the Earth's magnetic field at that time, then being moved away from the mid-ocean ridge. What is the result of cooled magma at the mid-ocean ridges?

Question 10:

A) Incorrect. Into the 1900s, many scientists believed that the Earth was relatively static. However, as a result of plate tectonics, mountain chains build and erode away, volcanoes erupt and go extinct, and seas advance and recede. What does this say about the Earth?

B) Correct! Into the 1900s, many scientists believed that the Earth was relatively static. However, plate tectonic theory reveals just how dynamic the Earth really is. As a result of plate tectonics, mountain chains build and erode away, volcanoes erupt and go extinct, and seas advance and recede.

C) Incorrect. The features on the ocean floor were an important dataset that led directly to the development of plate tectonic theory, but this was not the biggest change in how scientists viewed Earth. Look at the choices again.

D) Incorrect. Scientists knew that Earth's magnetic field had fluctuated, and its reversals were important to the development of plate tectonic theory. But this was not the biggest difference that the new theory brought. Look at the choices again.

Plates, Plate Boundaries, and Driving Forces

Comprehension Checkpoints:
p109: A; p111: B; p113: B

Question 1:

A) Incorrect. Earthquakes—as well as other types of geologic activity like volcanoes and the formation of mountain ranges—occur where plates meet along a boundary. Which choice identifies where earthquakes are concentrated?

B) Incorrect. Earthquakes—as well as other types of geologic activity like volcanic eruptions and the formation of mountain ranges—occur where plates meet along a boundary. Which choice identifies where earthquakes are concentrated?

C) Correct! Earthquakes are concentrated along plate boundaries. In fact, plate boundaries are the scene of not only earthquakes but of other geologic activity like volcanic eruptions and the formation of mountain ranges.

D) Incorrect. Earthquakes—as well as other types of geologic activity like volcanoes and the formation of mountain ranges—occur where plates meet along a boundary. Which choice identifies where earthquakes are concentrated?

Question 2:

A) Correct! Most boundaries are either convergent or divergent. However, transform boundaries occur in a few places to accommodate lateral motion, in which plates move horizontally past one another. Transform boundaries are rare on the continents, though they are more common in the oceans.

B) Incorrect. Most boundaries are either convergent or divergent. However, transform boundaries occur in a few places to accommodate lateral motion, in which plates move horizontally past one another. Which choice identifies this rare boundary type?

C) Incorrect. Most boundaries are either convergent or divergent. However, transform boundaries occur in a few places to accommodate lateral motion, in which plates move horizontally past one another. Which choice identifies this rare boundary type?

D) Incorrect. Most boundaries are either convergent or divergent. However, transform boundaries occur in a few places to accommodate lateral motion, in which plates move horizontally past one another. Which choice identifies this rare boundary type?

Question 3:

A) Correct! Divergent boundaries are the mid-ocean ridges characterized by shallow earthquakes and minor lava flows. Only shallow earthquakes (depths of 0 to 33 km) are recorded at the spreading ridges.

B) Incorrect. Divergent boundaries are the mid-ocean ridges characterized by shallow earthquakes and minor lava flows. Only shallow earthquakes (depths of 0 to 33 km) are recorded at the spreading ridges.

Question 4:

A) Incorrect. Everything on Earth is affected by gravity, including hotspots. However, hotspots act like Bunsen burners as plates move over them, creating volcanic islands and seamounts (islands eroded below sea level). Chains of volcanic islands and seamounts show the motion of a plate over a mantle plume. Which choice explains why hotspots can be used to trace plate motion history?

B) Incorrect. Plates are constantly moving, and hotspots are constantly erupting, but this does not explain why we can use hotspots to track plate motion. Hotspots act like Bunsen burners as plates move over them, creating volcanic islands and seamounts (islands eroded below sea level). Chains of volcanic islands and seamounts show the motion of a plate over a mantle plume. Which choice explains why hotspots can be used to trace plate motion history?

C) Correct! Since hotspots are relatively stationary, their tracks can be used to trace plate motion history. Hotpots are stationary plumes of hot magma that act like Bunsen burners as plates move over them, creating volcanic islands and seamounts (islands eroded below sea level). Chains of volcanic islands show the motion of a plate over a mantle plume.

D) Incorrect. Hotspots like Hawaii can erupt continuously, not only every 1,000 years. In fact, they act a little like Bunsen burners as plates move over them, creating volcanic islands and seamounts (islands

eroded below sea level). Chains of volcanic islands and seamounts show the motion of a plate over a mantle plume. Which choice explains why hotspots can be used to trace plate motion history?

Question 5:

A) Incorrect. Gravity and mantle convection are two driving forces for the movement of plates. In mantle convection, material rises along mid-ocean ridges and subsides at subduction zones, and the plates "ride" these convection cells. However, many geologists argue that gravity is the main cause of plate motion. Which choice does not fit with these possible causes of plate motion?

B) Correct! Earthquakes occur along plate boundaries and are a result of plate motion. Gravity and mantle convection are two driving forces for the movement of plates.

C) Incorrect. Gravity and mantle convection are two driving forces for the movement of plates. In mantle convection, material rises along mid-ocean ridges and subsides at subduction zones, and the plates "ride" these convection cells. However, many geologists argue that gravity is the main cause of plate motion. Which choice does not fit with these possible causes of plate motion?

D) Incorrect. Gravity and mantle convection are two driving forces for the movement of plates. In mantle convection, material rises along mid-ocean ridges and subsides at subduction zones, and the plates "ride" these convection cells. However, many geologists argue that gravity is the main cause of plate motion. Which choice does not fit with these possible causes of plate motion?

Question 6:

A) Incorrect. When oceanic crust meets oceanic crust, the older crust is usually subducted because it is colder and slightly denser. Which type of convergence results in a great pileup of continental material rather than in subduction?

B) Incorrect. In transform motion, plates move horizontally past each other. Transform boundaries typically do not result in dramatic mountain ranges. Which type of convergence results in a great pileup of continental material?

C) Correct! When two pieces of continental crust come together, a great pileup of continental material results because both pieces are buoyant and therefore not easily subducted. The Himalayan mountain range is an example of continental convergence.

D) Incorrect. When oceanic crust meets continental crust, they form subduction zones where the thin, dense oceanic crust dives beneath the thicker, more buoyant continental crust. Which type of convergence results in a great pileup of continental material?

Question 7:

A) Correct! When oceanic crust meets oceanic crust, the older crust is usually subducted because it is colder and slightly denser.

B) Incorrect. When oceanic crust meets oceanic crust, the crust that is most likely to be subducted is the one that has become colder and denser with age. Which choice offers the correct explanation?

C) Incorrect. When oceanic crust meets oceanic crust, the crust that is most likely to be subducted is the one that has become colder and denser with age. Which choice offers the correct explanation?

D) Incorrect. When oceanic crust meets oceanic crust, the crust that is most likely to be subducted is the one that has become colder and denser with age. Which choice offers the correct explanation?

Question 8:

A) Correct! The San Andreas Fault is a continental transform boundary. Transform boundaries accommodate lateral motion, in which plates move horizontally past one another. This type of boundary is very rare on continents, and is characterized by frequent, shallow earthquakes.

B) Incorrect. In convergent boundaries, plates move toward each other. The San Andreas Fault is an example of the type of boundary that allows plates to move horizontally past each other. Which type of plate boundary allows for this kind of lateral motion?

C) Incorrect. In divergent boundaries, plates moves away from each other. The San Andreas Fault is an example of the type of boundary that allows plates to move horizontally past each other. Which type of plate boundary allows for this kind of lateral motion?

D) Incorrect. "Plate boundary zones" are boundaries that do not fit easily into a single boundary type. The San Andreas Fault is an example of the type of boundary that allows plates to move horizontally past each other. Which type of plate boundary allows for this kind of lateral motion?

Question 9:

A) Incorrect. Geologists had long realized that earthquakes are not randomly distributed on Earth, and volcanoes had been documented since humans first observed them. Plate tectonics provided an explanation of why the different types of earthquakes and volcanoes followed certain patterns. Which choice tells how the study of earthquakes and volcanoes supported plate tectonic theory?

B) Correct! Plate tectonics provided an explanation of why earthquakes and volcanoes followed certain patterns. Earthquakes are shallow at spreading ridges where plates are thin and deeper inland where plates are deep beneath the continents. With volcanoes, most

major eruptions take place near subduction zones, while eruptions that occur along spreading ridges are much gentler.

C) Incorrect. Earthquakes and volcanoes are not distributed randomly; they are concentrated along plate boundaries. Further, they behave differently along different types of plate boundaries. Which choice states how the study of earthquakes and volcanoes supported plate tectonic theory?

D) Incorrect. Earthquakes are shallow at spreading ridges but deeper inland where plates are deep beneath the continents. With volcanoes, most major eruptions take place near subduction zones, while eruptions that occur along spreading ridges are much gentler. Which choice states how the study of earthquakes and volcanoes supported plate tectonic theory?

Question 10:

A) Incorrect. Continental crust is thick and buoyant, while oceanic crust is thin and dense. Look again at the choices.

B) Incorrect. Continental crust is thick and buoyant, while oceanic crust is thin and dense. Look again at the choices.

C) Incorrect. Continental crust is thick and buoyant, while oceanic crust is thin and dense. Look again at the choices.

D) Correct! Continental crust is thick and buoyant, while oceanic crust is thin and dense.

___

Carbon Chemistry

Comprehension Checkpoints:
p119: A; p121 (top): A; p121 (bottom): B

Question 1:

A) Correct! Organic chemistry has to do with molecules that contain carbon bonded to hydrogen. Organic molecules may contain other elements as well.

B) Incorrect. Organic chemistry is defined by the elements that are bonded together to make organic molecules. Which choice has to do with the type of molecule that forms an organic compound?

C) Incorrect. Living organisms are made up of organic molecules. What defines organic chemistry is the composition of the molecules. Specific elements must combine to form organic compounds. Which choice defines organic chemistry by type of molecule?

D) Incorrect. Organic chemistry is defined by the specific elements that combine to form organic molecules. Which choice has to do with the type of molecule that forms an organic compound?

Question 2:

A) Incorrect. Although ethane is an alkane, which is clear from the suffix –ane, it is not the simplest alkane. The simplest alkane has the formula CH4, while ethane has the formula C2H6. What is the name of the alkane that contains one carbon atom bonded to four hydrogen atoms?

B) Incorrect. The suffix -ene tells you that ethene is an alkene, not an alkane. The simplest alkane contains one carbon atom bonded to four hydrogen atoms. Which choice fits this description?

C) Incorrect. The suffix -yne tells you that ethyne is an alkyne, not an alkane. The simplest alkane contains one carbon atom bonded to four hydrogen atoms. Which choice fits this description?

D) Correct! The simplest alkane is methane, which contains one carbon atom bonded to four hydrogen atoms.

Question 3:

A) Incorrect. The simplest organic compounds contain both carbon and hydrogen. Which choice names molecules that are formed with these component elements?

B) Correct! The simplest organic chemicals, which contain only carbon and hydrogen atoms, are called hydrocarbons.

C) Incorrect. Organic compounds contain carbon as well as hydrogen. Which choice sounds like a combination of these component elements?

D) Incorrect. The name of the simplest organic compounds, which are formed of only carbon and hydrogen, sound like a combination of their component elements. Which choice names these simple organic molecules?

Question 4:

A) Correct! Hydrocarbons—organic chemicals that contain only carbon and hydrogen atoms—come in different types depending on the number of carbon-carbon bonds in the molecule. The simplest hydrocarbons have only carbon-carbon single bonds. These are called alkanes.

B) Incorrect. Hydrocarbons—organic chemicals that contain only carbon and hydrogen atoms—come in different types depending on the number of carbon-carbon bonds in the molecule. Alkenes have at least one double-bonded carbon pair. Which choice has no double carbon bonds?

C) Incorrect. Hydrocarbons—organic chemicals that contain only carbon and hydrogen atoms—come in different types depending on the number of carbon-carbon bonds in the molecule. Alkynes have at least one triple-bonded carbon pair. Which choice has no double carbon bonds?

D) Incorrect. Isomers are molecules that have the same chemical formula but different structural formulas.

Hydrocarbons are organic chemicals that contain only carbon and hydrogen atoms. Hydrocarbons come in different types depending on the number of carbon-carbon bonds in the molecule. Which choice names a hydrocarbon that has only carbon-carbon single bonds?

Question 5:

A) Incorrect. It is true that chemical compounds with the prefix but- have four carbon atoms. The chemical formula for any alkane is expressed as CnH2n+2. Alkenes have the chemical formula CnH2n. Alkynes have the chemical formula CnH2n-2. Which choice has four carbon atoms and six hydrogen atoms?

B) Correct! Chemical compounds with the prefix but- have four carbon atoms. The chemical formula for any alkyne is expressed as CnH2n-2. Thus, C4H6 is the formula for butyne.

C) Incorrect. Chemical compounds with the prefix eth- have only two carbon atoms; those with but- have four carbon atoms. The chemical formula for any alkane is expressed as CnH2n+2. Alkenes have the chemical formula CnH2n. Alkynes have the chemical formula CnH2n-2. Which choice has four carbon atoms and six hydrogen atoms?

D) Incorrect. Chemical compounds with the prefix prop- have only 3 carbon atoms; those with but- have four carbon atoms. The chemical formula for any alkane is expressed as CnH2n+2. Alkenes have the chemical formula CnH2n. Alkynes have the chemical formula CnH2n-2. Which choice has four carbon atoms and six hydrogen atoms?

Question 6:

A) Incorrect. C7H12 is the chemical formula for heptyne. Heptene is an alkene with seven carbon atoms. The chemical formula for any alkene is expressed as CnH2n. Which choice gives the correct formula for heptene?

B) Incorrect. C7H12 is the chemical formula for heptyne. Heptene is an alkene with seven carbon atoms. The chemical formula for any alkene is expressed as CnH2n. Which choice gives the correct formula for heptene?

C) Correct! The chemical formula for any alkene is expressed as CnH2n. Therefore, an alkene with 7 carbon atoms, heptene, has the formula C7H14.

D) Incorrect. C7H12 is the chemical formula for heptane. Heptene is an alkene with seven carbon atoms. The chemical formula for any alkene is expressed as CnH2n. Which choice gives the correct formula for heptene?

Question 7:

A) Incorrect. Sometimes a single type of molecule can have different bonding configurations. There is a special name for these compounds that have the same chemical formula but different structural formulas. Look again at the choices.

B) **Correct!** Isomers are molecules that have the same chemical formula but different structural formulas.

C) **Incorrect.** Sometimes a single type of molecule can have different bonding configurations. There is a special name for these compounds that have the same chemical formula but different structural formulas. Look again at the choices.

D) **Incorrect.** Sometimes a single type of molecule can have different bonding configurations. Look again at the choices for the name of the name for these compounds that have the same chemical formula but different structural formulas.

Question 8:

A) **Incorrect.** Groups of atoms that occur within organic molecules are called functional groups. Alcohols are the group of hydrocarbons that contain a functional group that consists of a single oxygen atom bound to a single hydrogen atom. Which choice sounds like a combination of these component elements?

B) **Incorrect.** Groups of atoms that occur within organic molecules are called functional groups. Alcohols are the group of hydrocarbons that contain a functional group that consists of a single oxygen atom bound to a single hydrogen atom. Which choice sounds like a combination of these component elements?

C) **Correct!** Alcohols are the group of hydrocarbons that contain a hydroxyl functional group.

D) **Incorrect.** Groups of atoms that occur within organic molecules are called functional groups. Alcohols are the group of hydrocarbons that contain a functional group that consists of a single oxygen atom bound to a single hydrogen atom. Which choice sounds like a combination of these component elements?

Question 9:

A) **Incorrect.** Ethane has the chemical formula C2H6. Counting the carbon and hydrogen atoms in CH3CH2CH3 reveals that this structural formula is the same as the chemical formula C3H8. Look again at the choices for the name of this compound.

B) **Incorrect.** Methane has the chemical formula CH4. Counting the carbon and hydrogen atoms in CH3CH2CH3 reveals that this structural formula is the same as the chemical formula C3H8. Look again at the choices for the name of this compound.

C) **Incorrect.** Pentane has the chemical formula C5H12. Counting the carbon and hydrogen atoms in CH3CH2CH3 reveals that this structural formula is the same as the chemical formula C3H8. Look again at the choices for the name of this compound.

D) **Correct!** Counting the carbon and hydrogen atoms in CH3CH2CH3 reveals that this is the structural formula for propane (C3H8).

DNA I

Comprehension Checkpoints:
p128: A; p129 (top): B; p129 (bottom): A

Question 1:

A) **Incorrect.** Scientists wondered which molecule within a chromosome carried hereditary information: protein or DNA. There are 20 different amino acids for building a protein polymer, while DNA polymers are made of only four nucleotide bases. Which of the two did scientists believe was more complex?

B) **Correct!** Scientists wondered which component of a chromosome carried hereditary information: protein or DNA. There are 20 different amino acids for building a protein polymer, while DNA polymers are made of only four nucleotide bases. Because proteins appeared far more complex, most scientists of the day believed that protein carried genetic information within the chromosome.

C) **Incorrect.** Scientists wondered which molecule within a chromosome carried hereditary information: protein or DNA. But while DNA polymers are made of only four nucleotide bases, there are 20 different amino acids for building a protein polymer. Which of the two did scientists believe was more complex?

D) **Incorrect.** Scientists wondered which molecule within a chromosome carried hereditary information: protein or DNA. There are 20 different amino acids for building a protein polymer, while DNA polymers are made of only four nucleotide bases. Which of the two did scientists believe was more complex?

Question 2:

A) **Incorrect.** During the First World War, hundreds of thousands of servicemen died from pneumonia. In the early 1920s, Frederick Griffith began studying the bacteria that caused the disease in hopes of developing a vaccine against it. Which choice names the bacterium that causes pneumonia?

B) **Incorrect.** During the First World War, hundreds of thousands of servicemen died from pneumonia. In the early 1920s, Frederick Griffith began studying the bacteria that caused the disease in hopes of developing a vaccine against it. Which choice names the bacterium that causes pneumonia?

C) **Incorrect.** During the First World War, hundreds of thousands of servicemen died from pneumonia. In the early 1920s, Frederick Griffith began studying the bacteria that caused the disease in hopes of developing a vaccine against it. Which choice names the bacterium that causes pneumonia?

D) Correct! During the First World War, hundreds of thousands of servicemen died from pneumonia, caused by the bacterium Streptococcus pneumoniae (or S. pneumoniae). In the early 1920s, Frederick Griffith began studying the bacteria in hopes of developing a vaccine against it. Although he was unable to develop a vaccine for pneumonia, he made one of the most important discoveries in the field of biology: "transformation."

Question 3:

A) Correct! Dr. Griffith mixed living R bacteria (which are not pathogenic) with heat-killed S bacteria (that causes pneumonia) and injected the mix into mice, who developed pneumonia. The harmless live R strain was somehow "transformed" into the pathogenic S strain. This discovery showed that organisms can be genetically "re-programmed" into a slightly different version of themselves.

B) Incorrect. In Dr. Griffith's experiments, a harmless R strain of bacteria was "transformed" into the pathogenic S strain that causes pneumonia. This discovery showed that organisms can somehow be genetically "re-programmed" into a slightly different version of themselves. Which choice fits this description?

C) Incorrect. In Dr. Griffith's experiments, a harmless R strain of bacteria was somehow "transformed" into the pathogenic S strain that causes pneumonia. This discovery showed that organisms can somehow be genetically "re-programmed" into a slightly different version of themselves. Which choice fits this description?

D) Incorrect. In Dr. Griffith's experiments, a harmless R strain of bacteria was somehow "transformed" into the pathogenic S strain that causes pneumonia. This discovery showed that organisms can somehow be genetically "re-programmed" into a slightly different version of themselves. Which choice fits this description?

Question 4:

A) Incorrect. The scientists added different enzymes to test tubes to see which could prevent the harmless R strain bacteria from transforming into the pathogenic S strain. Each enzyme would destroy one possible transforming agent. Lipase would destroy lipids, but this did not stop the R bacteria. Only the tube that was treated with the enzyme that breaks down DNA lost the ability to transform the R strain bacteria into the S strain. Which choice names the enzyme that breaks down DNA?

B) Incorrect. The scientists added different enzymes to test tubes to see which could prevent the harmless R strain bacteria from transforming into the pathogenic S strain. Each enzyme would destroy one possible transforming agent. RNase would destroy RNA, but this did not stop the R bacteria. Only the tube that was treated with the enzyme that breaks down DNA lost the ability to transform the R strain bacteria into the S strain. Which choice names the enzyme that breaks down DNA?

C) Correct! The scientists added different enzymes to test tubes to see which could prevent R strain bacteria from transforming into the S strain. Each enzyme would destroy one possible transforming agent: RNA, protein, DNA, lipids, and carbohydrates. The tube that was treated with the enzyme to break down DNA lost the ability to transform the R strain into the S strain, while the others were unaffected.

D) Incorrect. The scientists added different enzymes to test tubes to see which could prevent the harmless R strain bacteria from transforming into the pathogenic S strain. Each enzyme would destroy one possible transforming agent. Protease would destroy protein, but this did not stop the R bacteria. Only the tube that was treated with the enzyme that breaks down DNA lost the ability to transform the R strain bacteria into the S strain. Which choice names the enzyme that breaks down DNA?

Question 5:

A) Incorrect. S. pneumoniae is a bacterium that causes pneumonia. For their experiment, Hershey and Chase used an extremely small virus which only infects bacterial cell and "reprograms" the bacterium produce more of these viruses. Which choice names a specific virus?

B) Incorrect. For their experiment, Hershey and Chase used an extremely small virus which only infects bacterial cell and "reprograms" the bacterium produce more of these viruses. Which choice names a specific virus?

C) Incorrect. For their experiment, Hershey and Chase used an extremely small virus which only infects bacterial cell and "reprograms" the bacterium produce more of these viruses. Which choice names a specific virus?

D) Correct! For their experiment, Hershey and Chase used an extremely small virus called a bacteriophage (or just phage), which only infects bacterial cells. When these phage infect a bacterial cell, they somehow "reprogram" the bacterium produce more phage.

Question 6:

A) Incorrect. Dr. Griffith's experiment showed that organisms can be genetically "re-programmed" into a slightly different version of themselves. In Griffith's experiment, the harmless R strain of S. pneumoniae bacteria was transformed into the pathogenic S strain of S. pneumoniae bacteria, presumably because of the transfer of genetic material from a donor. Which choice fits this description?

B) Correct! Dr. Griffith's experiment showed that organisms can be genetically "re-programmed" into a slightly different version of themselves. In Griffith's experiment, the harmless R strain of S. pneumoniae bacteria was transformed into the pathogenic S strain of S. pneumoniae bacteria, presumably because of the transfer of genetic material from a donor (the S strain).

C) Incorrect. Dr. Griffith's experiment showed that organisms can be genetically "re-programmed" into a slightly different version of themselves. In Griffith's experiment, the harmless R strain of S. pneumoniae bacteria was transformed into the pathogenic S strain of S. pneumoniae bacteria, presumably because of the transfer of genetic material from a donor. Which choice fits this description?

D) Incorrect. In Griffith's experiment, it is true that the harmless R strain of S. pneumoniae bacteria was transformed into the pathogenic S strain of S. pneumoniae bacteria. But Dr. Griffith's discovery was significant because it showed that organisms can be genetically "re-programmed" into a slightly different version of themselves. Which choice fits this description?

Question 7:

A) Incorrect. Griffith had made one of the most important discoveries in the field of biology. Although it was clear that a genetic transformation occurred, the "transforming agent" was still unclear. Scientists needed to experiment further to find out exactly what was happening during genetic transformation. In which choice did scientists intend to build on Griffith's work?

B) Correct! Although it was clear that a genetic transformation occurred, the question remained: Which molecule is the "transforming agent"? Protein, RNA, DNA, lipids, and carbohydrates were all possibilities, and scientists needed to experiment further to find out exactly what was happening during genetic transformation.

C) Incorrect. Griffith had made one of the most important discoveries in the field of biology. Although it was clear that a genetic transformation occurred, the "transforming agent" was still unclear. Scientists needed to experiment further to find out exactly what was happening during genetic transformation. In which choice did scientists intend to build on Griffith's work?

D) Incorrect. Griffith had made one of the most important discoveries in the field of biology. Although it was clear that a genetic transformation occurred, the "transforming agent" was still unclear. Scientists needed to experiment further to find out exactly what was happening during genetic transformation. In which choice did scientists intend to build on Griffith's work?

DNA II

Comprehension Checkpoints:
p136: A; p137: B; p138: B; p139: A

Question 1:

A) Incorrect. In the early 1900s, biochemist Phoebus Levene deduced that the DNA molecule was made of smaller molecules linked together. Which choice identifies the smaller molecules that form the building blocks of DNA?

B) Incorrect. In the early 1900s, biochemist Phoebus Levene deduced that DNA molecules were made of smaller molecules linked together -- although he believed that protein rather than DNA contained the genetic material of an organism. Which choice identifies the smaller molecules that form the building blocks of DNA?

C) Incorrect. The double helix structure of DNA was discovered after the building blocks of DNA molecules were identified. In the early 1900s, biochemist Phoebus Levene deduced that the DNA molecule was made of smaller molecules linked together. Which choice names these smaller molecules that form the building blocks of DNA?

D) Correct! In the early 1900s, biochemist Phoebus Levene deduced that the DNA molecule was made of smaller molecules linked together. These smaller molecules, which he named nucleotides, form the building blocks of DNA.

Question 2:

A) Incorrect. Nucleotides, the building blocks of DNA, are made of a five-carbon sugar, a phosphate group, and one of four possible nitrogen bases – adenine, cytosine, guanine, or thymine. Which choice lists the three components of a nucleotide?

B) Incorrect. Nucleotides, the building blocks of DNA, are made of a five-carbon sugar, a phosphate group, and one of four possible nitrogen bases – adenine, cytosine, guanine, or thymine. Which choice lists the three components of a nucleotide?

C) Correct! Nucleotides, the building blocks of DNA, are made of a five-carbon sugar, a phosphate group, and one of four possible nitrogen bases – adenine, cytosine, guanine, or thymine.

D) Incorrect. Adenine, thymine, and cytosine are among the nitrogen bases that make up a nucleotide. The other components of a nucleotide are a five-carbon sugar and a phosphate group. Which choice lists the three components of a nucleotide?

Question 3:

A) Correct! In the 1940s, scientist Erwin Chargaff showed that different organisms had different amounts of the four nitrogen bases of DNA – adenine, cytosine, guanine, or thymine (often abbreviated A, C, G, and T).

B) Incorrect. In the late 1800s, chemist J. Friedrich Miescher discovered "nuclein", which was later renamed "nucleic acid". Look again at the choices.

C) Incorrect. Chemist Rosalind Franklin is best known for her work on X-ray diffraction pictures of DNA,. Look again at the choices.

D) Incorrect. James Watson, along with Frances Crick, received the Nobel Prize in 1962 for their model of DNA. Watson and Crick built upon earlier work by others, including work that demonstrated that different organisms had different amounts of the four nitrogen bases of DNA and that the four nitrogen bases of DNA were always predictably paired. Look again at the choices.

Question 4:

A) Incorrect. Though Pauling proposed a triple helix structure, he was later proven incorrect by Watson and Crick. What helped Watson and Crick develop a model for DNA?

B) Correct! Franklin's high quality pictures confirmed that DNA is actually a double helix – two strands wrapped around each other.

C) Incorrect. DNA has four nucleotides – adenosine, guanine, thymine, and cytosine. How did looking at an X-ray of DNA help Watson and Crick develop their model of DNA?

D) Incorrect. It was Franklin's work that actually helped Watson and Crick to develop their model. What did her X-ray show that helped Watson and Crick develop their model?

Question 5:

A) Correct! The connections between the nucleotides are "phosphodiester bonds." These bonds are referred to as "5' to 3' connections" because a phosphate molecule (PO4) serves as the bridge between the 5' carbon of one nucleotide and the 3' carbon of the next.

B) Incorrect. The connections between the nucleotides are "phosphodiester bonds." These bonds are referred to as "5' to 3' connections" because a PO4 molecule connects the 5' carbon of one nucleotide to the 3' carbon of the next. Which choice best fits this description?

C) Incorrect. Cytosine is one of the nitrogen bases in a nucleotide.The connections between the nucleotides are "phosphodiester bonds." These bonds are referred to as "5' to 3' connections" because a PO4 molecule serves as the bridge between the 5' carbon of one nucleotide and the 3' carbon of the next. Which choice best fits this description?

D) Incorrect. Hydrogen bonds hold the two separate DNA strands together, but "phosphodiester bonds" form the connections between the nucleotides of the same strand. These bonds are referred to as "5' to 3' connections" because a PO4 molecule serves as the bridge between the 5' carbon of one nucleotide and the 3' carbon of the next. Which choice fits this description?

Question 6:

A) Incorrect. The two DNA strands wrap around each other in an anti-parallel configuration--"upside down" relative to each other--and the nitrogen bases fit perfectly together through a hydrogen bond. Which choice does not accurately describe the two strands of DNA?

B) Incorrect. The two DNA strands wrap around each other in an anti-parallel configuration, and the nitrogen bases fit perfectly together through a hydrogen bond. Which choice does not accurately describe the two strands of DNA?

C) Correct! The sugars and the phosphate groups, which are soluble in water, point out towards the water, while the nitrogen bases of the DNA, which are not very soluble in water, stay tucked into the interior of the molecule.

D) Incorrect. The two DNA strands twist around each other in an anti-parallel configuration, and the nitrogen bases fit perfectly together through a hydrogen bond. Which choice does not accurately describe the two strands of DNA?

Question 7:

A) Incorrect. Watson and Crick were referring to the fact that the four nucleotide bases are always paired with each other in predictable ways. Based on this information, how could one tell by looking at either DNA strand exactly what was on the complementary strand?

B) Incorrect. Watson and Crick were referring to the fact that the four nucleotide bases are always paired with each other in predictable ways: A always base-pairs with T, and C always pairs with G. Based on this information, how could one tell by looking at either DNA strand exactly what was on the complementary strand?

C) Incorrect. Hydrogen bonds hold the two DNA strands together, but not permanently. What Watson and Crick were referring to was the fact that the four nucleotide bases are always paired with each other in predictable ways. Based on this information, how could one tell by looking at either DNA strand exactly what was on the complementary strand?

D) Correct! The four nucleotide bases are always paired in predictable ways, so an adenine on one side of the DNA molecule would be paired with a thymine on the other side, and cytosine would be paired with guanine. Thus, if the two strands were separated, it would be possible to look at either strand and know exactly what was on the complementary strand.

The Discovery and Structure of Cells

Comprehension Checkpoints:
p145: A

Question 1:

A) Incorrect. All cells have chromosomes, but basic structural and functional unit of life is the cell itself. Look again at the choices.

B) Incorrect. All cells have membranes, but basic structural and functional unit of life is the cell itself. Look again at the choices.

C) Correct! The cell is the basic structural and functional unit of life; all organisms are composed of cells.

D) Incorrect. All cells have ribosomes, but basic structural and functional unit of life is the cell itself. Look again at the choices.

Question 2:

A) Incorrect. All cells contain three basic features: (1) a plasma membrane, (2) cytoplasm, and (3) genetic material (DNA and RNA). Which choice includes all these shared features?

B) Correct! All cells contain three basic features: (1) a plasma membrane, (2) cytoplasm, and (3) genetic material (DNA and RNA).

C) Incorrect. All cells contain three basic features: (1) a plasma membrane, (2) cytoplasm, and (3) genetic material (DNA and RNA). Which choice includes all these shared features?

D) Incorrect. All cells contain three basic features: (1) a plasma membrane, (2) cytoplasm, and (3) genetic material (DNA and RNA). Which choice includes all these shared features?

Question 3:

A) Incorrect. Reproduction is a basic cell function. However, not all cells have a nucleus. While protozoan, animal, and plant cells contain a nucleus, other organisms such as bacteria do not. Look again at the choices.

B) Incorrect. One major difference among cells is the presence or absence of a nucleus, which contains genetic material. While protozoan, animal, and plant cells contain a nucleus, other organisms such as bacteria do not. Look again at the choices.

C) Correct! Tne major difference among cells is the presence or absence of a nucleus, which contains genetic material. Protozoan, animal, and plant cells contain a

nucleus, whereas bacteria and some other organisms do not.

D) Incorrect. All cells have a plasma membrane, but not all cells have a nucleus. While protozoan, animal, and plant cells contain a nucleus, other organisms such as bacteria do not. Look again at the choices.

Question 4:

A) Incorrect. The cells of plants, protists, and fungi are surrounded by a cell wall to help these cells maintain their shape. Animal cells maintain their shape by a network of long protein strands that attach to the inner surface of the plasma membrane. Which choice explains why plant cells are typically more rigid than animal cells?

B) Incorrect. All cells have a membrane, but only plant cells have a cell wall. Animal cells maintain their shape by a network of long protein strands that attach to the inner surface of the plasma membrane. Look again at the choices Which choice explains why plant cells are typically more rigid than animal cells?

C) Correct! The cells of plants, protists, and fungi are surrounded by a cell wall to help these cells maintain their shape. Animal cells lack a cell wall but instead have a network of long protein strands that attach to the inner surface of the plasma membrane and help them maintain their shape.

D) Incorrect. The cells of plants, protists, and fungi are surrounded by a cell wall to help these cells maintain their shape. Animal cells maintain their shape by a network of long protein strands that attach to the inner surface of the plasma membrane. Which choice explains why plant cells are typically more rigid than animal cells?

Question 5:

A) Incorrect. All cells have a plasma membrane, but not all cells have a nucleus. Prokaryotic cells (which include bacteria) lack a nucleus, whereas eukaryotic cells (which include protozoan, animal, and plant cells) contain a nucleus. Which choice identifies this feature that distinguishes prokaryotic from eukaryotic cells?

B) Incorrect. One major difference among cells is the presence or absence of a nucleus, which contains genetic material. Prokaryotic cells (which include bacteria) lack a nucleus, whereas eukaryotic cells (which include protozoan, animal, and plant cells) contain a nucleus. Which choice identifies this feature that distinguishes prokaryotic from eukaryotic cells?

C) Correct! One major difference among cells is the presence or absence of a nucleus, which contains the genetic material. Prokaryotic cells (which include bacteria) lack a nucleus, whereas eukaryotic cells (which include protozoans, animal, and plant cells) contain a nucleus.

D) Incorrect. One major difference among cells is the

presence or absence of a nucleus, which contains genetic material. Prokaryotic cells (which include bacteria) lack a nucleus, whereas eukaryotic cells (which include protozoan, animal, and plant cells) contain a nucleus. Which choice identifies this feature that distinguishes prokaryotic from eukaryotic cells?

Question 6:

A) Incorrect. Cells can vary widely in their structure, and these differences reflect the different functions that the cells serve.

B) Correct! Cells can vary widely in their structure, and these differences reflect the different functions that the cells serve.

Question 7:

A) Incorrect. The cell membrane, which forms an outer boundary layer, allows certain substances to move in and out of the cell. Which of the choices gives an example of why this "gatekeeper" function of the cell membrane is important?

B) Incorrect. The cell membrane, which forms an outer boundary layer, allows certain substances to move in and out of the cell. Which of the choices gives an example of why this "gatekeeper" function of the cell membrane is important?

C) Correct! The cell membrane, which forms an outer boundary layer, allows certain substances to move in and out of the cell.

D) Incorrect. The cell membrane, which forms an outer boundary layer, allows certain substances to move in and out of the cell. Which of the choices gives an example of why this "gatekeeper" function of the cell membrane is important?

Theories, Hypotheses, and Laws

Comprehension Checkpoints:
p150: B; p152: A; p156: A

Question 1:

A) Incorrect. In everyday speech, people often use the term theory to mean a hunch, but this is not the way scientists use the word. In science, theories explain phenomena in nature and are based on large amounts of data and observations that have been collected over time. Which choice fits the scientific description of a theory?

B) Correct! Scientists use the term "theory" to refer to a comprehensive set of ideas that explains some broad aspect of the natural world. Theories are supported by

evidence based on large amounts of data and observations that have been collected over time.

C) Incorrect. A theory is a comprehensive set of ideas that explains some broad aspect of the natural world. Laws define relationships, but don't explain them. Which choice fits this definition of the term "theory"?

D) Incorrect. Scientists use the term "theory" to refer to a comprehensive set of ideas that explains a phenomenon in nature. Theories are not based on assumptions. Rather they are based on evidence drawn from large amounts of data and observations that have been collected over time. Which choice fits this definition of the term "theory"?

Question 2:

A) Incorrect. Theories integrate a broad, comprehensive set of ideas and are based on large amounts of data and observations that have been collected over time. Which choice best fits the scientist's statement?

B) Incorrect. A scientific law describes natural phenomena, often mathematically. Which choice best fits the scientist's statement?

C) Incorrect. A scientific law describes natural phenomena, often mathematically. Which choice best fits the scientist's statement?

D) Correct! A hypothesis is a proposed explanation for an observation before it is confirmed by research. Scientists propose a hypothesis before doing research as a way of predicting the outcome of study. In contrast, theories explain some broad aspect of the natural world and are based on solid evidence that has been confirmed over time. Scientific laws describe natural phenomena, often mathematically.

Question 3:

A) Correct! Scientific theories can be tested and then refined by additional research.

B) Incorrect. Scientific theories can be tested and then refined as new information or new perspectives on existing data become available.

Question 4:

A) Incorrect. Theories are not merely assumptions; rather, they are supported by substantial evidence. Theories are based on large amounts of data and observations that have been collected over time. Which choice describes the foundation of a scientific theory?

B) Incorrect. Theories are based on large amounts of data and observations that have been collected over time. Scientific theories can be tested and then refined as new information or new perspectives on existing data become available. Which choice describes the foundation of a scientific theory?

C) Correct! Scientific theories are based on large amounts of data and observations that have been collected over time. They are broad, comprehensive ideas that are supported by substantial evidence that has been integrated.

D) Incorrect. Scientific theories are based on large amounts of data and observations that have been collected over time. Theories are often based on a long chain of research by different scientists in various scientific disciplines. Which choice describes the foundation of a scientific theory?

Question 5:

A) Correct! Theories provide a framework for additional research and allow scientists to make predictions.

B) Incorrect. Scientists cannot rely only on theories; they must still collect data and build evidence for their interpretation. Theories provide a framework for additional research and allow scientists to make predictions. Which choice tells why theories are important?

C) Incorrect. Scientific theories can guide research but do not determine the work that future scientists do. Theories provide a framework for additional research and allow scientists to make predictions. Which choice tells why theories are important?

D) Incorrect. Scientific theories can guide research but do not determine the subjects that scientists study. Theories provide a framework for additional research and allow scientists to make predictions. Which choice tells why theories are important?

Question 6:

A) Incorrect. Scientific theories can be expanded and revised as new evidence is introduced or as existing data are interpreted differently.

B) Correct! Scientific theories can be expanded and revised as new evidence is introduced or as existing data are interpreted differently.

Question 7:

A) Correct! Scientific laws describe natural phenomena, often mathematically, while theories explain phenomena.

B) Incorrect. Scientific laws describe natural phenomena, often mathematically. In contrast, theories explain some broad aspect of the natural world. Which choice fits this description?

C) Incorrect. Scientific laws describe natural phenomena, often mathematically. In contrast, theories explain some broad aspect of the natural world. Which choice fits this description?

D) Incorrect. Scientific laws describe natural phenomena, often mathematically. In contrast, theories explain some broad aspect of the natural world. Which choice fits this description?

Question 8:

A) Incorrect. Hypotheses can be tested and further supported or proved incorrect, so research results may not support the original hypothesis. Scientists propose a hypothesis before doing research to (1) predict the outcome of a study and (2) guide them as they design their research. Which choice states a valid reason for developing a hypothesis?

B) Correct! Scientists often propose a hypothesis before doing research to (1) predict the outcome of a study and (2) guide them as they design their research.

C) Incorrect. The outcome of the research may not support the original hypothesis. Hypotheses can be tested and further supported or proved incorrect. Scientists propose a hypothesis before doing research to (1) predict the outcome of a study and (2) guide them as they design their research. Which choice states a valid reason for developing a hypothesis?

D) Incorrect. Hypotheses can be tested and further supported or proved incorrect. Researchers must therefore record all observations. Scientists propose a hypothesis before doing research to (1) predict the outcome of a study and (2) guide them as they design their research. Which choice states a valid reason for developing a hypothesis?

Question 9:

A) Incorrect. Some theories, like the theory of evolution by natural selection, are broad and encompass many concepts. Others focus on smaller-scale concepts.

B) Correct! Some theories, like the theory of evolution by natural selection, are broad and encompass many concepts. Others focus on smaller, more targeted concepts.

Question 10:

A) Correct! Theories are supported by a long chain of research in various scientific disciplines. For example, the work of many researchers in several scientific fields over the course of hundreds of years contributed to the theory of evolution by natural selection.

B) Incorrect. Theories are supported by a long chain of research in various scientific disciplines. Studies in different scientific fields can expand the scope of a theory. Which choice describes how theories can interact?

C) Incorrect. Theories are based on a long chain of research that came before and are supported by research that comes after. Theories in every field of science are based on scientific principles and can influence theories in other disciplines. Which choice describes how theories can relate to each other?

D) Incorrect. Theories are based on the accumulation of evidence and ideas of many scientists in many different scientific disciplines. However, it often takes the insight and creativity of individuals to put together all of the pieces and propose a new theory. Which choice most accurately describes theories?

Charles Darwin I

Comprehension Checkpoints:
p162: A; p164: B; p165: B

Question 1:

A) **Incorrect.** In 1831, Darwin set sail on the H.M.S. Beagle as the ship's naturalist, but his On the Origin of Species wasn't published until almost 30 years later. Which choice fits this timeframe?

B) **Correct.** Darwin's On the Origin of Species was published in 1859.

C) **Incorrect.** In 1871, Darwin published a book titled Sexual Selection and the Descent of Man. This came about 12 years after On the Origin of Species. Which choice fits this timeframe?

D) **Incorrect.** In 1831, Darwin set sail on the H.M.S. Beagle as the ship's naturalist, but his On the Origin of Species wasn't published until almost 30 years later. Which choice fits this timeframe?

Question 2:

A) **Incorrect.** In his book On the Origin of Species, Darwin developed the following major themes: (1) species evolve as they develop protective adaptations ; (2) natural selection is the driving force behind evolution; (3) all life forms are related genealogically. Which choice is not included among these themes?

B) **Incorrect.** In his book On the Origin of Species by Means of Natural Selection, Darwin developed the following major themes: (1) species evolve as they develop protective adaptations; (2) natural selection is the driving force behind evolution; (3) all life forms are related genealogically. Which choice is not included among these themes?

C) **Correct!** In his book On the Origin of Species, Darwin developed the following major themes: (1) species evolve as they develop protective adaptations; (2) natural selection is the driving force behind evolution; (3) all life forms are related genealogically.

D) **Incorrect.** In his book On the Origin of Species by Means of Natural Selection, Darwin developed the following major themes: (1) species evolve as they develop protective adaptations; (2) natural selection is the driving force behind evolution; (3) all life forms are related genealogically. Which choice is not included among these themes?

Question 3:

A) **Incorrect.** In 1863, Thomas Henry Huxley wrote about people evolving in Evidence as to Man's Place in Nature. Look again for the title of Darwin's 1871 work about how human beings descended.

B) **Correct!** In 1871 Darwin published a book specifically about human evolution, Sexual Selection and the Descent of Man.

C) **Incorrect.** In 1859, Darwin published his legendary book, On the Origin of Species by Means of Natural Selection. Twelve years later, Darwin published a book specifically about human evolution. Look again for the title of Darwin's 1871 work about how human beings descended.

D) **Incorrect.** In 1859, Darwin published his legendary book, On the Origin of Species by Means of Natural Selection. Twelve years later, Darwin published a book specifically about human evolution. Look again for the title of Darwin's 1871 work about how human beings descended.

Question 4:

A) **Correct!** Creationists in the 19th century argued that since God's creations were perfect, there was no reason or even possibility for the structure of any species to change. In contrast, Darwin thought it was important that individuals vary within a same species; he realized that the variations were key to evolutionary change.

B) **Incorrect.** Creationists in the 19th century argued that since God's creations were perfect, there was no reason or even possibility for the structure of any species to change. In contrast, Darwin thought it was important that individuals vary within a same species; he realized that the variations were key to evolutionary change.

Question 5:

A) **Incorrect.** Darwin's ideas challenged the prevailing view at the time, that species were unchanging fixtures of nature based on an ideal model. Which choice offers a contrasting view?

B) **Incorrect.** Darwin's ideas challenged the prevailing view at the time, that species were unchanging fixtures of nature based on an ideal form. According to this "fixity" notion, there was no reason or possibility for any species to change. Which choice offers a contrasting view?

C) **Correct!** Darwin thought it was important that individuals vary even though they belong to the same species. He realized that the variations could become the raw material for evolutionary change.

D) **Incorrect.** Darwin believed that evolution is an ever-present, unstoppable, fundamental law of nature. It applied to every species. Which choice accounts for the variations that could become raw material for evolutionary change?

Question 6:

A) Correct! Darwin collected pieces of the evolutionary puzzle during his five years on the Beagle, but it took him decades to put the pieces together into a basic model for the public to understand. His work was capped by publication of the legendary, On the Origin of Species, which has been called one of the greatest books ever written.

B) Incorrect. The idea of evolution posed a serious challenge to the then-popular view of Fixity of Species, but not everyone subscribed to the idea that species were unchanging fixtures of nature. Darwin's work was significant because he presented evolution as a basic model that people could grasp. Which choice explains why Darwin's contribution changed the world?

C) Incorrect. The idea of evolution has been part of Western thought since the time of Aristotle. It had been discussed and written about often before Darwin's legendary On the Origin of Species. But Darwin presented evolution as a basic model that people could grasp in what has has been called one of the greatest books ever written. Which choice explains why Darwin's contribution changed the world?

D) Incorrect. During Darwin's years on the Beagle as it sailed around the world on a mapping expedition, he described a vast number of specimens and became the best naturalist in the world. But more importantly, decades later Darwin presented evolution as a basic model that people could grasp in what has been called one of the greatest books ever written. Which choice explains why Darwin's contribution changed the world?

Question 7:

A) Incorrect. Darwin saw evolution as a fundamental law of nature that applied to every species, including humans. But evolution represented a way of looking at life that challenged the religious ways of thinking that had been accepted for centuries. Which choice expresses Darwin's hesitation at going against the cultural mindset of the time?

B) Incorrect. Darwin's findings presented evidence that Fixity of Species was just an untested assumption. He saw evolutionary change as a fundamental law of nature that applied to every species, including humans. But evolution represented a way of looking at life that challenged the religious ways of thinking that had been accepted for centuries. Which choice expresses Darwin's hesitation at going against the cultural mindset of the time?

C) Incorrect. Darwin knew all along that evolutionary biology could be applied to human beings the same way it applied other species. But evolution represented a way of looking at life that challenged the religious ways of thinking that had been accepted for centuries. Which choice expresses Darwin's hesitation at going against the cultural mindset of the time?

D) Correct! Darwin saw evolutionary change as a fundamental law of nature that applied to every species, including humans. But evolution represented a way of looking at life that challenged the religious ways of thinking that had been accepted for centuries.

Charles Darwin II

Comprehension Checkpoints:
p170: B; p171: A; p172: B

Question 1:

A) Correct! Differential reproduction promotes the reproduction of certain members of a population that can pass on desired traits to offspring. In this way, an adaptation that puts the population at an advantage is passed on to future generations.

B) Incorrect. Differential reproduction results in offspring with desirable characteristics through the selective mating of members within a population that have desired traits. Which choice results in adaptations that put a certain population at an advantage?

C) Incorrect. Differential reproduction results in offspring with desirable characteristics through the selective mating of members within a population that have desired traits. Which choice results in adaptations that put a certain population at an advantage?

D) Incorrect. Differential reproduction results in offspring with desirable characteristics through the selective mating of members within a population that have desired traits. Which choice results in adaptations that put a certain population at an advantage?

Question 2:

A) Correct! Selective pressure refers to the forces that shape reproductive success. This results in a "pruning" effect in lean times so those best equipped to survive have more success reproducing.

B) Incorrect. In lean times, there is a "pruning" effect so that those organisms that are best equipped to survive have more success reproducing. Which choice identifies the forces that shape reproductive success?

C) Incorrect. In lean times, there is a "pruning" effect so that those organisms that are best equipped to survive will have more success reproducing. Which choice identifies the forces that shape reproductive success?

D) Incorrect. In lean times, there is a "pruning" effect so that those organisms that are best equipped to survive will have more success reproducing. Which choice identifies the forces that shape reproductive success?

Question 3:

A) Correct! Because the rate at which species produce offspring is greater than the rate at which the environment can provide food and shelter, individuals who carry advantageous traits will come to outnumber those without them. This causes a shift in the common characteristics of the species over time.

B) Incorrect. Because the rate at which species produce offspring is greater than the rate at which the environment can provide food and shelter, individuals who carry advantageous traits will come to outnumber those without them. This causes a shift in the common characteristics of the species over time.

Question 4:

A) Incorrect. Natural selection is always present and ongoing. However, it is impossible to know what threats to survival will occur in the future or how well a species will be able to resist these threats. Which choice takes this into account?

B) Correct! Natural selection is ever present and ongoing. However, it is impossible to predict what threats to survival will occur in the future or how well a species will be able to resist these threats.

C) Incorrect. Natural selection is always present and ongoing. However, it is impossible to know what threats to survival will occur in the future or how well a species will be able to resist these threats. Which choice takes this into account?

D) Incorrect. Natural selection is always present and ongoing. However, it is impossible to know what threats to survival will occur in the future or how well a species will be able to resist these threats. Which choice takes this into account?

Question 5:

A) Incorrect. While disease sometimes kills off portions of populations, Darwin's proposal was much broader in scope. Individuals who have traits that are better adapted to the conditions of the environment will survive and pass those traits on. As a result, individuals with advantageous traits will come to outnumber those without. Which choice explains this shift in characteristics of a population over time?

B) Correct! Natural differences always exist among individuals, with some individuals having traits that are better adapted to the conditions of the environment. One of the key points of the idea of natural selection is that individuals who carry advantageous traits will come to outnumber those without them, causing a shift in the common characteristics of the species over time.

C) Incorrect. Natural differences always exist among individuals. Individuals who have traits that are better adapted to the conditions of the environment will survive and pass those traits on. As a result, individuals with advantageous traits will come to outnumber those without. Which choice explains this shift in characteristics of a population over time?

D) Incorrect. While it is true that natural differences always exist among individuals, Darwin's proposal was broader in scope. Individuals who have traits that are better adapted to the conditions of the environment will survive and pass those traits on. As a result, individuals with advantageous traits will come to outnumber those without. Which choice explains this shift in characteristics of a population over time?

Question 6:

A) Correct! Individuals whose traits are best adapted to the conditions of the environment have the greatest ability to survive and reproduce.

B) Incorrect. Individuals whose traits are best adapted to the conditions of the environment have the greatest ability to survive and reproduce.

Question 7:

A) Incorrect. It is difficult to tell what types of traits will be favored by natural selection in the long run because no one knows what threats to survival will occur or how species may be able to resist these threats. Which choice takes this into account?

B) Correct! While we can make educated guesses based on our experience and prior research, there are factors in the natural world that we cannot control. It is difficult to tell what types of traits will be favored by natural selection in the long run. No one knows what threats to survival will occur or how species may be able to resist these threats.

C) Incorrect. It is difficult to tell what types of traits will be favored by natural selection in the long run because no one knows what threats to survival will occur or how species may be able to resist these threats. Which choice takes this into account?

D) Incorrect. It is difficult to tell what types of traits will be favored by natural selection in the long run because no one knows what threats to survival will occur or how species may be able to resist these threats. Which choice takes this into account?

Charles Darwin III

Comprehension Checkpoints:
p177: B; p178: A; p179: A

Question 1:

A) Correct! A phylogenetic tree is a kind of family tree. It shows the evolutionary development of a species.

B) Incorrect. A phylogenetic tree is a kind of family tree. It shows the evolutionary development of a species.

Question 2:

A) Incorrect. Before Darwin's phylogenetic tree, scientists thought that the vast range of living organisms was a feature of divine creation meant to highlight our own superiority. According to this view, life was arranged like a set of stairs, with "lower" forms situated on the bottom and "higher" forms, humans, appearing at the top. Which choice identifies this pattern of biodiversity?

B) Correct! Before Darwin's phylogenetic tree, scientists had thought that the most important pattern of biodiversity was the Scale of Nature. This was the notion that the vast range of living organisms was a feature of divine creation meant to highlight our own superiority. According to this view, life was arranged like a set of stairs, with "lower" forms situated on the bottom and "higher" forms, humans, appearing at the top.

C) Incorrect. Before Darwin's phylogenetic tree, scientists thought that the vast range of living organisms was a feature of divine creation meant to highlight our own superiority. According to this view, life was arranged like a set of stairs, with "lower" forms situated on the bottom and "higher" forms, humans, appearing at the top. Which choice identifies this pattern of biodiversity?

D) Incorrect. Before Darwin's phylogenetic tree, scientists thought that the vast range of living organisms was a feature of divine creation meant to highlight our own superiority. According to this view, life was arranged like a set of stairs, with "lower" forms situated on the bottom and "higher" forms, humans, appearing at the top. Which choice identifies this pattern of biodiversity?

Question 3:

A) Incorrect. Rather than being linear like the ladder, the tree model spreads out in different directions. New branches sprout, allowing for new varieties or species. The ladder model shows a hierarchy, with some species better or worse than others. But in the tree model, all are adapted to their specific environments. Which choice states how the tree model represents evolution?

B) Incorrect. The tree model sprouts branches, allowing for new varieties or species. In contrast to the ladder model, none of the branches of the tree is superior or inferior to others. Some branches grow straight up, while most develop in different directions, resembling alternative adaptations. Some branches die out, becoming extinct. Which choice states how the tree model represents evolution?

C) Correct! Rather than being linear like the ladder, the tree model spreads out in different directions. New branches sprout, allowing for new varieties or species. Some branches grow straight up, while most develop in different directions, resembling alternative adaptations. Some branches die out, becoming extinct. None of the branches of a tree is superior or inferior to other branches. They are all simply different, adapted to their specific environments.

D) Incorrect. The ladder model has "lower" forms on the bottom and progresses linearly to "higher" forms, with humans at the top. The tree model, in contrast, sprouts branches, allowing for new varieties or species. None of the branches of a tree is superior or inferior to other branches. They are all simply different, adapted to their specific environments. Which choice states how the tree model represents evolution?

Question 4:

A) Correct! With the tree of life as a metaphor for evolution, Darwin changed the way both scientists and the public viewed the origin of species. In the view of evolution that Darwin proposed, all species, at some level, share a common source of origin.

B) Incorrect. With the tree of life as a metaphor for evolution, Darwin changed the way both scientists and the public viewed the origin of species. In the view of evolution that Darwin proposed, all species, at some level, share a common source of origin. Which choice fits this description?

C) Incorrect. With the tree of life as a metaphor for evolution, Darwin changed the way both scientists and the public viewed the origin of species. In the view of evolution that Darwin proposed, all species, at some level, share a common source of origin. Which choice fits this description?

D) Incorrect. With the tree of life as a metaphor for evolution, Darwin changed the way both scientists and the public viewed the origin of species. In the view of evolution that Darwin proposed, all species, at some level, share a common source of origin. Which choice fits this description?

Question 5:

A) Incorrect. Clusters of similar species form because they have a common origin. This can be seen in Darwin's tree model of biodiversity, where all the branches are interconnected. You can trace their origins from their endpoints to the parent shoots from which they grew to their original ancestral species. Which choice points to a shared ancestor?

B) Incorrect. Clusters of similar species form because they have a common origin. This is can be seen in Darwin's tree model of biodiversity, where all the branches are interconnected. You can trace their origins from their endpoints to the parent shoots from which they grew to their original ancestral species. Which choice points to a shared ancestor?

C) Correct! Clusters of similar species can form because they have a common origin. This is can be seen in Darwin's tree model of biodiversity. All the branches are interconnected. You can trace their origins from their endpoints to the parent shoots from which they grew to their original ancestral species.

D) Incorrect. Clusters of similar species can form because they have a common origin. This is can be seen in Darwin's tree model of biodiversity. You can trace their origins from their endpoints to the parent shoots from which they grew to their original ancestral species. Which choice points to a shared ancestor?

Question 6:

A) Correct! At that time, "evolution" described both physical maturation and the structural change in a species over time (also called "transmutation"). Darwin chose the term "descent with modification" to make clear that his discussion of evolution dealt with transmutation ("modification"), not growth and development. He also wanted to emphasize that biological evolution involved the linking of species genetically, through "descent."

B) Incorrect. At that time, "evolution" described both physical maturation and the structural change in a species over time (also called "transmutation"). Darwin chose the term "descent with modification" to make clear that his discussion of evolution dealt with transmutation ("modification"), not growth and development. He also wanted to emphasize that biological evolution involved the linking of species genetically, through "descent." Which choice fits this explanation?

C) Incorrect. At that time, "evolution" described both physical maturation and the structural change in a species over time (also called "transmutation"). Darwin chose the term "descent with modification" to make clear that his discussion of evolution dealt with transmutation ("modification"), not growth and development. He also wanted to emphasize that biological evolution involved the linking of species genetically, through "descent." Which choice fits this explanation?

D) Incorrect. At that time, "evolution" described both physical maturation and the structural change in a species over time (also called "transmutation"). Darwin chose the term "descent with modification" to make clear that his discussion of evolution dealt with transmutation ("modification"), not growth and development. He also wanted to emphasize that biological evolution involved the linking of species genetically, through "descent." Which choice fits this explanation?

Question 7:

A) Incorrect. Before Darwin, scientists promoted a "natural order" of organisms according to divine creation.

In this pattern of biodiversity, the vast array of living organisms was arranged much like a set of stairs, with "lower" forms on the bottom and "higher" forms, humans, at the top. Which choice proposes an explanation of biodiversity that includes a "natural order" of different species?

B) Incorrect. Before Darwin, scientists promoted a "natural order" of organisms according to divine creation. In this pattern of biodiversity, the vast array of living organisms was arranged much like a set of stairs, with "lower" forms on the bottom and "higher" forms, humans, at the top. Which choice proposes an explanation of biodiversity that includes a "natural order" of different species?

C) Incorrect. Before Darwin, scientists promoted a "natural order" of organisms according to divine creation. In this pattern of biodiversity, the vast array of living organisms was arranged much like a set of stairs, with "lower" forms on the bottom and "higher" forms, humans, at the top. Which choice proposes an explanation of biodiversity that includes a "natural order" of different species?

D) Correct! Before Darwin, scientists explained biodiversity by the Scale of Nature. This model of biodiversity proposed a "natural order" of living organisms arranged like a set of stairs, with "lower" forms situated on the bottom and "higher" forms, humans, appearing at the top.

Mendel and Inheritance

Comprehension Checkpoints:
p185: A; p186: B; p187: B; p188: A

Question 1:

A) Incorrect. Mendel's aim was to reveal the genetic makeup of pea plants to understand how traits were inherited. When we talk about the combined underlying genetic factors in an organism that result in traits such as height in Mendel's pea plants – represented as TT, tt, or Tt – we are referring to the genotype of those plants. DNA encodes the genetic makeup of an organism and serves as a blueprint for replicating genetic information. Which choice best defines genotype?

B) Correct! "Genotype" refers to the genetic makeup of an organism.

C) Incorrect. Mendel's aim was to reveal the genetic makeup of pea plants to understand how traits were inherited. When we talk about the combined underlying genetic factors in an organism that result in traits such as height in Mendel's pea plants – represented as TT, tt, or Tt – we are referring to the genotype of those plants. The individual "factors" that Mendel studied are now known to be genes, which are encoded by DNA. Which choice best defines genotype?

D) Incorrect. Phenotypes are the physical traits of an organism. Mendel's aim was to reveal the genetic makeup of the plants, so he observed phenotypes in order to understand the genotype of his pea plants. When we talk about the combined underlying genetic factors in an organism that result in traits such as tallness or shortness, we are referring to the genotype of those plants. Which choice best defines genotype?

Question 2:

A) Incorrect. Earlier theories suggested that only sperm carried traits to offspring, but Mendel determined that an organism inherits genetic material from both parents.

B) Correct! Unlike earlier theories that suggested that only sperm carried traits, Mendel's first law says that both egg and sperm carry physical traits to the offspring.

Question 3:

A) Incorrect. When parents produce offspring, those offspring are the first filial generation. The offspring of this generation is called the second filial generation. Which choice identifies the first generation of offspring produced by two parents?

B) Incorrect. When parents produce offspring, recessive traits may be hidden in the first generation but show up in future generations. Which choice identifies the first generation of offspring produced by two parents?

C) Correct! When parents produce offspring, the offspring are the first filial generation, known as the F1 generation.

D) Incorrect. The genotype, or genetic makeup, of offspring is made up of genes contributed by both parents. Which choice identifies the first generation of offspring produced by two parents?

Question 4:

A) Correct! In his experiments with peas, Mendel carefully bred male and female plants and observed traits in offspring. His work showed that an organism inherits genetic material that determines physical traits from both the male and female parent.

B) Incorrect. Mendel carefully pollinated plants with different physical traits, using the male parts of some plants and the female parts of others. The results of Mendel's experiments went against the popular belief that only the male parent carried traits to its offspring. Which choice correctly states Mendel's discovery?

C) Incorrect. Earlier theories that suggested only the male parent carried traits to its offspring. However, the results of Mendel's experiments challenged this way

of thinking. Which choice correctly states Mendel's discovery?

D) Incorrect. Mendel cross-pollinated two parental lines of pea plants, one that always produced round peas and another that always gave wrinkled peas. He found that every plant among the first generation of offspring had round peas, whether the pollen came from a parent plant with round peas or with wrinkled peas. These results challenged the popular belief that only the male parent carried traits to its offspring. Which choice correctly states Mendel's discovery?

Question 5:

A) Incorrect. There is a special name for the chart that is used to calculate products from genetic crosses. In the chart, genes donated from each parent are displayed in quadrants. Which choice gives the name for this type of chart?

B) Correct! A chart called a Punnet square is a useful way to calculate products from genetic crosses.

C) Incorrect. A special type of chart is used to calculate products from genetic crosses. In the chart, genes donated from each parent are displayed in quadrants. Which choice gives the name for this type of chart?

D) Incorrect. In this special type of chart useful for calculating products from genetic crosses, genes donated from each parent are displayed in boxes. Which choice gives the name for this type of chart?

Question 6:

A) Correct! From his experiments with pea plants, Mendel proposed his second law, which proposed that gene pairs randomly and independently segregate into an organism's gametes.

B) Incorrect. Mendel believed that two factors, or genes, must be involved in producing a physical trait: one donated by the male and one from the female parent. Each parent had a pair of factors, or alleles of a gene, that separated randomly during reproduction. Thus, the offspring could inherit either allele from each parent. The resulting combination of donated alleles would determine physical traits in the offspring.

Question 7:

A) You are partly correct. You are right that incomplete dominance results in the offspring having a trait that is a mix of those seen in the two parents. For example, when pure snapdragon plants with red flowers are bred with pure plants with white flowers, the offspring have pink flowers. What else can be said about pink snapdragons, which result from incomplete dominance?

B) You are partly correct. You are right that incomplete dominance results in the offspring having traits that are different from either parent. For example, when pure snapdragon plants with red flowers are bred with pure plants with white flowers, the offspring have pink flowers. What else can be said about pink snapdragons, which result from incomplete dominance?

C) Correct! Genes that show "incomplete dominance" result in traits from the combined action of multiple genes. For example, when pure snapdragon plants with red flowers are bred with pure plants with white flowers, the offspring have pink flowers. Pink is both (a) a mix of the colors in both parents (b) different from the color of either parent.

D) Incorrect. Snapdragons show incomplete dominance. When pure snapdragon plants with red flowers are bred with pure plants with white flowers, the offspring have pink flowers. What can be said about pink snapdragons, which result from incomplete dominance of the traits in the red and white parent snapdragons?

Question 8:

A) Incorrect. Snapdragons demonstrate incomplete dominance in flower color, and the offspring show a blend of traits seen in the parents. Which choice presents a blend of traits?

B) Correct! Snapdragons demonstrate incomplete dominance in flower color, and the offspring show a blend of traits seen in the parents. When pure plants with red (RR) flowers are bred with pure plants with white (rr) flowers, the offspring will have a blend of traits (Rr), resulting in pink flowers.

C) Incorrect. Snapdragons demonstrate incomplete dominance in flower color, and the offspring show a blend of traits seen in the parents. Which choice presents a blend of traits?

D) Incorrect. Snapdragons demonstrate incomplete dominance in flower color, and the offspring show a blend of traits seen in the parents. When pure plants with red (RR) flowers are bred with pure plants with white (rr) flowers, all of the offspring will inherit one red gene and one white gene. Which choice presents a blend of these traits?

Taxonomy I

Comprehension Checkpoints:
p192: B; p193: A; p194: B

Question 1:

A) Incorrect. The formal system organizing and naming plants and animals is called taxonomy. Look again at the choices.

B) Incorrect. The formal system organizing and naming plants and animals is called taxonomy. Look again at the choices.

C) Correct! Taxonomy has to do with classifying and naming plants and animals.

D) Incorrect. The formal system organizing and naming plants and animals is called taxonomy. Look again at the choices.

Question 2:

A) Incorrect. Carolu s Linnaeus wrote Systema Naturae, in which he listed all organisms known in the world at the time. He revised it many times. The 10th revision, published in 1758, is considered the official start of modern taxonomy and is still used today. Look again at the choices.

B) Incorrect. Carolus Linnaeus wrote Systema Naturae, in which he listed all organisms known in the world at the time. He revised it many times. The 10th revision, published in 1758, is considered the official start of modern taxonomy and is still used today.

C) Correct! Carolus Linnaeus wrote one of the great classic works in the history of science, Systema Naturae, in which he listed all organisms known in the world at the time. He revised it many times. The 10th revision, published in 1758, is considered the official start of modern taxonomy and is still used today.

D) Incorrect. Carolus Linnaeus wrote Systema Naturae, in which he listed all organisms known in the world at the time. He revised it many times. The 10th revision, published in 1758, is considered the official start of modern taxonomy and is still used today.

Question 3:

A) Incorrect. In our modern classification system, every species is known by a unique genus and species name that distinguishes it from other species. Which choice accomplishes this goal?

B) Correct! In our modern classification system, every species is known by a unique genus and species name that distinguishes it from other species.

C) Incorrect. In our modern classification system, every species is known by a unique genus and species name that distinguishes it from other species. Which choice accomplishes this goal?

D) Incorrect. In our modern classification system, every species is known by a unique genus and species name that distinguishes it from other species. Which choice accomplishes this goal?

Question 4:

A) Incorrect. Folk taxonomy is the root of modern biological classification. It is important to modern research scientists, who often rely on traditional knowledge when learning about native species. Which choice identifies the correct term?

B) Correct! Folk taxonomy is the root of modern biological classification. It is important to modern research scientists, who often rely on traditional knowledge when learning about native species. In complex tropical environments, local people are likely to recognize a vast number of organisms.

C) Incorrect. Folk taxonomy is the root of modern biological classification. It is important to modern research scientists, who often rely on traditional knowledge when learning about native species. Which choice identifies the correct term?

D) Incorrect. Folk taxonomy is the root of modern biological classification. It is important to modern research scientists, who often rely on traditional knowledge when learning about native species. Which choice identifies the correct term?

Question 5:

A) Incorrect. Naturalists such as John Ray are credited with developing a scientific basis for arranging species into logical classes based on their appearance and characteristics. In the 18th century, the Swedish scientist Carolus Linnaeus more or less invented our modern system of taxonomy and classification. Which choice correctly identifies this pair?

B) Incorrect. Naturalists such as John Ray are credited with developing a scientific basis for arranging species into logical classes based on their appearance and characteristics. In the 18th century, the Swedish scientist Carolus Linnaeus more or less invented our modern system of taxonomy and classification. Which choice correctly identifies this pair?

C) Correct! Naturalists such as John Ray are credited with developing a scientific basis for arranging species into logical classes based on their appearance and characteristics. In the 18th century, the Swedish scientist Carolus Linnaeus more or less invented our modern system of taxonomy and classification.

D) Incorrect. Ancient Greek naturalist Theophrastus classified plants as early as 300 BCE. In Europe, this is the historical beginning of an organized, written taxonomy. Later, explorers like Magellan collected samples of plants and animals from distant parts of the globe. However, Naturalists such as John Ray are credited with developing a scientific basis for arranging species into logical classes based on their appearance and characteristics. And in the 18th century, the Swedish scientist Carolus Linnaeus more or less invented our modern system of taxonomy and classification. Which choice identifies the two best known for their contributions to taxonomy?

Question 6:

A) Incorrect. Linnaeus adhered rigidly to the principal that each species must be identified by a set of names, which are termed the "genus" and "species" that the plant or animal belongs to. Which choice identifies the two terms that form a Linnaean name?

B) Incorrect. Linnaeus adhered rigidly to the principal that each species must be identified by a set of names, which are termed the "genus" and "species" that the plant or animal belongs to. Which choice identifies the two terms that form a Linnaean name?

C) Correct! Linnaeus adhered rigidly to the principal that each species must be identified by a set of names, which are termed the "genus" and "species" that the plant or animal belongs to.

D) Incorrect. Linnaeus adhered rigidly to the principal that each species must be identified by a set of names, which are termed the "genus" and "species" that the plant or animal belongs to. Which choice identifies the two terms that form a Linnaean name?

Question 7:

A) Incorrect. Linnaeus identified each species by their genus and species and classified them on the basis of their similarities and differences. Which choice states how Linnaeus grouped species?

B) Incorrect. Linnaeus identified each species by their genus and species and classified them on the basis of their similarities and differences. Which choice states how Linnaeus grouped species?

C) Correct. Linnaeus identified each species by their genus and species and classified them on the basis of their similarities and differences.

D) Incorrect. Linnaeus identified each species by their genus and species and classified them on the basis of their similarities and differences. Which choice states how Linnaeus grouped species?

Scientific Controversy

Comprehension Checkpoints:
p199: B; p203: A; p204: B

Question 1:

A) Incorrect. For a controversy to be resolved, it is not necessary for all scientists to agree. A controversy is resolved when multiple lines of evidence support one argument. Then, the other arguments fade away. Which choice fits this explanation?

B) Incorrect. A controversy in science does not get resolved when scientists vote on the explanation they favor. Rather, when multiple lines of evidence support one argument, the other arguments fade away. Which choice fits this explanation?

C) Correct! Controversies in science are resolved when multiple lines of evidence strongly support one argument. The evidence comes from different research methods and even from different scientific fields. Then, the other arguments fade away.

D) Incorrect. Controversies in science are resolved when multiple lines of evidence strongly support one argument. The evidence often comes from different research methods and even from different scientific fields. Then, the other arguments fade away.

Question 2:

A) Incorrect. When there is a controversy in science, the debate takes place in peer-reviewed journal articles, not in newspapers and other popular media. It is only through this process that the debate becomes part of the scientific literature and helps advance science. Which choice fits this description?

B) Incorrect. A controversy in science is more than a discussion among individuals. A scientific controversy must meet the following criteria: (1) A number of scientists are engaged in research that addresses the controversy. (2) The research is ongoing. (3) The debate takes place within the broader scientific community in peer-reviewed journal articles. Which choice meets at least one of these criteria?

C) Incorrect. When there is a controversy in science, the debate takes place in peer-reviewed journal articles. It is only through this process that the debate becomes part of the scientific literature and helps advance science. Which choice fits this description?

D) Correct! When there is a controversy in science, the debate takes place in peer-reviewed journal articles. It is only through this process that the debate becomes part of the scientific literature and helps advance science.

Question 3:

A) Correct! In 2005, Hurricane Katrina caused great destruction. After this, many studies were published on the relationship between global warming and hurricanes. Scientists disagreed and debated. There were so many articles on different sides of the issue that in 2010 the World Meteorological Organization appointed an expert panel to summarize new research.

B) Incorrect. Hurricane Katrina hit in 2005. After this, many studies were published on the relationship between global warming and hurricanes. There were so many articles on different sides of the issue that in 2010 the World Meteorological Organization appointed an expert panel to summarize new research. In this way, the controversy could be clarified but not necessarily resolved. Which choice best fits this explanation?

C) Incorrect. Hurricane Katrina hit in 2005. After this, many studies were published on the relationship between global warming and hurricanes. There were so many articles on different sides of the issue that in 2010 the World Meteorological Organization appointed an expert panel to summarize the research. The authors reported on the state of the controversy, pointed out where there was agreement, and emphasized that controversy is a natural outcome of the process of discovery in science. Which choice best fits this description?

D) Incorrect. In general, the more people that are involved in a scientific controversy and conduct research to address the issues, the more rapidly progress is made. After Hurricane Katrina, numerous studies addressed global warming and hurricanes. Scientists disagreed and debated. In 2010, the World Meteorological Organization appointed an expert panel to summarize new research and report on the state of the controversy. Which choice fits this explanation?

Question 4:

A) Incorrect. In a scientific controversy, arguments are not based on personal disagreements but on data. Scientists must consider all data and have evidence to support their claim. Which choice states this?

B) Correct! In a scientific controversy, all of the data must be explained and taken into account-- not just the data collected to support one side. In this way, scientists garner evidence to support their claim.

C) Incorrect. In science, although a controversy may have social or political implications, these are not the basis of the argument. In a scientific controversy, valid arguments are based on evidence that comes from an analysis of all available data. Which choice states this?

D) Incorrect. In a scientific controversy, all of the data must be explained and taken into account. If scientists select only a portion of the data to analyze or report on, then the explanation may not account for all data and the result may not be valid. Which choice could form the basis of a valid argument?

Question 5:

A) Incorrect. Science is full of controversy. Controversy in science often creates progress because it spurs new research. It is therefore an essential part of the process of science.

B) Correct! Controversies are ongoing in every field of science on a regular basis.

Question 6:

A) Incorrect. In a true scientific controversy, a community of scientists takes part in the debate. Further, the arguments are based on evidence. In this case, the arguments are not research-based. Rather, they center on freshwater demands to meet different needs and criticism of the government agencies that regulate water use.

B) Correct! A scientific controversy is a debate among the broader scientific community in which arguments are based on evidence. Scientific controversies are different from political, ethical, and personal controversies, though they sometimes overlap.

Question 7:

A) Correct! A scientific controversy is a debate among the broader scientific community in which arguments are based on evidence. The debate is ongoing so that new data can shed light on the argument. In this case, arguments are research-based and multiple lines of evidence are being investigated.

B) Incorrect. A scientific controversy is a debate among the broader scientific community in which arguments are based on evidence. The debate is ongoing so that new data can shed light on the argument. In this case, arguments are research-based and multiple lines of evidence are being investigated.

Uncertainty, Error, and Confidence

Comprehension Checkpoints:
p211: B; p214: B; p215: A; p216: B

Question 1:

A) Incorrect. Reporting uncertainty is an important part of reporting the results of research. There is variability in all scientific measurements. Which answer best captures the scientific meaning of "uncertainty"?

B) Incorrect. When scientists use the word uncertainty, it does not mean that they are unsure about their research results. There is variability in all measurements in science. Scientists report this as uncertainty. Which answer best captures the scientific meaning of "uncertainty"?

C) Incorrect. When scientists use the word uncertainty, it does not mean that they are unsure about their research results. In science, uncertainty means that all data have a range of values as opposed to a precise value. Which answer best captures this scientific meaning of "uncertainty"?

D) Correct! All data have a degree of error and variability. Uncertainty is a measurement of that variability.

Question 2:

A) Incorrect. Accuracy refers to how close a measurement comes to the target (the bullseye in this case).

Precision refers to how close different measurements are to each other. Which choice describes the picture?

B) Correct! Accuracy refers to how close a measurement comes to the target. Precision refers to how close different measurements are to each other. The picture shows poor accuracy since the marks are not close to the bullseye but high precision since the marks are grouped closely together.

C) Incorrect. Accuracy refers to how close a measurement comes to the target (the bullseye in this case). Precision refers to how close different measurements are to each other. Which choice describes the picture?

D) Incorrect. Accuracy refers to how close a measurement comes to the target (the bullseye in this case). Precision refers to how close different measurements are to each other. Which choice describes the picture?

Question 3:

A) Incorrect. Pearson proposed that even the most careful and rigorous science cannot yield exact measurements. Rather, uncertainty is part of nature and so there will always be some scatter of measurements. Which choice allows for natural variability?

B) Incorrect. Even when following careful procedures, scientists cannot completely eliminate error in their measurements. This is because variations are part of nature. Which choice accounts for natural variability?

C) Incorrect. Before Pearson, scientists assumed that when measurements varied, it was due to instrument error. But Pearson proposed that natural variability causes some scatter of measurements in even the most careful and rigorous scientific investigation. Which choice fits this description?

D) Correct! Pearson proposed that there is natural variability in all measurements. Even the most careful research and best instruments cannot yield an exact measurement. When measurements are repeated, natural variability causes an unavoidable scatter of measurements around some central value.

Question 4:

A) Correct! Statistical error is described as the inherent uncertainty of a measurement caused by random fluctuations in a system. Systematic error is the result of a bias introduced by instrument error, human mistakes, poor research design, or incorrect assumptions.

B) Incorrect. Statistical error is the inherent uncertainty of a measurement. It is caused by random fluctuations in a system. Systematic error can be caused by instrument bias, human mistakes, poor research design, or incorrect assumptions. Which choice provides the correct definition of the terms?

C) Incorrect. Statistical error is the inherent uncertainty of a measurement caused by random fluctuations in a system. Systematic error is the result of a bias introduced by instrument error, human mistakes, poor research design, or incorrect assumptions. Which choice fits this description?

D) Incorrect. Statistical error is caused by random fluctuations in a system. Although it can be reduced by repeating a measurement or observation many times, it cannot be completely eliminated. Systematic error is due to a non-random fluctuation, such as instrument bias or human mistake. If the source of a systematic error can be identified, it can often be eliminated or controlled. Which choice correctly distinguishes statistical error from systematic error?

Question 5:

A) Correct! Measurements always show a range of values rather than one precise value. The more times you measure something, the more certain you can be of the value. Repeated measurements therefore decrease uncertainty and increase confidence.

B) Incorrect. Measurements always show a range of values rather than one precise value. The more times you measure something, the more certain you can be of the value. Repeated measurements therefore decrease uncertainty and increase confidence.

Question 6:

A) Incorrect. All scientists find some degree of error in their measurements, but that does not mean that their research is wrong. When scientists report error in their data, they are putting a number to the variability associated with their measurements. Which choice describes stating uncertainty in numerical terms?

B) Incorrect. Even the most careful measurements have some degree of error and variability, but this does not mean that they made mistakes. Error in science refers the difference between the true value and the measured value. When scientists report error in their data, they are putting a number to the variability associated with their measurements. Which choice describes stating uncertainty in numerical terms?

C) Correct! All measurements have some degree of error and variability. Error in science refers the difference between the true value and the measured value. When scientists report error in their data, they are putting a number to the variability associated with their measurements.

D) Incorrect. All measurements have some degree of error. Error in science refers the difference between the true value and the measured value. When scientists report error in their data, this does not mean that they have made a mistake. Rather, they are putting a number to the variability associated with their measurements. Which answer best explains error reporting in science?

Question 7:

A) Incorrect. Confidence statements do not tell us how "correct" a conclusion is. Instead, they describe the probability that a measurement range will overlap a mean value when a study is repeated. Which choice fits this definition?

B) Correct! Confidence statements do not tell us how "correct" a measurement is. Instead, they describe the probability of obtaining a certain measurement when a study is repeated.

C) Incorrect. Confidence statements do not tell us how "correct" a measurement is. Instead, they describe the probability that a measurement range will overlap a mean value when a study is repeated. Which choice fits this definition?

D) Incorrect. All measurements have some variability rather than one precise value. Confidence intervals state the probability that a measurement range will overlap a certain value when a study is repeated. Which choice fits this definition?

Question 8:

A) Incorrect. Propagating an error means to continue to transmit and increase that error. Quality assurance refers to the plans that a researcher has for minimizing and measuring error, while quality control refers to the actual procedures implemented to minimize error in the research. Look again at the choices.

B) Not necessarily. Replicating—or repeating—measurements will determine precision and is one of many possible techniques for minimizing error in research. Efforts to measure and reduce errors in scientific research are generally referred to as quality assurance and quality control. Look again at the choices.

C) Incorrect. Confidence statements describe the probability that a similar result will be found if a study is repeated. Quality assurance refers to the plans that a researcher has for minimizing and measuring error, while quality control refers to the actual procedures implemented to minimize error in the research. Look again at the choices.

D) Correct! Quality assurance and quality control refer to the steps that a researcher takes to measure and reduce error. These steps can include calibrating instruments, standardizing procedures, documenting methods, repeating measurements, and other techniques.

Data Analysis and Interpretation

Comprehension Checkpoints:
p223: A; p226: B; p228: B

Question 1:

A) Correct! A dictionary definition is not raw data. Instead, creating a dictionary definition requires analyzing the meaning of a word and then using judgment to produce a description that is clear, concise, and accurate.

B) Incorrect. Raw data includes information that can be observed and recorded, so a temperature measurement is an example of raw data. Which of the choices does not rely on an instrument to measure or record?

C) Incorrect. A satellite image is an example of raw data. Weather scientists can analyze and interpret these raw data to map the size of the hurricane. Which choice already includes interpretation?

D) Incorrect. The location coordinates are an example of raw data. Scientists can use these data to propose the conditions that the tree species needs in order to grow. Which of the choices does not allow scientists to make deductions or predictions?

Question 2:

A) Incorrect. You are right that statistical analysis is one way to analyze data, but there are also other types of analysis.

B) Incorrect. You are right that filtering is one way to analyze data, but there are also other types of analysis.

C) Incorrect. You are right that removing bad data is one part of data analysis, but what are some other ways to process data?

D) Correct! All of these—statistical analysis, filtering, and removing bad data—can be steps in data analysis.

Question 3:

A) Incorrect. Scientists bring their unique perspectives to the task of explaining data, and that includes intuition. Which of the choices takes into account the skills and experience that scientists rely on?

B) Incorrect. Assumptions are always a part of explaining data, but it's important to define what they are. Which choice allows for making assumptions?

C) Correct! Scientists interpret data in the context of what they already know.

D) Incorrect. It takes a creative mind to explain observations and relate data to existing scientific ideas. Which of the choices indicates that scientists bring their unique insights and experiences to the task of data interpretation?

Question 4:

A) Incorrect. Even high quality data can yield different interpretations. Which choice shows that data interpretation can be a subjective process?

B) Incorrect. Different scientists can look at the same data in different ways, but that doesn't mean they don't understand it. Which of the choices explain why scientists may come up with different interpretations?

C) Correct! Scientists bring their unique perspectives, background knowledge, and experience to the task of data analysis. Therefore, different scientists can come up with different interpretations for the same data.

D) Not necessarily. Individual scientists bring their unique perspectives and judgments to the task of data interpretation. Which choice best states that different scientists can propose different explanations for the same set of data?

Question 5:

A) Correct! It is important for the scientists to report all data and describe how they processed the data. This allows others in the scientific community to evaluate the research.

B) Incorrect. A detailed description of their data collection and processing procedures allows others to evaluate the study and use the data in further research. Which choice best fits this description?

C) Incorrect. Publishing data and how it is processed is one way to help others learn from what you have done. Which choice helps other scientists learn about the complete procedure and processing?

D) Incorrect. Honesty is an important component of scientific research, and that includes publishing all data involved in a study and how it is processed. Which choice would provide the most information for other researchers?

Question 6:

A) Incorrect. Even when data have been properly collected, scientists can come to different conclusions based on their background and experience. Disagreement in the scientific community is not a bad thing since it often leads to more research and discussion. This ends up building the body of scientific knowledge.

B) Correct! There is more than one way to interpret data. Disagreement over data interpretation is common in the scientific community. This type of disagreement often leads to new data collection and research.

Question 7:

A) Incorrect. If the data was systematically collected and analyzed in the first place, it does not need to be reanalyzed for the purpose of other studies. Which of the choices might lead to new research results?

B) Correct! When new ways to analyze data are available, the scientist may uncover patterns in the data that were not seen before.

C) Incorrect. Replication is a healthy part of science, but it does not require that original data be reanalyzed. Which of the choices might uncover new patterns in the data that were not seen before?

D) Incorrect. The scientist does not need to reanalyze the data for the journal article if the data was systematically collected and analyzed in the first place. Which of the choices might uncover new patterns in the data and produce different results?

Question 8:

A) Incorrect. The red line represents CO_2 concentrations in the atmosphere. Which choice describes the trend of CO_2 concentrations when you read the chart from left to right?

B) Correct! The red line on the graph representing CO_2 concentrations shows a steady increase from 1974 to 2010.

C) Incorrect. The red line in the graph represents CO_2 concentrations in the atmosphere. Although this line is a little wavy, it shows a clear trend across the graph. What is the overall trend in CO_2 concentrations from 1974 to 2010?

D) Incorrect.

If concentrations of CO_2 remained constant, the red line would remain flat from one end of the graph to the other. Which choice describes the rise across the chart from the left to the right?

Utilizing the Scientific Literature

Comprehension Checkpoints:
p238: A; p239: B

Question 1:

A) Correct! The vast majority of the scientific literature is published in the form of peer reviewed journal articles. The scientific literature is a reliable archive of research in science. Its purpose is to provide a growing, stable base for new scientific investigations.

B) Incorrect. Science textbooks generally explain concepts in science and report on existing literature in the field. Which of the choices contributes new research upon which future scientific work can build?

C) Incorrect. Newspapers publish information on current events, including recent scientific advances. However, newspaper articles are not part of the scientific literature. The scientific literature is a reliable archive of research in science. Which of the choices contributes new research upon which future scientific work can build?

D) Incorrect. Science fiction is entertaining, but it does not contribute to the scientific literature. The scientific literature is a reliable archive of research in science. Which of the choices contributes new research upon which future scientific work can build?

Question 2:

A) Incorrect. The scientific literature provides an archive of research, which scientists make use of throughout the entire process of investigation. Which choice shows the central importance of the scientific literature to the process of research?

B) Incorrect. Science builds on previous findings, so scientists draw on available information to conduct their research. The scientific literature provides an archive of research, which scientists make use of throughout the process of investigation. Which choice shows the central importance of the scientific literature to the process of research?

C) Incorrect. Since science builds on previous findings, scientists draw on available information to conduct their research. Scientists are expected to support their ideas with knowledge of the scientific literature and the work that has come before them, and even old studies can provide important information. Which choice shows the central importance of the scientific literature to the process of research?

D) Correct! Since science builds on previous findings, scientists draw on available information to conduct their research. The scientific literature is a reliable archive of scientific research, which scientists make use of throughout the process of investigation. It provides a growing, stable base for new research investigations.

Question 3:

A) Correct! The scientific literature is a reliable archive of scientific research. When mistakes are discovered, a paper can be retracted. This removes it from the literature and ensures that the record continues to be reliable.

B) Incorrect. The scientific literature is a reliable archive of scientific research. When mistakes are discovered, a paper can be retracted. Which choice ensures that the record will continue to be reliable?

C) Incorrect. The scientific literature is a reliable archive of scientific research. When mistakes are discovered, a paper can be retracted. Which choice ensures that the record will continue to be reliable?

D) Incorrect. The scientific literature is a reliable archive of scientific research. Sometimes mistakes get published, but when they are discovered the paper can be retracted. Which choice ensures that the record will continue to be reliable?

Question 4:

A) Incorrect. Scientists can look at existing data in new ways and arrive at different results. Researchers use the literature to learn all they can about a specific area of study, and then cite those articles. Which choice acknowledges the original study and helps readers understand the researcher's reasoning in coming to her own conclusions?

B) Incorrect. Scientists can look at existing data in new ways and arrive at different results. Researchers use the literature to learn all they can about a specific area of study, and then cite those articles. . Which choice acknowledges the original study and helps readers understand the researcher's reasoning in coming to her own conclusions?

C) Correct! Scientists can look at existing data in new ways and arrive at different results. Researchers use the literature to learn all they can about a specific area of study, and then cite those articles. This acknowledges the original authors and helps readers understand the researcher's reasoning in coming to her own conclusions.

D) Incorrect. Scientists can look at existing data in new ways and arrive at different results. They consult the literature to learn all they can about a specific area of study, and then cite those articles. . Which choice acknowledges the original study and helps readers understand the researcher's reasoning in coming to her own conclusions?

Question 5:

A) Incorrect. Having access to the scientific literature is critical to the work of scientists, but bookstores are not the place to find the scientific literature. Vast online databases of published research make it easy for researchers to search the literature. Look at the choices again for the most efficient way to search the scientific literature.

B) Incorrect. Having access to the scientific literature is critical to the work of scientists, but far more research is being published every day than is possible to read – even when subscribing to several journals in a particular discipline. Vast digital databases make it easier to search the literature. Look at the choices again for the most efficient way to search the scientific literature.

C) Correct! Having access to the scientific literature is critical to the work of scientists, but far more research is being published every day than is possible to read. Digital and online databases make it easier to search the literature. Here researchers can find titles of published articles along with a short summary.

D) Incorrect. Having access to the scientific literature is critical to the work of scientists, but common search engines are not the place to find the scientific literature. Specialized databases of research that has been published in scholarly journals make it easy for re-

searchers to search the literature. Look at the choices again for the most efficient way to search the scientific literature.

Question 6:

A) Incorrect. New research questions can be investigated by reanalyzing data that were previously published in the scientific literature. In addition, our evolving understanding of the natural world can reveal mistakes in interpretation in the existing literature.

B) Correct! New research questions can be investigated by reanalyzing data that were previously published in the scientific literature. In addition, our evolving understanding of the natural world can reveal mistakes in interpretation in the existing literature

Question 7:

A) Incorrect. Solid research requires a thorough investigation of the scientific literature. Researchers use the literature to learn all they can about a specific area of study, and then cite those articles to acknowledge the original authors. Which choice shows that science builds on previous findings?

B) Correct! Science builds on previous findings, so solid research requires a thorough investigation of the scientific literature. Thorough researchers use the literature to learn all they can about a specific area of study, and then cite those articles to acknowledge the original authors.

C) Incorrect. Solid research requires a thorough investigation of the scientific literature. Researchers use the literature to learn all they can about a specific area of study, and then cite those articles to acknowledge the original authors. Which choice shows that science builds on previous findings?

D) Incorrect. Solid research requires a thorough investigation of the scientific literature. Researchers use the literature to learn all they can about a specific area of study, and then cite those articles to acknowledge the original authors. Which choice shows that science builds on previous findings?